Preface

THIS TEXT is based upon a belief that an introductory one-semester course in quantitative analysis should emphasize fundamental techniques and principles rather than attempt a survey of the general field. To this end, basic techniques and principles are systematically introduced in connection with eight recommended and three optional determinations that can be performed in the laboratory time normally available. Throughout the text, techniques are presented through functional illustrations, that clearly show the required operational steps. In Chapter 2, non-essential details of balance construction and adjustment have been eliminated—only the factors of direct concern to the use of a balance are discussed. The treatment of the quantitative effect of various factors on solubility in Chapter 5 stresses the use of the method of successive approximations for the solution of practical problems. In Chapter 6, the discussion of factors that influence the physical character and purity of precipitates is a compromise between the very detailed consideration sometimes found and the very sketchy treatments frequently given. The propagation of errors in the calculation of results is emphasized in Chapter 7, but the general theory of errors is considered only in connection with the evaluation of the limited sets of data ordinarily obtained. The discussion of precipitation methods in Chapter 9 is used primarily to introduce the general principles of volumetric methods. The treatment of acid-base reactions in Chapter 10 is more detailed than usual because we feel it is a particularly important topic in an introductory course. In Chapter 11, the treatment of the theory of oxidation-reduction reactions is based very largely upon the general analogy that exists between acid-base reactions and oxidation-reduction reactions. The treatment of cells is limited to that required to introduce the meaning of oxidation potentials.

The introductory course in quantitative analysis at the University of California at Berkeley consists of one lecture and two three-hour laboratory periods per week for a sixteen-week semester. Chemists and chemical engineers, who comprise less than half of the students in the course, normally enroll in the first semester of their sophomore year. The course is required or recommended for students in many other curricula; in this category, the pre-medical students comprise the largest single group. Over a period of years, a selection of material has been made, and methods of presentation have been developed to meet the special problems encountered in teaching the course. Instruction sheets issued to clarify particular points in regard to specific determinations, or specific elements of theory, grew into a syllabus that has served as the basis for this text.

It is a privilege at this point to acknowledge our obligations to the many people who have assisted in this course during the formative years and have offered constructive criticisms, particularly Dr. Estelle Katzenellenbogen and Dr. Thomas Simonson. We are indebted also to Dr. Gerald Ballou for helpful suggestions and constructive criticism made in connection with the preparation of this text. We shall be grateful to anyone who will draw our attention to errors.

A. R. OLSON
E. F. ORLEMANN
C. W. KOCH

Berkeley, California
April, 1948

INTRODUCTORY QUANTITATIVE ANALYSIS

By

AXEL R. OLSON
Professor of Chemistry, University of California

EDWIN F. ORLEMANN
Assistant Professor of Chemistry, University of California

CHARLES W. KOCH
Instructor of Chemistry, University of California

ILLUSTRATIONS BY
LEONARD W. TREGILLUS

1948

W·H·FREEMAN AND COMPANY
SAN FRANCISCO · CALIFORNIA

*Copyright, 1948, by Axel R. Olson,
Edwin F. Orlemann, and Charles W. Koch*

All rights to reproduce this book in whole or in part are reserved, with the exception of the right to use short quotations for review of the book.

PRINTED IN THE UNITED STATES OF AMERICA
DESIGN AND TYPOGRAPHY BY MACKENZIE & HARRIS, INC.
SAN FRANCISCO, CALIFORNIA

Table of Contents

Chapter	Page
1. Introduction	1
2. Introductory Laboratory Techniques (determination of water in a hydrate)	6
3. Fundamental Calculations	28
4. Equilibrium and Equilibrium Constants	43
5. Gravimetric Techniques and the Control of Solubility (determination of chloride)	51
6. Gravimetric Determination of Sulfate, Physical Character and Purity of Precipitates, and the Gravimetric Determination of Iron	78
7. Evaluation of Analytical Data	102
8. Volumetric Apparatus	114
9. Introduction to Volumetric Principles (determination of chloride)	130
10. Principles and Analytical Applications of Acid-Base Reactions (standardization of sodium hydroxide and hydrochloric acid; determinations of acid phthalate and carbonate-bicarbonate mixtures)	150
11. Principles and Applications of Oxidation-Reduction Reactions (determination of iron, calcium, copper)	202
12. Relation of This Introduction to the General Field of Quantitative Analysis	256
Appendices	263
Tables of Logarithms	271
Index	293

Table of Illustrations

Figure	Page
2-1(a). The analytical balance.	9
2-1(b). The bearing surfaces of a balance.	11
2-1(c). The beam arrest of a balance.	11
2-2. Balance pointer scale.	13
2-3. The water vapor pressure of copper sulfate and its hydrates.	20
2-4. Preparation and use of the desiccator.	22
2-5. A simple muffle furnace.	25
2-6. Holding a weighing bottle.	26
4-1. The equalization of pressures to show equilibrium.	44
4-2. Graphical representation of equalization of pressures.	45
5-1. Protection of a weighing bottle in the drying oven.	52
5-2. Suction flask assembly.	53
5-3. Insertion of Witt plate in a Gooch crucible.	55
5-4. Transfer of a dry sample.	55
5-5. Decantation in the filtering process.	57
5-6. Washing a precipitate into a filter.	58
5-7. Use of the rubber policeman.	59
6-1. Ignition over a Bunsen flame.	81
6-2. Preparation of a filter.	82
6-3. Preparation of a filtered precipitate for ignition.	83
6-4. Schematic growth of a solid.	87
6-5. The ion regions around a precipitated crystal.	89
6-6. Effect of counter ions on the flocculation of a colloid.	90
7-1. Effect of precision on an error distribution curve.	103
7-2. Effect of a systematic error on an error distribution curve.	105
8-1. Cleaning and greasing a buret stopcock.	116
8-2. Cleaning a buret barrel.	117
8-3. Removal of grease from a buret tip.	118
8-4. Manipulation of a buret stopcock.	119
8-5. Method of approaching an endpoint.	120
8-6. Reading a buret.	121
8-7. Cleaning a pipet.	124
8-8. Use of the pipet.	125
8-9. Use of the volumetric flask.	127
9-1. Concentration relationships near the endpoint.	135
9-2. A linear titration curve of chloride ion with silver nitrate.	136
9-3. Linear and logarithmic scales.	136
9-4. Titration curve of chloride ion with silver nitrate.	138
10-1. Titration curves of strong acids with strong bases.	155
10-2. Titration curves of strong and weak acids with a strong base.	171
10-3. The titration of HAc with NaOH, showing all species.	174
10-4. Titration curves of H_2CO_3 and Na_2CO_3.	182
10-5. A sodium hydroxide storage bottle.	188
10-6. Titration curves of H_3PO_4 and Na_3PO_4.	189
11-1. Diagram of an electrolytic cell.	215
11-2. Comparison of acid-base titration curves with oxidation-reduction titration curves.	224

Chapter 1

INTRODUCTION

The Nature of Quantitative Analysis

Quantitative analysis is the application of chemical fact, theory, and experimental technique to the precise determination of the composition of samples of matter. Such determinations are an essential part of chemical research and are routinely used to control chemical processes and partially to evaluate raw materials and finished products. Apart from the importance of quantitative analytical data, a study of the methods used is an excellent introduction to the general problems of quantitative chemical investigation.

An almost endless variety of analytical problems arises in chemical research and technology. Materials to be analyzed range from complex natural products to quite simple compounds. At one extreme, the constituents of interest may comprise the bulk of the sample and, at the other extreme, they may be present only to the extent of a few parts per million. An analysis in terms of the elements present may suffice in some cases, while in others it is necessary to determine constituent ions and molecules or less specific units such as proteins. The degree of precision is also variable since it depends primarily upon the use that is to be made of the analytical data.

Because of this wide range of analytical problems, there is no practical set of standard methods applicable to any and all samples. Instead, there are analytical methods of a limited range of application which must be evaluated and frequently modified with respect to specific problems. As new techniques of measurement are developed and as the general fund of chemical fact and theory increases, new methods of analysis result and older methods are improved and extended.

Methods of Determination

The analysis of a reasonably complex material usually involves four steps. The first is the isolation of a representative sample small enough to be handled efficiently in the laboratory. At this stage, the problem is to make certain that the small portion taken does have the average composition of the bulk portion of the material. As the second step, the sample is brought into solution, in whole or in part. Next, some degree of separation of the sample into individual constituents is required. Finally, after each constituent has been satisfactorily isolated, the amount of it is determined by the measurement of a suitable physical or chemical property.

The methods of determination used in the last step usually are classified in accordance with the physical property which is directly measured.

Gravimetric methods are characterized by the fact that the determination of mass is the final measurement. The constituent to be determined is isolated as a compound of known composition or, less frequently, as the element, which then is weighed. The constituent also may be weighed indirectly by volatilizing it as a compound of known composition or by measuring a change in weight caused by a known reaction.

Volumetric methods depend upon the measurement of the volume of a solution of known concentration.* The reagent is added to a solution of the suitably isolated constituent, under conditions where a known reaction occurs. The point at which a chemically equivalent amount of reagent has been added is found by observing a physical or chemical property of the solution, which undergoes a marked change at this point. The volume of reagent required for the reaction is then measured and used to calculate the amount of the constituent present.

Physicochemical methods include all those which depend

---

* Sometimes the weight of the solution is measured in order to obtain greater precision.

upon the measurement of physical properties other than mass and volume. These methods are, of course, further divided in accordance with the particular physical property used. Because of considerable progress in instrumentation, the development and widespread application of various of these methods have been among the major recent advances in quantitative analysis.

Scope of the Text

The text is restricted to a consideration of a limited number of gravimetric and volumetric methods in the field of inorganic analysis. No attempt to survey the field has been made. The laboratory experience with a small number of precise determinations provides only an introduction to the most basic operations and the principles employed. It is expected that additional work in quantitative analysis will be undertaken by chemistry majors and that the application of various physicochemical methods will be surveyed by work in instrumental analysis or in the physical chemistry laboratory.

Laboratory Records

Quantitative analysis requires experimental skill as well as an understanding of the principles and facts which underlie the various methods. It is essential to learn to make careful observations and to record them immediately in clear, complete, and permanent form. It is not necessary that such records conform exactly to a fixed pattern, but some general principles should be followed.

A bound notebook containing about one hundred numbered pages of approximately letter size should be used. Allow about ten pages for each determination and reserve the first ten pages for an index, a tabulation of weight corrections, and such miscellaneous data as stock reagent concentrations, molecular weights of various compounds, etc., which are convenient to have at hand.

The entries in connection with any determination consist of experimental data and calculations. The actual observations that are made such as the readings of a buret at the beginning and at the end of a titration, the weights on the balance pan, or the swings of a balance pointer are experimental data. *All such data must be recorded directly in the notebook at the time the observations are made.* The use of loose pieces of paper for temporary records cannot be tolerated. If a mistake has been made in recording an observation, do not erase or obliterate the entry. Draw a single line through the incorrect entry so that it still is legible, record the correct observation close to it, and enter a short explanation for the change. Never tear a page out of the notebook.

Such quantities as the volume of liquid delivered from a buret or the weight of an object are calculated from the experimental data and may be entered whenever it is convenient. If the calculations and experimental data are not on adjacent pages, give a page reference to the data used. It is immaterial whether or not the actual calculations are made directly in the notebook, but it is important that they be recorded there so that possible errors of computation may be easily checked. Quite commonly the left-hand pages of the notebook are reserved for calculations and the right-hand pages for data. It also is very desirable to prepare, for easy reference, a table of the important quantities required in a determination.

All pertinent observations must be recorded. These include the date and approximate time of making the observation; the general appearance of samples, precipitates, and solutions; any real or suspected errors of technique, i. e., such things as observed or suspected spattering, poor removal of a precipitate from a vessel, etc.; room temperature and humidity if these seem unusual. Such qualitative data may be of considerable importance in the final evaluation of the results of a determination. They may suggest various sources of error and provide a basis for the estimation of their possible importance.

The notebooks are subject to examination at any time. An inadequate record of any determination may be used as a basis for rejecting the results.

Organization of Laboratory Time

Because all operations must be carried out with particular care, quantitative work is time consuming. In any particular determination, there are usually some steps which must be performed in unbroken sequence, certain stages at which the determination may be interrupted if necessary, and some operations which require very little direct attention such as the evaporation, and digestion of solutions. The laboratory work must be planned, before coming to the laboratory, with these factors in mind, in order to use the limited amount of time efficiently. It is necessary to work on more than one determination at the same time so that operations on some part of one of the determinations can be carried out while the others are in stages that require little direct attention. The experimental procedures that are given include a consideration of the stages at which the operation may be interrupted and the steps that must be performed in unbroken sequence. It is essential to study the determinations before coming to the laboratory and to organize your time as indicated above.

Chapter 2

INTRODUCTORY LABORATORY TECHNIQUES

USE OF AN ANALYTICAL BALANCE

Importance

Ultimately, all quantitative analyses depend upon the measurement of mass. Indeed, precise weighing is one of the most frequent operations in analytical work. It is necessary, therefore, to master the techniques associated with precision weighings so that they can be performed with reasonable speed.

Standard Weights

The mass of an object is never directly measured. It always is compared with the mass of some standard by means of a balance. This operation is, of course, called a weighing and it is customary to refer to the **weight** of an object as synonymous with its **mass**. Technically, this usage is incorrect, but little confusion results since the units employed make the physical meaning of the measurement clear. The terms mass and weight will, therefore, be used interchangeably in the text in accordance with common practice.

Various sets of standard weights are employed, depending upon the range of weight that is to be considered and upon the type of balance used. A set frequently employed in ordinary analytical work consists of the following units:

g..........20	10	10'	5	2	2'	1		
mg........500	200	100	100'	50	20	10	10'	5

This subdivision of the total permits the assembly of any weight from 5 mg to 51 g in steps of 5 mg. Weights smaller than 5 mg are added or subtracted by means of a rider or other device on the balance. The smallest weight needed in a set depends, of course, upon the balance used and the resultant range of weight that can be covered by its manipulation. Duplicate weights are marked in some way to distinguish them, since the individual units must be calibrated, as discussed later.

It obviously is essential that the mass of the standard weights remain constant. The major difficulty in this regard is an accidental change of weight through chemical or mechanical action.

The gram weights often are made of brass and plated with an inert metal such as gold to minimize chemical attack under normal conditions of exposure. For the same reason, the small weights frequently are made of platinum. All but the very cheap sets are reasonably resistant to attack under ordinary atmospheric conditions, but no set can be expected to withstand continued exposure to the usual laboratory atmosphere without corrosion.

Careless handling is a serious source of trouble. Material may be picked up by such acts as setting weights on the balance table or by handling them with the fingers. The weights sometimes are dropped or seriously scratched by rough handling with forceps. In this regard, it is worth noting that a precision tolerance of 0.1 mg is represented by about 0.00001 ml of brass. This corresponds to a 1 cm scratch 0.01 cm wide and 0.001 cm deep.

The above difficulties can be minimized by adhering to the following rules:
1. Never handle the weights with fingers.
2. Use forceps gently to avoid possible abrasion of the weights.
3. Never place a weight anywhere except on the balance pan or in its *proper* position in the box.
4. Keep the box closed when not in use and keep it out of the laboratory.
5. If a weight has been dropped or otherwise subjected to possible injury, do not use it until it has been checked.

Calibration of Weights

It is expensive to make weights with masses that are precisely equal to fixed values. Moreover, it is unnecessary to do so, since the individual weights can be more easily calibrated than precisely tailored. Methods of calibration are described in more extensive analytical texts. They will not be discussed here because the experience gained in making the calibrations does not justify the time required.

In practically all analyses, the final result is calculated as the ratio of two experimentally determined weights multiplied by some numerical factor. It therefore is essential that the set of weights be self-consistent, but it seldom is necessary that it be calibrated so that the sum of the two 10 g weights is exactly equal to the value of the 20 g weight and so on.

However, it is not necessary that the absolutely correct values of the individual weights be known. In the rare cases where an absolute calibration is required, it is customary to send an acceptable grade of weights to the Bureau of Standards where they can be calibrated against carefully maintained absolute standards.

Use of Weight Corrections

The correction to each individual weight in a calibrated set usually is given as the number of milligrams that must be added (no sign) or subtracted (− sign) from the nominal value of the weight to obtain its precise mass. To obtain the weight of an object, the sum of the nominal values of the individual weights is obtained and the corrections are algebraically added separately. The resultant total correction is now algebraically added to the nominal total to obtain the correct weight. The latter is then rounded off to the nearest 0.1 mg which is the precision limit of the ordinary analytical balance.

As an example, suppose an object has been balanced exactly by use of the following weights:

Weights...	5 g	2 g	2′g	200 mg	10 mg	10′mg
Corr.(mg).	−1.61	0.45	−0.14	0.83	−0.20	0.11

Sum of the weights.................... 9.2200 g
Sum of the corrections................ −0.00056 g
Correct weight (nearest 0.1 mg)........ 9.2194 g

Operation of an Analytical Balance

The most frequent analyses involve techniques for quantitative operations with amounts of material between 0.01 and 1 g. The analytical balance used for these *macro scale* de-

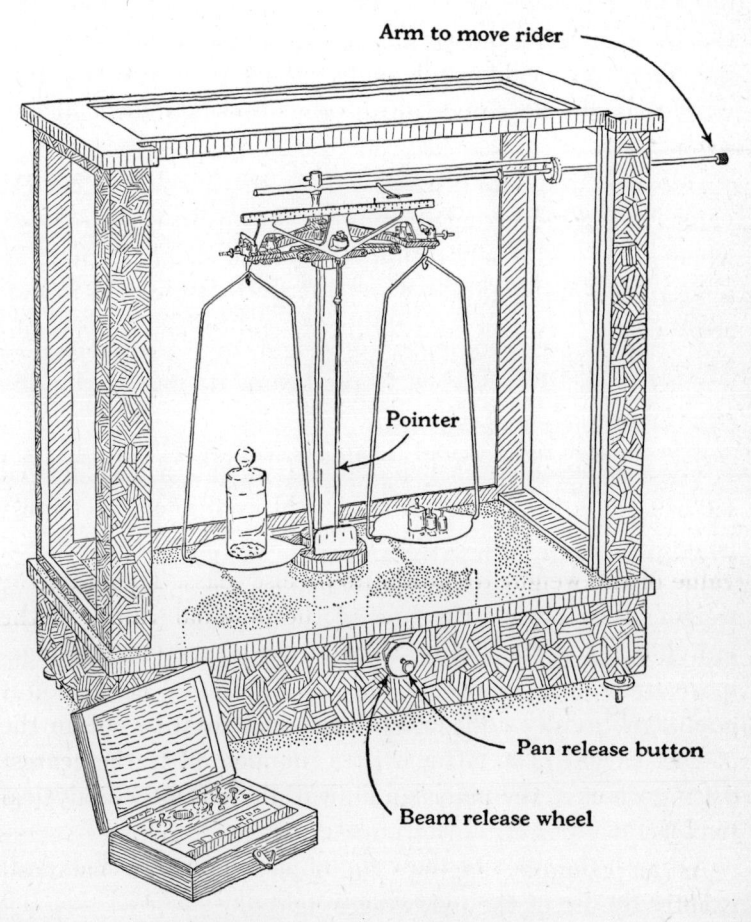

FIG. 2-1(a). The analytical balance.

terminations is an instrument which can be used to weigh from 1 mg to about 50 g with a precision of approximately 0.1 mg. Effective techniques also have been developed for quantitative operations with amounts of material ranging from 10 mg to one microgram (10^{-6} g). Quantitative work with such small amounts involves the use of semimicro or micro analytical balances. Micro scale analyses are particularly useful in dealing with material which may be hazardous in bulk and with materials which are very limited in quantity.

The following discussion applies to the use of an analytical balance for the weighings required in macro scale operations. Detailed descriptions of other types of analytical balances may be found in more comprehensive discussions of analytical procedures and in the literature.

One type of macro scale analytical balance is shown in Figure 2-1 (a). The knurled wheel controls the beam release as discussed later. The button in the center of the wheel controls the pan arrests which can be seen by their reflection in the bottom of the balance case. The arm is used to move a small platinum rider along the scale on the beam to obtain differences of weight up to 10 mg. The pointer is rigidly attached to the beam. Its use will be discussed later.

The light-weight, rigid beam is supported on a rigid central column through a knife edge which rests on a carefully ground plane surface as shown in Figure 2-1(b). The edge and plane frequently are made of agate to minimize corrosion and abrasion. The two pans are suspended from the beam by minimal friction junctions which involve the use of ground planes resting on knife edges as shown. The pan and beam suspensions must be carefully machined and aligned in order to obtain a satisfactory balance.

The lengths from the central knife edge to the pan knife edge supports are made equal, within technical limits, so that the mass of an object on one pan can be directly compared with the mass of the weights placed on the other pan.

In order to protect the beam and pan suspensions, the beam arrest shown in Figure 2-1(c) is provided. When the

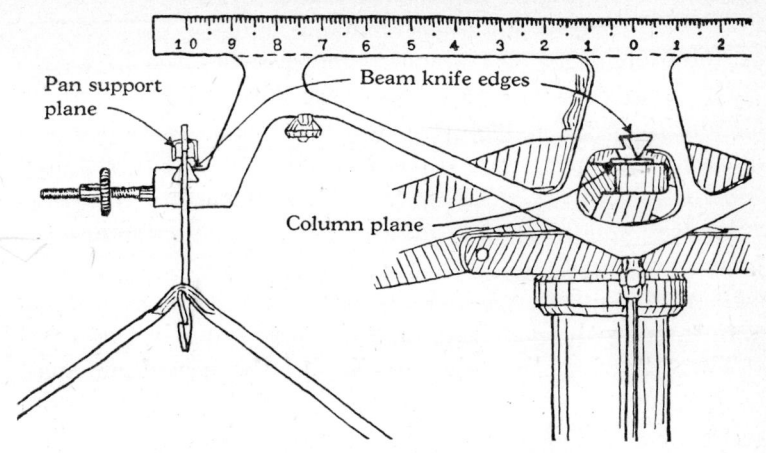

FIG. 2-1(b). The bearing surfaces of a balance.

wheel is turned counter-clockwise, the support moves into the position shown in the figure. When it is turned clockwise, the pan supports are held above their knife edges and the beam knife edge is lifted above its central beam support. If the beam arrest is released abruptly, the knife edges strike their supporting surfaces with a force which can blunt or crack the edges and can sometimes fracture the planes. If objects on the pans are changed without using the beam arrest, the critical suspensions are subjected to sudden jars that can injure them. Three rules should be followed strictly in using the beam arrest:

1. Release the beam slowly.

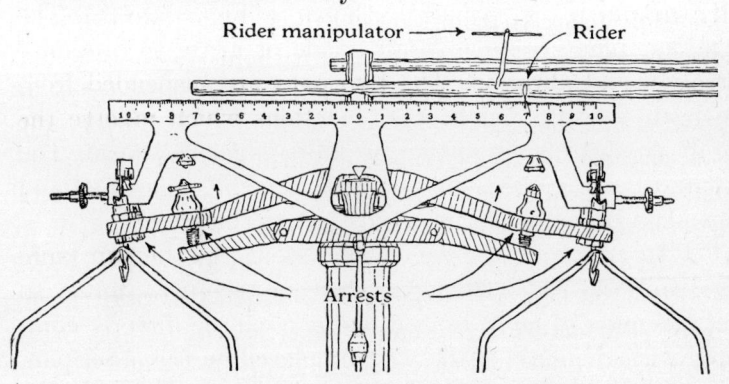

FIG. 2-1(c). Detail of beam arrest mechanism.

2. Arrest the beam when changing weights or objects on the pans.

3. Arrest the beam when the balance is not in use.

The type of balance frequently used has a rider that can be moved along the beam by a control which projects through the upper right-hand side of the balance case. A scale on the beam has 5 or 10 main divisions each of which is subdivided into 10 small divisions corresponding to 0.1 mg. Changing the position of the rider permits the addition or subtraction of 5 to 10 mg of weight in units as small as 0.1 mg.

The balance must always be level and properly adjusted as to sensitivity, rest point, and period of oscillation. All such adjustments will be made by the instructor. They should not be attempted by the student.

A Method of Determination of the Zero and Rest Points

The operations involved in a weighing are considered here without elaboration as to technique for this can best be learned by observation.

The zero point is the scale reading that corresponds to the equilibrium position of the pointer when the balance is empty. In the direct weighing of an object, it is necessary to determine the zero point of the balance as a reference position. When the beam and pan arrests of the balance are released, the pointer will swing back and forth across its equilibrium position. It is impractical to wait for the balance to come to rest or to release the pans without starting the balance swinging, and so the zero point is calculated from observations of the amplitudes of the pointer oscillation. The chief obstacle to simplicity is the continuous decrease in the oscillations, primarily due to air resistance which opposes a vertical movement of the large pan surfaces. Various methods of taking this damping effect into account are used in order to obtain the true rest point. The method described below is quite satisfactory for ordinary analytical weighings. Other methods are described in detail in many texts and can be tried and used if you prefer to do so.

In the following discussion, we shall assume that the scale on the balance is numbered as shown in Figure 2-2:

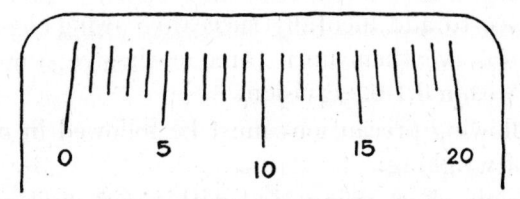

FIG. 2-2. Balance pointer scale.

To start the balance swinging, slowly release the beam arrest and manipulate the pan arrest to get the desired amplitude of swing. Do not attempt to control the swings by the beam arrest or to start the swings by fanning the pan or by tapping it in any manner.

While maintaining a position directly in front of the balance, observe the amplitude of successive swings, estimating them to 0.1 scale division. Disregard the first few swings because they may be erratic because of extraneous vibrations induced in releasing the beam. For small oscillations, between 5 and 15 on the scale, the damping of the swings is small and usually can be neglected. The average of two successive swings is taken as an approximate zero point. In taking the average with the scale numbered as shown, add the values observed for the amplitude of two successive swings and divide by two. However, the sum of the two amplitudes is as useful as the zero point itself and so we may use it for convenience.

To illustrate the method some typical data are shown below:

Scale Readings	7.5, 13.4	7.6, 13.2	7.6, 13.0	7.8, 12.8	7.9, 12.6
Sum of Two	20.9	20.8	20.6	20.6	20.5
Zero Point	10.5	10.4	10.3	10.3	10.3

In these data, the decreasing amplitude is seen, as is the fact that it is only of the order of 0.1 division per swing. Since observations of the amplitude are uncertain to this amount, the decrease is not important, and so a variation of 0.1 division in the zero point or 0.2 division in the sum is to be expected. In the data given above, it should be noted that the first four swings are less reliable than the subsequent ones in yielding a constant value for the sum. It should be standard practice to add mentally successive swings and to continue to observe them until three successive sums become constant within 0.1-0.2 division.

The following precautions must be followed in using this method of weighing:

1. Use only short swings, i.e., within ± 5 divisions of the equilibrium point.
2. Do not base a sum on just two swings. *Observe successive sums until three of them agree within 0.2 division.*

The application of this method to scales numbered 10, 5, 0, 5, 10 will not be described separately. Hereafter, we will use the term zero point to mean the sum described above, as well as the true zero point since there is a direct, simple relation between the two.

The zero point of a balance is not constant, particularly where the balance is used by several people. The zero point will vary through contamination of the pans, temperature changes, slight jarring of the balance, etc. Unless several objects are weighed in unbroken sequence, the zero point must be determined before every direct weighing. If it is more than two divisions from the midpoint, ask your instructor to readjust the balance.

The rest point of the balance is the equilibrium position of the pointer when the balance is loaded. It is determined, of course, in the same way as the zero point.

A Direct Weighing

Place the object to be weighed *in the center* of the left-hand pan and set the rider at zero. All objects to be weighed must be essentially at the balance temperature to avoid creating thermal air currents which interfere with the free oscillation of the balance. Place the weights systematically* on the right-hand pan in decreasing order of mass until the object is

---

* Considerable time can be saved in this step by obtaining an approximate weight of the object on a less sensitive balance. If this is done, care must be taken to prevent contamination.

INTRODUCTORY LABORATORY TECHNIQUES 15

balanced within 5 to 10 mg. The weights *must be grouped in the center of the pan* to eliminate sidewise oscillations when the pans are released. During this stage, the balance case may be left open to facilitate the exchange of individual weights. After the object has been balanced within 5 to 10 mg, close the case and move the rider systematically until the pointer swings within the limits of the scale. Then determine a rest point. Unless the rest point happens to coincide with the known zero point of the balance, move the rider, actually or by calculation, to the position where this is true. The simplest method for doing this is by calculation based upon a determination of the *sensitivity* of the balance. This procedure is illustrated by the following example in which the zero point and rest points are stated as the sums previously discussed.

Operation	Wts.	Rider	Pointer	Object Wt.
1. Determine the zero point.	0	0	20.5	......
2. Balance object within 10 mg.	12.570	0	off right	12.570
	12.580	0	off left	12.580
3. Move rider until pointer value is on scale near zero point.	12.570	3	22.1	12.573
4. Move rider 1 mg in direction to bracket zero point.	12.570	4	17.7	12.574
5. Calculate rider position where rest point equals the zero point.				

From steps (3) and (4), it is found that a weight of 1 mg shifts the pointer from 22.1 to 17.7 or 4.4 scale divisions. The *sensitivity* of the balance is therefore 1 mg divided by 4.4 scale divisions or 1/4.4 mg/div. From (3), it is evident that the object weighs 12.570 g plus 3 mg *plus* the weight needed to shift the pointer from a rest point of 22.1 to the zero point of 20.5, a shift of 1.6 scale divisions. This weight is 1.6 scale divisions times the sensitivity in milligrams per scale division and is therefore 1.6 × 1/4.4, or 0.4 mg.

6. List weights by empty spaces in the box and check this list as the weights are removed. Algebraically sum up the weights and the corrections.

```
                box      10 g    2 g    500 mg   50 mg   20 mg      12.570
Weights
         removed  √       √       √       √       √
Corrections (mg) −1.1    0.3    0.05    −0.06     0       −0.0008
Rider (with rest point 22.1 and zero point 20.5)..........    0.003
Weight to shift rest point from 22.1 to 20.5.............    0.0004
    Total Weight.......................................   12.5726
```

To try your understanding of the use of balance sensitivity independently, calculate the weight that must be subtracted to bring the rest point from 17.7 with the rider at 4 mg to 20.5 which is the required rest point. The result should check the above value of 12.5726 g for the final weight.

One more example is given below.

Weights   *Corrections (mg)*
  10 g   −0.14   Zero Point = 20.5
   5 g   0.05
   2 g   0.41   Rest Point with rider
 100 mg   −0.02   at 6 mg = 16.7
  50 mg   −0.03
  10 mg   −0.01   Rest Point with rider
                            at 5 mg = 23.1

From these data, you should obtain **a weight for the object of 17.1657 g.**

Weighing by Difference

It is not necessary to determine the zero point of a balance if the amount of material transferred out of a container such as a weighing bottle is determined by weighing it before and after the transfer. This method is commonly employed in weighing samples. In this case, the weighing bottle is balanced as described above. A rest point is determined as soon as the pointer swings freely on scale. The approximate amount of material required is carefully transferred to a beaker or other container and the weighing bottle is reweighed, using this rest point as the zero point of the balance. It should be clear that the correct weight of material transferred is obtained in this way even though the correct weight of the weighing bottle is not.

Errors in Recording Weights

During a weighing, it is easy to make arithmetical mistakes in adding swings, adding weights, etc. It therefore is essential to record all actual observations as they are made, so that the arithmetical operations can be checked to eliminate errors.

It also is easy to fail to record or to misread the value of one or more of the weights on the pan. To minimize this error, make a list of the weights on the pan by listing the empty spaces in the weight box. Check this list as the weights on the pan are individually removed and placed in their proper positions in the box.

Systematic Balance Errors

If l_1 and l_2 are the lengths of the balance arms and if w_1 and w_2 are the weights on the corresponding pans, balance is obtained when $w_1 l_1 = w_2 l_2$. Therefore, $w_1 = w_2 l_2 / l_1$, and $w_1 = w_2$ only if $l_1 = l_2$. It is impossible to make l_1 and l_2 exactly equal. Whenever an absolute weight comparison is made, as in the calibration of weights, this systematic error must be considered. Since most analyses involve the ratio of two experimentally measured weights, the error due to unequal balance arms cancels when both weighings are made on the same balance. In this case, there is no necessity for making a correction. However, if you must check a weight after it has been subject to possible injury, consult your instructor in regard to a method of correcting for balance arm inequalities.

One other systematic error which generally is negligible in analytical work should be mentioned. An object of mass m will have a volume V_0 equal to m/d_0 where d_0 is the density of the material. Similarly, the weights will have a volume V_w equal to m/d_w. If d_a is the density of air, there will be an upward "push" on the object equal to $V_0 d_a$ and an upward "push" on the weights equal to $V_w d_a$. If V_0 and V_w are equal, the buoyant effect of the air will cancel; if not, there will be a systematic error which depends upon the extent of the difference in density between the weights employed and the object weighed. This correction can be important in very precise analytical work. It is important when absolute weights must be obtained. In ordinary analyses, it seldom is significant and so the method of making buoyancy corrections will not be discussed further.

DRYING AND STORING SOLIDS

Water Content of Air

The pressure of water vapor in equilibrium with liquid water increases with the temperature as shown in Table 2-1.

TABLE 2-1

PARTIAL PRESSURE OF WATER IN AIR AT VARIOUS TEMPERATURES

Pressure (mm of Hg)	4.6	9.2	12.8	17.5	23.8	31.8	41.6
Temp. °C	0	10	15	20	25	30	35

Air which contains water vapor at the equilibrium pressure is described as having a relative humidity of 100%. If, as is usually the case, the air is not saturated, its water content can be expressed by stating that the air has a certain relative humidity. Thus, air at 25° C containing water at a pressure of 15 mm of mercury has a relative humidity of 15/23.8 (equilibrium pressure at 25° C) $\times$ 100 or 63%.

At 25° C, the equilibrium pressure of 23.8 mm of mercury corresponds to a water content of 23.1 mg of water per liter of air, and so it is evident that the weight of a substance can change significantly by either absorbing water from, or losing water to, even a small volume of air.

Water in Solids

The extent to which a given solid can gain or lose water

when exposed to air depends upon the humidity, the temperature, the state of subdivision of the solid, and the nature of the solid. Solids which take water from the air are said to be *hygroscopic*.

The water associated with solids may conveniently be divided into two kinds:

a) The water adsorbed on the surface.
b) The water chemically combined throughout the solid substance.

Surface adsorption occurs quite generally at the interface of a solid and a gas because the molecules in the gas are acted on by the field of force around the atoms in the surface of the solid. The amount of a gaseous substance adsorbed on a unit area of a given solid depends upon the temperature and upon the ratio p/p_0 where p is the partial pressure of the substance in the gaseous phase, and p_0 is the vapor pressure of this substance in the liquid state at the temperature considered. In the case of air, at room temperature, such components as oxygen, nitrogen, and carbon dioxide are considerably above their boiling points; p_0 is therefore very large and the corresponding p/p_0 values are very small. As a result, surface adsorption by these substances is rarely of analytical significance in changing the weight of a solid. However, the p/p_0 values for water in air at room temperature are generally in the range of 0.2 to 0.8, corresponding to relative humidities of 20 to 80%. Under these conditions, many solids condense water on their surfaces to form polymolecular films when exposed to air under ordinary conditions.

In the case of any given solid at a particular temperature and a definite value of p/p_0, the amount of water adsorbed per gram is directly proportional to the area of the solid. Such objects as weights, crucibles, and weighing bottles have relatively small surface areas and ordinarily do not adsorb significant quantities of water. On very humid days, the weight of a dried weighing bottle may increase by as much as a few tenths of a mg. However, finely divided materials present so much surface that they may adsorb analytically significant amounts of moisture under ordinary conditions.

Ordinarily, surface-adsorbed water can be removed by heating the solid between 100 and 120° C. In less frequent cases, such as that of silica gel, much higher temperatures are required. In cases where heating results in a chemical change in the solid, drying usually is done at lower temperatures and at reduced pressures.

Water of Hydration.—Various substances form hydrates in which water molecules are present as units in the solid. In these cases, the area of the solid does not determine the amount of water taken up; it is important only in determining the rate at which water is exchanged between the solid and air. The stability of a given hydrate at a given temperature depends upon the partial pressure of water, p, as shown by the typical vapor-pressure diagram in Figure 2-3.

The practical significance of Figure 2-3 can be expressed

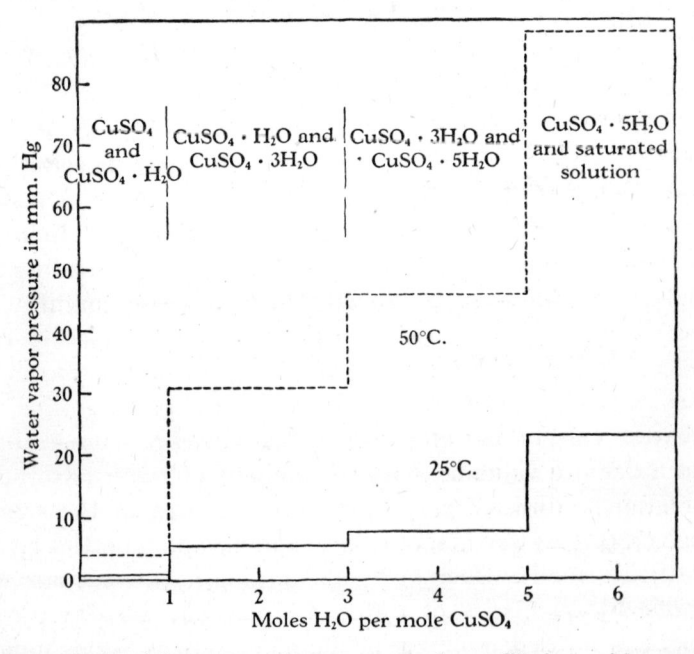

FIG. 2-3. Partial pressure of water vapor in equilibrium with copper sulfate, its crystalline hydrates, and the saturated solution at 25°C. and at 50°C.

in the following way. If anhydrous copper sulfate is exposed to air at 25° C when the partial pressure of water is less than 0.8 mm of mercury, the monohydrate, $CuSO_4 \cdot H_2O$, does not form. If the pressure is greater than 0.8 mm, water is taken up to form $CuSO_4 \cdot H_2O$ and this continues until the partial pressure of water is reduced to 0.8 mm or until all of the copper sulfate is converted to the monohydrate. At pressures between 0.8 and 5.6 mm, the monohydrate is stable. If the pressure is above 5.6 mm, the trihydrate forms until the pressure is reduced to 5.6 mm or until all of the monohydrate is converted to the trihydrate. When the pressure is between 5.6 and 7.8 mm, the trihydrate is stable; formation of the pentahydrate begins if the pressure exceeds 7.8 mm. The dotted curve shows the equilibrium pressure at 50° C. It should be clear that anhydrous copper sulfate can be obtained by heating the pentahydrate to 50° C if the partial pressure of water is kept below 4.5 mm of mercury.

When the anhydrous form of a solid is required, any water of hydration usually is removed by heating to the temperature required in the specific case. If this is not possible because of other chemical changes at the required temperature, the usual procedure is to dry the hydrate *in vacuo*. When a specific hydrate must be weighed, it usually is necessary to prepare a *hygrostat* that will maintain the vapor pressure in the range of stability of the desired hydrate.

Use of a Desiccator

A desiccator, of the type shown in Figure 2-4, is used to provide a dry, dust-free space for the storage of materials that have been suitably dried.

Water is removed from the air in the desiccator by the introduction of substances that combine with water to form hydrates or dry materials, such as silica gel, which very strongly binds adsorbed water. Among the commonly used desiccants are: anhydrous calcium chloride, sulfuric acid, phosphorus pentoxide, magnesium perchlorate, and silica gel. When equilibrium is reached, the final vapor pressure of

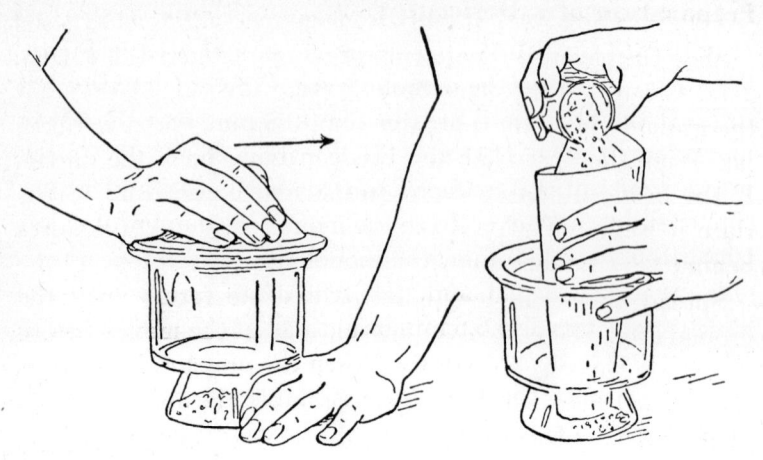

Fig. 2-4. (a) Opening a desiccator, and (b) adding the desiccant to a desiccator.

water in the desiccator depends upon the particular desiccant used. For the materials encountered in this course, anhydrous calcium chloride is a satisfactory desiccant.

It is very important to realize that water is removed slowly from the air in a desiccator even when the most effective desiccants are employed. Water molecules are not removed until they actually strike the desiccant. The diffusion of the water molecules through the other molecules in the air is a slow process and so the initial drying of the air in the desiccator may require two to four hours. For the desiccator to function properly, it must be opened as few times as possible and those times should be as brief as possible. Furthermore, the materials placed in the desiccator should be dry.

Hot objects must be cooled to somewhat above room temperature before being placed in the desiccator, for otherwise some air will be forced out, and so, on cooling, a vacuum will be produced. Such a vacuum will make it difficult to open the desiccator. In addition, air currents initiated at the time of opening may deposit desiccant on materials in the desiccator. If the lid is replaced before the air has expanded, it may be blown off.

Preparation of a Desiccator

Slide the cover of the desiccator off, as indicated in Figure 2-4a. Clean and dry the support, wipe the old grease from the ground glass, and pour the old desiccant into the waste jar. Wipe the dust from the inside with a clean, dry towel. If the inside is visibly dirty, wash it with soap and water, rinse it well, and wipe it dry. Keep the amount of lint left behind to a minimum.

Spread about one-fourth ml of vaseline evenly over the ground area. Slide the cover into place and rotate it to further distribute the vaseline. If the proper amount has been used, the contact area will be transparent and the cover will not readily slide out of place.

Make a funnel of a piece of paper and insert it into the bottom compartment of the desiccator as shown in Figure 2-4b.

Fill a 100 ml beaker with dry calcium chloride, lower it into the funnel, and then carefully empty the beaker so as not to raise a dust. Remove the paper, but do not permit it to come into contact with the upper part of the desiccator. Spread the calcium chloride uniformly by slightly tilting the desiccator. Replace the cleaned and dried support, slide the lid into place, and set the desiccator aside until needed.

Deposition of desiccant on objects to be weighed must be avoided. Should such deposition occur, the weights of the objects will change rapidly through moisture absorption. In addition, the possibility of transferring desiccant from the object to the balance pan is even more serious since this may result in permanent injury to the instrument.

DETERMINATION OF WATER IN BARIUM CHLORIDE DIHYDRATE

Outline of the Method

A determination of the percent of water in pure barium chloride dihydrate, $BaCl_2 \cdot 2H_2O$, is recommended as an introductory experiment to obtain familiarity with the use of a balance and with other manipulative techniques. If the determination is omitted, the procedure should be studied as an example of the techniques involved in a simple type of gravimetric determination.

Barium chloride dihydrate is stable in air within the ordinary extremes of humidity at room temperature. As the temperature is raised, the equilibrium water-vapor pressure in the reaction $BaCl_2 \cdot 2H_2O = BaCl_2 + 2H_2O$ also increases (See Fig. 2-3). Anhydrous barium chloride can be obtained in a reasonable time by heating the dihydrate somewhat above 100° C under ordinary atmospheric conditions. If a weighed sample that is known to be pure dihydrate is thus heated for a suitable time, the loss in weight is an experimental determination of the amount of water in the sample. The percent of water originally present can then be calculated within the experimental limits of error.

Preparation of a Simple Muffle Furnace

The hydrate can conveniently be decomposed in a small muffle-type furnace at 125 to 175° C. Such a furnace assembly is shown in Figure 2-5. Since new asbestos frequently contains volatile materials, the furnace should be heated to 125 to 175° C without the weighing bottle present until any evolution of smoke stops.

Preparation and Manipulation of the Weighing Bottle

Wipe the inside and the outside of a weighing bottle with a clean, dry towel. Avoid leaving lint behind. If the bottle is visibly dirty, wash it with soap and water, rinse it thoroughly with tap water, then with distilled water, and wipe it dry. Place the bottle in the muffle as shown in Figure 2-5 and tilt the stopper so that water vapor and air can escape. Heat for fifteen minutes at 125 to 175° C, and then remove the burner. When the thermometer registers about 50°, transfer the bottle (still not stoppered) to the desiccator. After the bottle has cooled to room temperature (which requires about 30 minutes), take the desiccator to the balance, remove the bottle, stopper it, and weigh it. Record the weight in the notebook. Again tilt the stopper, heat the bottle, and

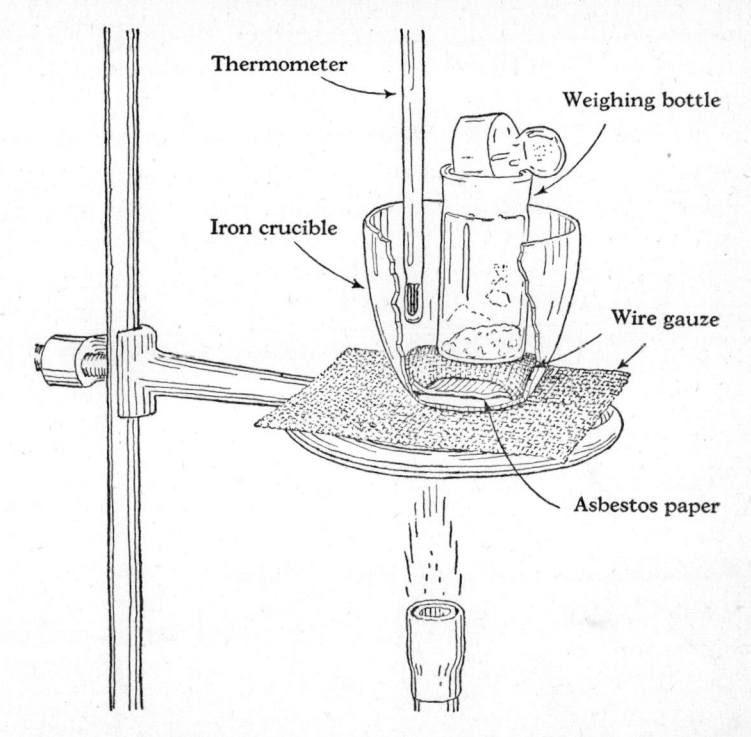

FIG. 2-5. Muffle furnace assembly for the determination of water in barium chloride dihydrate.

obtain a second weight as before. If the weighings agree within 0.2 mg, take the average as the weight of the empty bottle.

Pick-up of moisture and grease due to handling of the weighing bottle must be minimized. In this connection, it is worth noting that the expected precision tolerance of 0.2 mg corresponds to 0.0002 ml of water which is just barely visible as a drop. Since manipulation of the weighing bottle with crucible tongs is dangerously awkward, the procedure shown in Figure 2-6 is recommended.

Indirect Determination of Water

Place an estimated 1 to 2 g (about 0.5 ml) of barium chloride dihydrate in the dry bottle and accurately weigh the bottle plus the sample. Heat for 30 minutes at 125-175° C,

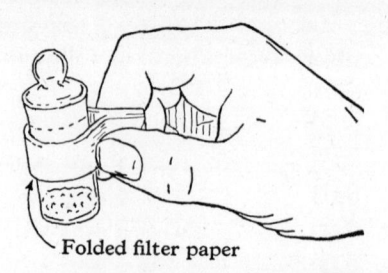

Fig. 2-6. Holding a weighing bottle.

as described in the preparation of the dry bottle, cool, and weigh. Repeat for ten-minute periods until successive determinations of the weight agree to ± 0.2 mg. It is important to keep the bottle stoppered during these weighings.

Assuming that the observed loss in weight is due to loss of water, calculate the percent water which was present in the sample. Compare your result with the theoretical value. If it agrees within five parts per thousand, you may consider your technique in regard to these fundamental operations as satisfactory at this time. If such agreement is lacking, consult your instructor.

Problems

1. Calculate to a tenth of a milligram the weight of an object from the data listed below:

Weight on right hand pan....................19.850 g
Zero Point...................................20.4
Rest Point with rider at 3 mg................22.3
Rest Point with rider at 4 mg................17.6

Ans. **19.8534 g**

2. The 500 mg fractional in a box of weights was damaged and so it was recalibrated against the following weights:

200 mg	0.04 mg		
100	−0.12	Zero Point............19.9	
100	−0.03	Rest Point with rider	
50	0.03	at 4 mg............21.5	
20	0.09	Rest Point with rider	
10	0.00	at 5 mg............16.9	
10	0.01		
5	0.05		

What is the correct weight of the fractional?

Ans. **499.4 mg**

3. An unknown sample is to be analyzed for residue after heating. From the following data calculate the percent residue in the sample.

Weight weighing bottle
Weights on right hand pan................. 18.750 g
Zero Point............................... 20.0
Rest Point with rider at 6 mg.............. 20.9
Rest Point with rider at 7 mg.............. 16.3

Weight weighing bottle plus sample
Weights on right hand pan................. 20.640 g
Rest Point with rider at 2 mg.............. 23.4
Rest Point with rider at 3 mg.............. 19.0

Weight weighing bottle plus sample after heating
Weights on right hand pan................. 19.985 g
Rest Point with rider at 4 mg.............. 21.1
Rest Point with rider at 5 mg.............. 16.6

Ans. **65.4%**

Chapter 3

FUNDAMENTAL CALCULATIONS

The Basis of Stoichiometric Calculations

The term stoichiometry refers to the relationships that exist between the weights of the various substances that take part in a chemical reaction. The three basic empirical laws of stoichiometry—the *Law of Constant Proportions*, the *Law of Simple Multiple Proportions*, and the *Law of Combining Weights*—acquired a theoretical foundation with the advent of the *Atomic Theory*. This theory, as you will recall, stated that all matter is composed of small particles called atoms and that the atoms of each *element* are alike in every respect.

The comparatively recent discovery of *isotopes*, however, made it necessary to rephrase the above statement somewhat, and to say that only the atoms of a given isotope of an element are exactly alike. Thus, the element chlorine contains two isotopes—an atom of the heavier isotope weighing 37/35 as much as an atom of the lighter one. In naturally occurring compounds of chlorine, the ratio of the amounts of the two isotopes is constant, and so we usually can ignore the existence of isotopes and assign an average atomic weight to the chlorine atom. All of the elements which are not products of naturally occurring radioactivity have essentially constant isotopic compositions as they are found on the earth, and so the average atomic weights can be used for stoichiometric calculations. The International Table of Atomic Weights is a compilation of average atomic weights relative to 16.000 for the average atomic weight of naturally occurring oxygen.

The weight of a single atom of any element is so small, and the number of atoms used in any reaction is so large, that it is convenient to use a larger unit—the **gram atom**. It is simply the average atomic weight of an element expressed in grams, and corresponds to the weight of 0.602×10^{24} atoms.

Considerations similar to the above also apply to molecules. The quantity corresponding to the weight of 0.602×10^{24} molecules is called a **mole**, and is equal to the molecular weight expressed in grams.

Stoichiometric calculations are based upon the Law of Simple Multiple Proportions and upon the fact that a gram atom of an element and a mole of a compound refer to the same number of particles. This law states that if two substances react, the relative amounts of the substances involved, expressed as gram atoms or moles, will be some simple fraction. In the use of this relationship, seemingly different types of calculation arise because it is necessary to convert directly measured quantities such as mass and volume, into gram atoms and moles.

For purposes of calculation, we may assume that all chemical reactions and physical separations required in an analysis can be quantitatively performed. Practically, this is a goal which can only be approached. In subsequent chapters, the factors that must be considered in this regard will be discussed; for the present, we are concerned only with a review of the basic calculations.

GRAVIMETRIC CALCULATIONS

In gravimetric methods, the constituent to be determined is isolated by suitable means and is then weighed, directly or indirectly, in the form of a compound of known composition or, more rarely, as the element. The calculations required involve the interconversion of moles as the units of reaction and grams, which are the directly measured units. The following examples illustrate the general way in which such calculations can be made.

Example 1.—Determine the weight of chloride ion in a sample by precipitating and weighing it as silver chloride.

Basis of Solution.—One mole of silver chloride can be obtained from one gram atom of chloride ion. The number of gram atoms of chloride ion in the sample is therefore equal to the number of moles of silver chloride obtained from it.

Pertinent Data.—0.7500 g of AgCl were obtained.
One mole of AgCl weighs 143.34 g.
One gram atom of chloride ion weighs 35.457 g.

Numerical Solution.—

$$\text{Weight of chloride ion} = \frac{0.7500}{143.34} \times 35.457 \text{ g.}$$

Of course, the sample in Example 1 must have contained the chloride ion in some combined state. In a specific case, we may know the chlorine compounds that are present, or we may wish to express the chlorine content in terms of an arbitrarily chosen compound for convenience. Suppose, for example, that it is necessary to state the chlorine content of the above sample in terms of its possible sodium chloride content or its possible barium chloride dihydrate content.

Example 2.—Assuming that the chloride ion in Example 1 is present as sodium chloride, calculate the weight of the latter in the sample.

Basis of Solution.—One mole of silver chloride can be obtained from one mole of sodium chloride. The number of moles of sodium chloride in the sample is equal to the number of moles of silver chloride obtained from it.

Pertinent Data.—0.7500 g of AgCl were obtained.
One mole of AgCl weighs 143.34 g.
One mole of NaCl weighs 58.45 g.

Numerical Solution.—

$$\text{Weight of NaCl in sample} = \frac{0.7500}{143.34} \times 58.45 \text{ g.}$$

Example 3.—Assume that the chloride ion in Example 1 is

present as barium chloride dihydrate, $BaCl_2 \cdot 2H_2O$, and calculate the weight of the latter in the sample.

Basis of Solution.—One mole of silver chloride can be obtained from one-half mole of barium chloride dihydrate. The number of moles of barium chloride dihydrate in the sample is equal to one-half the number of moles of silver chloride obtained.

Pertinent Data.—0.7500 g of AgCl were obtained.
One mole of AgCl weighs 143.34 g.
One mole of $BaCl_2 \cdot 2H_2O$ weighs 244.31 g.

Numerical Solution.—

$$\text{Weight of } BaCl_2 \cdot 2H_2O = \frac{1}{2} \times \frac{0.7500}{143.34} \times 244.31 \text{ g.}$$

Example 4.—Calculate the weight of ferroferric oxide, Fe_3O_4, in a sample that yields 0.7516 g of pure ferric oxide, Fe_2O_3, on analysis.

Basis of Solution.—One mole of Fe_3O_4 contains three gram atoms of Fe. Two gram atoms of Fe are needed to make one mole of Fe_2O_3. Therefore, one mole of Fe_2O_3 can be obtained from 2/3 mole of Fe_3O_4. The number of moles of Fe_3O_4 in the sample is equal to 2/3 the number of moles of Fe_2O_3 obtained.

Pertinent Data.—0.7516 g of Fe_2O_3 were obtained.
One mole of Fe_2O_3 weighs 159.70 g.
One mole of Fe_3O_4 weighs 231.55 g.

Numerical Solution.—

$$\text{Weight of } Fe_3O_4 = \frac{2}{3} \times \frac{0.7516}{159.70} \times 231.55 \text{ g.}$$

The preceding examples illustrate the principles applicable to all gravimetric calculations. They should be applied to the exercises at the end of this chapter until the necessary expressions can be set up with facility and confidence. It is strongly recommended that all the problems be solved in terms of the application of basic principles, as outlined above, and that a routine application of proportion or the use of a set of specific formulas be avoided.

Gravimetric Factors

An inspection of the preceding examples of gravimetric calculations will show that the final pattern of the calculation has the form:

Wt. Constituent =

Wt. Compound Obtained $\times \frac{a}{b} \times \frac{\text{M.W. Constituent}}{\text{M.W. Compound Obt.}}$

In this equation, a and b are small integers which make the number of atoms of the element in which we are interested the same in both the compound that is weighed and in the compound that is to be determined. Applied to the preceding Fe_3O_4—Fe_2O_3 example, the factor is $2Fe_3O_4/3Fe_2O_3$ because excess oxygen is available and it is the iron that determines how much Fe_2O_3 can be obtained from a given amount of Fe_3O_4.

A practical value of this expression lies in the fact that the quantity, $a \times M.W.\ Constituent/\ b \times M.W.\ Compound\ Obtained$, can be tabulated for commonly used analytical methods. This quantity is called the *Gravimetric Factor* or sometimes the *Chemical Factor*. Tables of the numerical value of these quantities may be found in various handbooks and in many quantitative texts; their use saves time in routine analytical work. However, it is recommended that the use of gravimetric factors in solving problems be deferred until the principles behind their use are clearly understood.

Calculation of Percent Composition

In practice, analyses are made upon known quantities of sample and the results are usually reported in terms of the percent of the designated constituent in the material. The additional calculation required is simply:

$$\%\ \text{constituent} = \frac{\text{Wt. Constituent}}{\text{Wt. Sample}} \times 100$$

A Method of Numerical Calculation

In the preceding discussion, the calculations have been divided into steps to make them clear. It should, however, be common practice to combine all steps into a single expression before making the actual numerical calculation. This facilitates checking the calculation for errors in method and frequently simplifies the arithmetic because some factors may cancel, and because the non-varying factors can be combined into a constant term.

The numerical calculations required in precise analyses usually are tedious and subject to error due to their length. They can be made less tedious and the possibility of error can be reduced by the use of logarithms. A table of logarithms and a short discussion of its use are given in the Appendix.

The following example of precise calculation is based upon the determination of sulfate in a sample by precipitation as barium sulfate. In this case, the percent sodium sulfate in the sample is to be reported. Two determinations yield the following results:

Determination	*I*	*II*
g sample	0.6543	0.6644
g BaSO$_4$	0.4978	0.5045

Combining the calculation steps into a single expression and then collecting all non-varying factors into a constant term gives:

$$\% Na_2SO_4 = \frac{g\ BaSO_4}{M.W.BaSO_4} \times M.W.Na_2SO_4 \times \frac{100}{g\ sample}$$

$$= \frac{g\ BaSO_4}{g\ sample} \times \frac{142.06}{233.43} \times 100$$

The constant term, $\frac{142.06}{233.43} \times 100$, is evaluated separately since it is used in each calculation. The logarithm of this term is:

$$\log 142.06 + \log 100 - \log 233.43 = 1.78431$$

The remaining calculations are made by means of logarithms as follows:

	I	II
log g BaSO$_4$	19.69705 − 20	19.70286 − 20
log g sample	9.81578 − 10	9.82243 − 10
log g BaSO$_4$/g sample	9.88127 − 10	9.88043 − 10
log factor	1.78431	1.78431
log % Na$_2$SO$_4$	11.66558 − 10	11.66474 − 10
% Na$_2$SO$_4$	46.30	46.21

Precise calculations are required in connection with each laboratory determination. These numerical calculations should be written in the notebook as an integral part of the determination. They should be labelled clearly in a manner similar to that used in the preceding example so that they can be checked in detail at any time. Numerical errors are serious and so every calculation should be systematically checked before reporting an analytical result. The use of a slide rule, to obtain the approximate value of an analytical result, is a simple and recommended way to check the general validity of a more exact calculation. Although the ordinary slide rule is not satisfactory for the evaluation of precise analytical results, it is entirely satisfactory for the problems in the text.

Once the experimental data have been obtained, numerical calculations can be carried out with any degree of precision. The precision implied by the calculated result should correspond to that set by the data. The use of significant figures in this connection and the general problem of evaluating a calculated result in terms of the precision of the experimental data are discussed in Chapter 7.

COMMON VOLUMETRIC CALCULATIONS

An amount of a dissolved substance can conveniently be measured in terms of the volume of a solution of known concentration. This is, of course, the routine method of measuring required amounts of reagents in laboratory work and is the characteristic feature of volumetric analysis. The stoichiometric calculations of volumetric analysis will be discussed in detail in subsequent chapters. At this point, we are concerned with the calculations required in laboratory operations and with a review of the calculation of molar concentrations because of their use in the discussion of solubility equilibria in Chapters 4 and 5.

Concentration Units

The concentration of a component of a solution may be expressed in various ways, the choice in any particular case being one of convenience. Solutions frequently are prepared by dissolving a weighed amount of a substance in enough solvent to produce a predetermined volume of solution. For such solutions, the concentration can conveniently be expressed as grams per unit volume.

Sometimes the composition is more loosely stated on a percentage basis. Unfortunately, the term percent may mean percent by weight or percent by volume. For example, a 10% alcohol solution may mean 10 g of alcohol dissolved in 100 g of solution (percent by weight) or 10 ml of alcohol dissolved in 100 ml of solution (percent by volume). In the case of water solutions, the term percent often is interpreted as the number of grams of substance dissolved in 100 ml of water. Because of this ambiguity, it has become common practice to use percent in connection with reagents whose concentration is only approximately known. It is possible to specify composition carefully by stating which percentage is meant; unless this is done, it can be assumed that the percentage given is approximately the number of grams of solute in 100 ml of water solution.

In stoichiometric calculations, the most useful designations are: *molarity* (M)* which is the number of moles of a component in one liter of solution, and *normality* (N) which is the number of equivalents of a component in one liter of solution. Discussion of the latter term will be deferred until

---

*This definition of the term *molarity* is used throughout the analytical literature with very few exceptions. We have therefore retained it in this text and departed from the usage found in the preceding texts of this series.

neutralization reactions are considered. Sometimes *formality* is used in place of molarity in cases where the true molecular weight is in doubt. Formality corresponds to the number of formula weights, in grams, per liter of solution.

Some solids, like iodine, are built up of molecular groups. However, this is not the case for most of the substances with which we shall be concerned. For these solids, the molecular weight has no physical significance. The formula describes only the average composition without implying the existence of distinguishable molecules in the solid. When a solid is dissolved, molecules of the formula composition may be found in the solution or there may be dissociation, association, or reaction with the solvent to yield a variety of ions and other molecules. We shall use the term *molar* to mean that one formula weight, in grams, of a substance is contained in one liter of solution without implying that molecules of this substance are present. Whenever it is necessary to specify the concentration of one or more of the ions or molecules that actually exist in a solution, the terms *molarity* and *normality* will be used. For example, the formula weight of Na_2SO_4 is 142.06 g. A solution that contains 14.206 g of sodium sulfate per liter will be designated as 0.1 M Na_2SO_4. With the further knowledge that there is almost complete dissociation into sodium and sulfate ions, the corresponding concentrations of these species will be designated as 0.1 M SO_4^{--} and 0.2 M Na^+.

Relation of Grams per Unit Volume to Molarity

The conversion of grams per unit volume to molarity follows directly from the definitions of a mole and the molarity of a solution as illustrated below.

Example 1.—Calculate the molarity of a solution prepared by dissolving 5.845 g of pure sodium chloride in enough water to make 250 ml of solution.

Basis of Solution.—

$$\text{Molarity} = \frac{\text{No. of moles dissolved}}{\text{No. of liters of solution obtained}}$$

Pertinent Data.—5.845 g of NaCl were dissolved.
250 ml of solution were obtained.
A mole of NaCl weighs 58.45 g.

Numerical Solution.—

$$M = \frac{\frac{5.845}{58.45}}{\frac{250}{1000}} = 0.400$$

Example 2.—Calculate the weight of silver nitrate required to prepare 150 ml of 0.250 M AgNO$_3$ solution.

Basis of Solution.—The number of moles of silver nitrate required is equal to the number of liters of solution times the molarity. The weight of silver nitrate in grams is equal to the molecular weight of silver nitrate times the number of moles.

Pertinent Data.—A mole of AgNO$_3$ weighs 169.9 g.
The volume of solution is 0.150 l.
The concentration is 0.250 M.

Numerical Solution.—
Weight of AgNO$_3$ = 0.250 × 169.9 × 0.150 g.

Conversion of Percent Concentration to Molarity

In the case of the common concentrated acids and bases, the concentration is known approximately in terms of weight percent and the corresponding molarity must be estimated. Since the density of such solutions may differ largely from unity, a calculation of this kind requires a knowledge of the density of the solution as shown in the following example.

Example 3.—Calculate the approximate molarity of concentrated hydrochloric acid.

Basis of Solution.—If d is the density of the acid, one liter weighs d × 1000 g.

The weight in grams of hydrochloric acid in one liter is $\frac{\text{percent HCl}}{100}$ times the weight of one liter.

Pertinent Data.—Density of concentrated HCl is 1.2 g/ml.

The percent HCl by weight is 39.11.
A mole of HCl weighs 36.47 g.

Numerical Solution.—

$$M = \frac{1.2 \times 1000 \times \frac{39.11}{100}}{36.47}$$

Some Routine Calculations

One of the calculations most frequently required in the laboratory is that of the volume of a solution of known concentration required to precipitate, or otherwise to react with, a known amount of another substance. The following examples illustrate how such calculations can be made using general principles.

Example 1.—Estimate the volume of $0.25 M$ $AgNO_3$ required to precipitate the chloride in a sample of impure sodium chloride.

Basis of Solution.—One mole of sodium chloride requires one mole of silver nitrate to precipitate silver chloride according to the reaction:

$$Ag^+ + Cl^- = AgCl_{(s)}$$

Since the percent purity is unknown, assume the sample to be pure sodium chloride and estimate the number of moles present. Each ml of the $0.25\ M$ $AgNO_3$ solution must, by definition, furnish $\frac{0.25}{1000}$ moles of Ag^+.

Pertinent Data.—The NaCl sample weighs 0.2923 g.
A mole of NaCl weighs 58.45 g.
The $AgNO_3$ is $0.25\ M$.

Numerical Solution.—

Approximate volume of $0.25\ M\ AgNO_3 = \dfrac{\frac{0.29}{58}}{\frac{0.25}{1000}}$ **ml.**

FUNDAMENTAL CALCULATIONS

Example 2.—Estimate the volume of 10% $BaCl_2$ required to precipitate the sulfate in a weighed sample of impure sodium sulfate.

Basis of Solution.—One mole of sodium sulfate will require one mole of barium chloride for precipitation according to the reaction:

$$Ba^{++} + SO_4^{--} = BaSO_{4(s)}$$

Assume that the sample is pure sodium sulfate in order to estimate the moles present.

Pertinent Data.—The sample weighs 0.50 g.

A 10% $BaCl_2$ solution contains approximately 10 g of $BaCl_2$ per 100 ml.

A mole of Na_2SO_4 weighs approximately 142 g.

A mole of $BaCl_2$ weighs approximately 173 g.

Numerical Calculation.—

$$\text{Approximate volume} = \frac{\frac{0.50}{142} \times 173}{\frac{10}{100}} \text{ ml.}$$

Example 3.—Calculate the volume of 0.15 M $AgNO_3$ required to precipitate the chloride in 35 ml of 0.16 M NaCl.

Basis of Solution.—One mole of sodium chloride requires one mole of silver nitrate for precipitation according to the reaction:

$$Ag^+ + Cl^- = AgCl_{(s)}$$

Pertinent Data.—

A ml of 0.16 M NaCl contains $\frac{0.16}{1000}$ moles of Cl^- ion.

A ml of 0.15 M $AgNO_3$ contains $\frac{0.15}{1000}$ moles of Ag^+ ion.

Numerical Calculation. —

$$\text{Approximate volume} = \frac{0.16 \times 35}{0.15} \text{ ml}$$

The Approach to Stoichiometric Calculations

The calculations reviewed in this chapter should be familiar from a study of general chemistry. They have been presented in detail to emphasize the fact that the solution of stoichiometric problems can, and should be, divorced from an attempt to memorize a pattern of formulas and routine proportion. A real understanding of the chemical reactions involved, as well as the physical significance of the terms mole and molarity, are the most important concepts used in the logical solution of almost all of the common stoichiometric calculations.

Problems

1. How many moles of substance are represented by 0.5016 g of a solid if it is: (a) pure KCl; (b) pure NaCl; (c) one-half NaCl and one-half KCl by weight?
   Ans. (a) **0.00673**; (b) **0.00858**; (c) **0.00765**.

2. How would you measure 0.0187 moles of AgCl with a balance?   *Ans.* **Weigh 2.68 g**.

3. A sample yields 0.1433 g of AgCl upon analysis. How many moles of (a) NaCl, (b) $KClO_4$, (c) $CrOCl_2$ could have been present in the sample?
   Ans. (a) **0.001**; (b) **0.001**; (c) **0.0005**.

4. What weight of KCl could have been present in the sample of Problem 3? If the sample weighed 0.5000 g what was the percent KCl?   *Ans.* **0.0746 g; 14.92%**.

5. How many grams of $AgNO_3$ are required to precipitate the halide in 0.7500 g of (a) NaCl, (b) KBr?
   Ans. (a) **2.180 g**; (b) **1.070 g**.

6. What is the logarithm of the weight of the bromine in 15.000 g of (a) NaBr, (b) KBr, (c) $NaBrO_3$?
   Ans. (a) **1.06629**; (b) **1.00316**; (c) **0.90003**.

7. A sample of Na_2SO_4 weighing 0.2841 g yields 0.3501 g

of $BaSO_4$ upon analysis. What is the logarithm for (a) the number of moles of $BaSO_4$ precipitated, (b) the number of grams of sulfur in the sample, (c) the percent sulfur in the sample? *Ans.* (a) **7.17609-10;** (b) **8.68206-10;** (c) **1.22858.**

8. A 0.6000-g sample of $BaCl_2 \cdot 2H_2O$ is heated until anhydrous $BaCl_2$ is obtained. How many moles of H_2O are evolved? What weight of H_2O is evolved? What is the percent H_2O in the sample?
Ans. **0.0049 moles; 0.0885 g; 14.75%.**

9. A mixture of $NaCl$ and $Na_2SO_4 \cdot 7 H_2O$ loses 25.00% of its weight on heating to a high enough temperature to form Na_2SO_4. Calculate the percent composition of the sample.
Ans. **53.2% $Na_2SO_4 \cdot 7H_2O$; 46.8% $NaCl$.**

10. A 1.5000-g sample yields 0.3700 g Fe_2O_3 upon analysis. Write expressions for (a) the percent Fe in the sample, (b) the grams of $Fe_2(SO_4)_3 \cdot 6H_2O$ in the sample.

11. A 1.000-g sample of an equimolar mixture of $NaCl$ and KBr is dissolved in dilute HNO_3 and treated with an excess of $AgNO_3$. The precipitate is filtered, washed, and dried. What is the weight of the precipitate obtained? *Ans.* **1.866 g.**

12. A 1.000-g sample consisting of $LiCl$ and KBr is dissolved and treated with excess $AgNO_3$. The precipitate, after washing and drying, weighs 2.500 g. Calculate the percent composition of the original sample.
Ans. **51.2% $LiCl$; 48.8% KBr.**

13. How many ml of a 0.1500 M HCl solution are required to obtain 0.00285 moles of HCl? *Ans.* **19.00 ml.**

14. Ten grams of each of the following substances are dissolved in water and diluted to 200 ml: (a) KCl, (b) Na_2SO_4, (c) $BaCl_2 \cdot 2H_2O$, (d) $Na_2CO_3 \cdot 10H_2O$. Write expressions for the molarity of each solution.

15. The chloride ion contained in 25 ml of 0.100 M $NaCl$ is to be precipitated with 0.055 M $AgNO_3$. What is the minimum volume of silver nitrate that must be used?
Ans. **45.5 ml.**

16. What is the minimum volume of 5% $BaCl_2$ required to precipitate the sulfate ion in a sample of pure potassium sulfate weighing 0.4500 g? *Ans.* **10.8 ml**

17. How many grams of silver bromide will be precipitated if 25.00 ml of 0.075 M $AgNO_3$ are added to 60 ml of 0.050 M KBr? *Ans.* **0.352 g**

18. The sulfate ion contained in 50.0 ml of a sodium sulfate solution is precipitated by an excess of a 5% $BaCl_2$ solution. The weight of barium sulfate, after washing and drying, is 1.500 g. What is the molarity of the sodium sulfate solution? *Ans.* **0.129 M**

19. What weight of silver nitrate is required to precipitate the halide ion contained in (a) 20 ml of 0.5 M KCl? (b) 25 ml of 0.25 M KI? (c) 40 ml of 0.10 M NaBr? *Ans.* (a) **1.7 g**; (b) **1.06 g**; (c) **0.68 g**

20. How many milligrams of chlorine can be precipitated by
(a) 1.00 ml of 0.120 M $AgNO_3$? (b) 40.0 ml of 0.120 M $AgNO_3$. (c) 25.0 ml of 0.045 M $AgNO_3$? *Ans.* (a) **4.3 mg**; (b) **170 mg**; (c) **40 mg**

21. Calculate the molarity of each of the following solutions:
 a. HCl of density, 1.17, containing 37.7% HCl by weight
 b. HNO_3 of density, 1.31, containing 50.0% HNO_3 by weight
 c. H_2SO_4 of density, 1.79, containing 85.7% H_2SO_4 by weight
 d. NaOH of density, 1.39, containing 36.0% NaOH by weight
 e. NH_4OH of density, 0.90, containing 28.4% NH_3 by weight
Ans. (a) **12.1 M**; (b) **10.4 M**; (c) **15.6 M**; (d) **12.5 M**; (e) **15.0 M**

Chapter 4

EQUILIBRIUM AND EQUILIBRIUM CONSTANTS

In the preceding discussion of elementary calculations, it was tacitly assumed that the chemical reactions employed in analytical methods convert all of a constituent to a specified product. Under certain reaction conditions, this assumption is justified; under other conditions, an equilibrium may be established in which a significant amount of a reactant may remain unaltered; under still other conditions, the formation of some other product may be favored either because of changes in rates of reaction or because of equilibrium considerations. It thus becomes desirable to review the concept of equilibrium and the use of equilibrium constants even though they furnish only a part of the essential picture.

Characteristic Features of an Equilibrium State

The essential features of a system in equilibrium may be illustrated by an example which involves a physical change.

The apparatus shown in Figure 4-1 consists of two chambers, of equal size, equipped with pressure gauges. The valve between the two chambers can be opened to any desired degree.

With the valve closed, chamber A is filled with gas to one atmosphere pressure and chamber B is evacuated to zero pressure. The temperature of the whole apparatus is kept constant and the pressure gauges are observed at various times after the valve is opened slightly. The pressure in A decreases, and the pressure in B increases with time as shown graphically in Figure 4-2 until a final pressure of one-half atmosphere is established. This state in which no change occurs with time is the equilibrium state of the system. It is

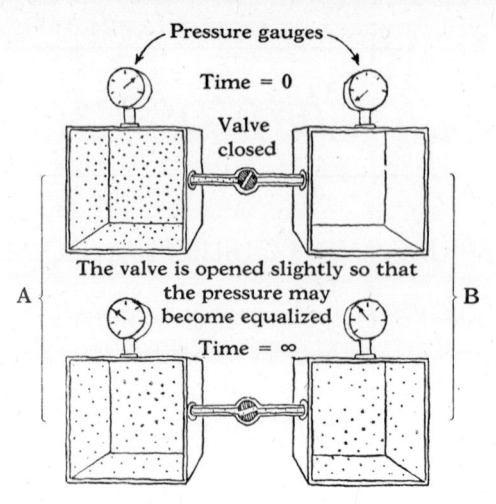

FIG. 4-1. The equalization of pressures as an example of equilibrium.

characterized by the fact that the molecules are still moving freely back and forth between chambers A and B under conditions where the rate of transfer of molecules from A to B is equal to the rate of transfer of molecules from B to A. If the process of transferring molecules could be called a reaction, the example would be termed a reversible reaction because the product (a molecule in B) can "react" to form the reactant (a molecule in A) under the same conditions that molecules in A can "react" to go to B. Chemical systems come to a state of equilibrium only when the reactions involved are reversible in this sense.

If we repeat the experiment but open the valve to a different extent, the equilibrium state where the final pressure is one-half atmosphere will not be affected. However, the rate at which the system approaches equilibrium by the net flow of molecules from A to B will be directly determined by the effective area at the valve. This independence of the rate at which equilibrium is established and the equilibrium state itself are of importance in chemical reactions and the two should not be confused.

The final pressure of one-half atmosphere is the result of our choice of initial conditions—one and zero atmospheres

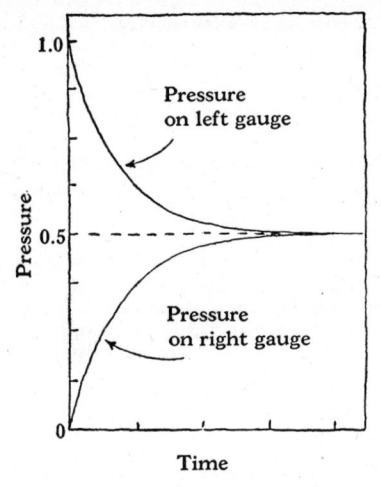

FIG. 4-2. Graphical representation of equalization of pressures, Fig. 4-1.

pressure and chambers of equal volume. For some other set of initial conditions, a different equilibrium pressure would be obtained subject only to the basic condition that the pressures in *A* and *B* must be equal at equilibrium. Similarly, in chemical reactions, there is a fundamental relationship that must exist at equilibrium but the amount of a given substance that reacts can be altered by changing the initial condition.

The Equilibrium Constant

Consider a reaction represented by the equation:

$$A + B = C + D$$

If this reaction is reversible, in the sense previously mentioned, an equilibrium state will be established after some required period of time has elapsed. At equilibrium, the relative amounts of the molecules A, B, C, and D will show no change with time only because the rate of reaction between A and B is exactly equal to the rate of reaction between C and D. A relation between the amounts of A, B, C, and D at equilibrium can be derived if we know how the rates of these reactions depend upon the relative number of these molecules.

In order for A and B to react, they must come very close to each other. However, when an A and a B molecule "collide" there may or may not be a reaction. At a fixed temperature, the fraction of such collisions that do result in reaction is a constant value. It is called the probability of reaction, P_1. If v_1 designates the rate at which A and B react, then:

$$v_1 = P_1 \times \text{No. of A, B collisions per unit time.}$$

Assume for convenience, that the molecules A, B, C, and D are either ideal gases confined in a volume of one liter or components of an ideal solution whose volume is one liter. If we have one molecule of A in the liter volume, the number of collisions it makes with B molecules as it moves at random depends only on the number of B molecules in this same volume. The number of collisions of any particular A molecule is therefore directly proportional to the concentration of B molecules. If the number of A molecules in this liter volume is increased, the number of A, B collisions is increased. Each A molecule makes collisions at random entirely unaffected by the fact that other A molecules are doing the same thing. The number of A, B collisions per unit time in a unit volume is therefore directly proportional to the concentration of A and to the concentration of B. At fixed concentrations, the number of A, B collisions per second will depend upon the average speed of the molecules and upon their sizes. The effects of speed and size can be combined in a single factor f_1, the value of which will depend on the temperature. We thus obtain the expression:

$$\text{No. of A, B collisions per unit time} = f_1 [A][B]$$

In this equation, [A] and [B] represent the concentrations of A and B in moles per liter.

Using this relation in the equation for the rate of reaction and combining the constants P_1 and f_1 into a single term we obtain the relation:

$$v_1 = P_1 f_1 [A][B] = k_1 [A][B]$$

By exactly the same reasoning, the rate of reaction between C and D molecules is given by the equation:

$$v_2 = k_2 [C] [D]$$

Equilibrium is established when v_1 and v_2 are equal and, therefore, the following relation between [A], [B], [C], and [D] must hold:

$$[C] [D] k_2 = [A] [B] k_1$$

Since we rarely can derive values of k_1 and k_2, it is convenient to combine the ratio k_1/k_2 into a single term and write the relation in the form:

$$\frac{[C] [D]}{[A] [B]} = K$$

where K is the equilibrium constant of the reaction.

Applying reasoning similar to the above to the more complex reaction:

$$A + B + C = ABC$$

we obtain

$$\frac{[ABC]}{[A] [B] [C]} = K$$

In this case, the formation of the molecule ABC involves the collision of three particles A, B, and C. This does not mean that the three separate particles must come together at the same instant. It is more likely that two particles combine and then this combined particle collides with the third component. In accord with this assumption, there are three possible reaction paths:

$$A + B = AB$$
$$AB + C = ABC$$

$$A + C = AC$$
$$AC + B = ABC$$

$$B + C = BC$$
$$BC + A = ABC$$

These paths lead to identical expressions for the equilibrium constant:

$$\frac{[ABC]}{[A] [B] [C]} = K$$

The equilibrium state does not depend on the path or paths by which the system arrives at that state.

If two of the substances in the preceding reaction are identical; for example, A and C, the reaction becomes:

$$2A + B = A_2B$$

and the corresponding expression for the equilibrium constant becomes:

$$\frac{[A_2B]}{[A]^2 [B]} = K$$

Extension of the above reasoning to the general equation:

$$aA + bB + cC + \ldots = lL + mM + nN + \ldots$$

leads to the general expression:

$$\frac{(L)^l (M)^m (N)^n \cdots}{(A)^a (B)^b (C)^c \cdots} = K$$

This relation is a general statement of the **Law of Mass Action**.

Activities and Activity Coefficients.—Throughout the preceding discussion, we have used concentrations in expressions for the equilibrium constants. The result applies exactly to ideal systems but is not correct when applied to most reactions under practical conditions for we should have used corrected concentrations, called *activities*. The activity, *a*, of a chemical species is related to the concentration by the equation:

$$a = \gamma \times \text{concentration}$$

In this relation the correction term, γ, is called an *activity coefficient*. In dilute solutions, the activity coefficients approach unity; in more concentrated solutions, they are complex functions of the concentration of each substance present. Inasmuch as we shall use equilibrium considerations to establish orders of magnitude rather than exact values, we will continue to neglect the correction terms.

Equilibria in Simple Hydrate Systems

The apparent form of the mass action law may change as it is applied to various systems. For example, the reaction involved in the determination of water in barium chloride dihydrate in Chapter II is:

$$BaCl_2 \cdot 2H_2O_{(s)} = BaCl_{2\,(s)} + 2\,H_2O_{(g)}$$

Formal application of the law yields the relation:

$$\frac{[BaCl_{2(s)}] \cdot [H_2O_{(g)}]^2}{[BaCl_2 \cdot 2H_2O_{(s)}]} = K''$$

However the "concentration" of barium chloride in solid barium chloride, [BaCl$_2$], is a fixed quantity at a given temperature and pressure. The solid contains the same number of moles of barium chloride per liter whether there is 1 or 100 mg present. Similarly the "concentration" of the solid dihydrate is independent of the amount present, and so, we can simplify the equilibrium expression as follows:

$$[H_2O_{(g)}]^2 = K'' \frac{[BaCl_2 \cdot 2H_2O_{(s)}]}{[BaCl_{2(s)}]} = K'$$

The concentration of water is the gas phase, [H$_2$O$_{(g)}$], is proportional to the partial pressure of water, P_{H_2O}. The simplest form, therefore, in which to write the equilibrium constant is:

$$P_{H_2O} = \text{constant} \times K' = K$$

According to this simple relation, water can be removed from the dihydrate at any temperature if the water vapor pressure is less than the corresponding equilibrium constant. Barium chloride dihydrate is stable in air at room temperature because the equilibrium pressure, K, is less than the normal range of the water vapor pressure in air. When the temperature is raised, the value of K increases as illustrated in the case of the hydrates of copper sulfate in Figure 2-4, and so dehydration can be accomplished in air at elevated temperatures. It should be clearly recognized that the rate at which water can be removed is not determined by the value of K. Equilibrium considerations define only the conditions under which a desired reaction is permitted. Even if the reaction is possible, it may often be too slow to be of practical value. For example, water can be removed from barium chloride dihydrate at room temperature in a vacuum or at a temperature around 90° C in air but in both cases the process is slow. A temperature of 125 to 175° C was used for the experimental determination in Chapter 2 in order to increase the rate of dehydration.

Solubility Equilibria

Estimation of the effect of various factors upon the solubility of precipitates is of considerable practical value in quantitative separations and determinations. The general application of the mass action law to solubility equilibria is reviewed here as a basis for the discussion of solubility product calculations in Chapter 5.

With few exceptions, inorganic precipitates dissociate into their component ions when they dissolve in water and this fact must be recognized in writing the reaction and expressing the equilibrium constant. For example, when silver chloride dissolves, the reaction is:

$$AgCl_{(s)} = Ag^+ + Cl^-$$

The formal expression for the equilibrium constant becomes:

$$\frac{[Ag^+] \cdot [Cl^-]}{[AgCl_{(s)}]} = K'$$

Again combining the concentration of solid silver chloride, [AgCl], with the equilibrium constant as discussed in the barium chloride dihydrate example the expression becomes:

$$[Ag^+] \cdot [Cl^-] = K' \cdot [AgCl_{(s)}] = K_{sp}$$

The notation K_{sp} is used because the constants for inorganic salts are referred to as solubility products.

Chapter 5

GRAVIMETRIC TECHNIQUES AND THE CONTROL OF SOLUBILITY
•
GRAVIMETRIC TECHNIQUES

General Use of Precipitation

The samples ordinarily encountered in analytical work contain several constituents, although only one or two may have to be determined. Frequently, the major problem is to obtain some separation of these constituents before the required determinations can be made.

Precipitation is a particularly important method of making such separations in inorganic analysis. This more general use of precipitation should be borne in mind in connection with the importance of the principles and techniques discussed here and in Chapter 6.

Outline of a Gravimetric Determination of Chloride

A sample containing chloride is dried, weighed, and dissolved in water which is then acidified with nitric acid. Silver nitrate solution is added in excess to precipitate silver chloride. This precipitate is carefully washed, dried, and weighed after separation on a suitable filter crucible. From the weight of the sample and the weight of the precipitate, the percent potassium chloride in the unknown is calculated.

Apart from the weighings required, the most important techniques involve the transfer of the original sample and the transfer and washing of the precipitate. The importance of careful manipulation is illustrated by the fact that 0.00008 ml of silver chloride weighs about 0.4 mg which corresponds to an error of approximately one part per thousand in this and in similar determinations.

The choice of the exact conditions for carrying out any particular determination is fundamentally empirical. It is conditioned by the nature of the sample, the accuracy desired, the facilities available, and the importance of time in analysis. The procedure used for these samples differs from the commonly accepted one in that the digestion period at elevated temperatures is omitted. A digestion period does facilitate coagulation of the precipitate, but it also increases the time required for the analysis. It likewise increases the amount of photo-reduction of silver chloride to silver. Satisfactory results can be obtained without digestion.

General Preparations

Pour the chloride sample into a clean, dry, weighing bottle. With a lead pencil, enter some identifying mark on the ground area of the bottle. Gummed labels should not be used since they may fall off; if they do stick, they are hygroscopic. Place the bottle in a 50 ml beaker as shown in Figure 5-1 and set it in the drying oven.

After the sample has been dried for at least one hour at 105 to 115° C, place it in a desiccator to cool. Weigh the sample when convenient but not before it has cooled for at least one-half hour.

FIG. 5-1. To dry a crucible or weighing bottle, place it in a marked beaker before placing it in a drying oven.

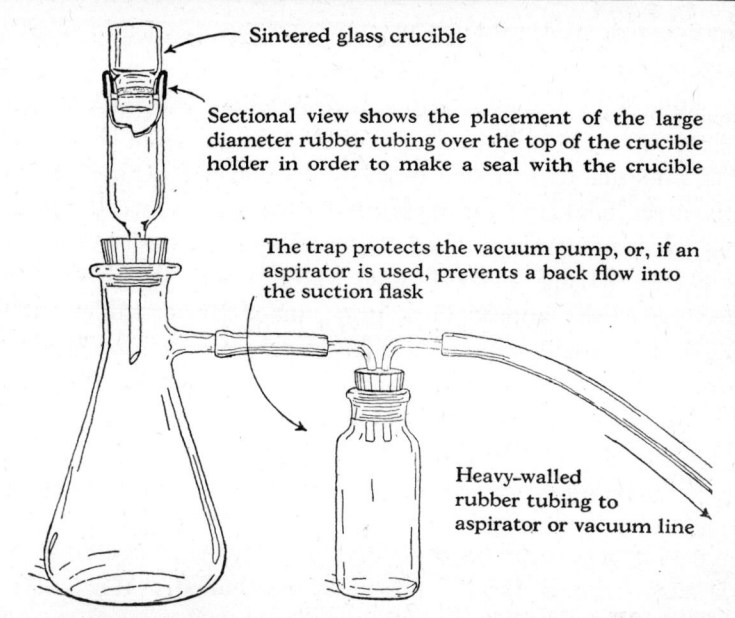

GRAVIMETRIC TECHNIQUES AND THE CONTROL OF SOLUBILITY   53

FIG. 5-2. Suction flask assembly for use with filtering crucibles.

Wash three 400 ml beakers, three watch glasses, and four stirring rods with cleanser. Rinse thoroughly with tap water and then with distilled water. Do not attempt to wipe them dry. Mount a rubber policeman on one of the rods. Mark the beakers for identification and cover them with watch glasses.

Use of Filter Crucibles

Non-gelatinous precipitates which do not have to be heated to high temperatures can conveniently be separated from the supernatant liquid on filter crucibles. These crucibles are of two types—the Gooch crucible and the sintered or fritted crucible. The latter type usually is preferable.

Cleaning a Sintered Glass Filter.—Insert a sintered glass crucible in the suction flask assembly as shown in Figure 5-2 and draw tap water through it.

The choice of solvents for cleaning a crucible depends of course on the contamination. In this case, we will assume that it is necessary to remove silver and possibly silver chloride. Cover the sintered disk with concentrated nitric acid and draw it through. Wash again with tap water. If the crucible appears to be clean and if water flows through freely when suction is applied, draw three portions of distilled water through it. Wash all three crucibles in this manner and place each one in a small, marked beaker. Then place the beakers in a drying oven for one to two hours or longer, if convenient. Cool the crucibles in a desiccator and weigh to 0.1 mg. If the flow of water is very slow, or if the sintered disks appear dark gray, place the crucibles in a beaker, add 6 N ammonium hydroxide and let the beaker stand in a hood for thirty minutes. Pour off the ammonium hydroxide, rinse with tap water, using suction, and proceed as above. If the rate still is slow, consult your instructor.

Preparation of the Gooch Crucible.—The Gooch crucible is made of porcelain with a flat perforated base upon which a mat of asbestos can be deposited. The mat is protected from damage by a perforated porcelain disc called a Witt plate.

Clean the crucible and plate with cleaning solution and rinse with water. Mount the crucible in a suction flask assembly as shown previously in Figure 5-2. Prepare a suspension of acid-washed, long-fiber asbestos by adding about a gram of it to 300 ml of distilled water, stir well, and let it settle for a few seconds. Pour some of the opalescent liquid into the crucible. Do not use suction at this stage. The asbestos accumulates on the base, building a retentive mat. After the asbestos has settled, use suction to pull it firmly into place. Remove the crucible and hold it toward a light. The perforations will appear just translucent if the mat has been properly prepared. If the mat is too thick, remove it with a stirring rod, return the material to the beaker, and begin again. If the mat is satisfactory, place the Witt plate carefully on top of it. This can be done conveniently by inserting the plate in the inverted crucible, as shown in Figure 5-3, and then righting the whole assembly. Mount the crucible on the suction flask, apply suction, and add a small amount of the opalescent suspension. Rinse with distilled water until the filtrate is free from small asbestos fibers. Place the crucible in a small beaker and dry in the oven for

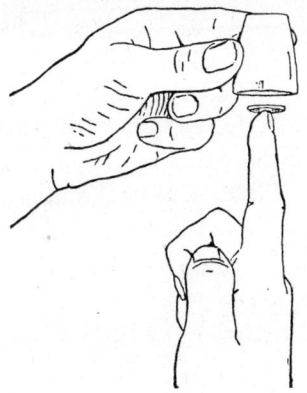

FIG. 5-3. Insertion of Witt plate.

at least one hour. Cool the crucible in the desiccator and weigh it to 0.1 mg.

Weighing of Samples

The weights of the samples are obtained from the differences of a series of consecutive weighings and so no zero point determination of the balance is needed. If the unloaded

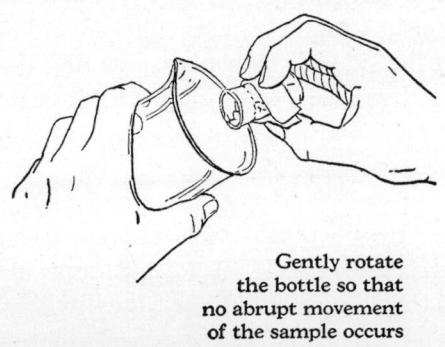

Gently rotate
the bottle so that
no abrupt movement
of the sample occurs

FIG. 5-4. Transfer of a sample.

balance swings freely across the midpoint of the scale, assume the rest point of the first weighing to be the zero point. Weigh the bottle plus the sample to the nearest 0.1 mg.

Transfer 0.2-0.4 g of the sample from the weighing bottle to the beaker as shown above in Figure 5-4. Without removing the bottle from the beaker, tilt it and carefully slide the remaining sample back on to the bottom. Remove the bottle, replace the cover gently to avoid loss of material, and weigh the bottle. Cover the beaker with a watch glass. The decrease in weight of the bottle is taken as the weight of the sample in the beaker. Obviously, low overall results will be obtained in direct proportion to the amount of material that may have been lost due to poor handling. The second and third samples are weighed in a similar manner so that only four weighings are required for the three samples.

In all handling of the weighing bottle, be careful not to deposit moisture or grease on to the bottle as pointed out in connection with the determination of water in barium chloride dihydrate in Chapter 2.

Precipitation of AgCl

Add approximately 50 ml of distilled water and 1 ml of 6 N HNO_3 to each beaker. Assume that the sample is pure potassium chloride and calculate the volume of 0.1 N $AgNO_3$ required for precipitation (the calculation should show that 0.37 g of sample require about 50 ml). Measure the calculated amount of 0.1 N $AgNO_3$ in a graduate. Stir the solution continuously with a clean stirring rod and add the silver nitrate down the side of the beaker. Usually, the bulk of the precipitate settles rapidly and the supernatant remains somewhat cloudy.

Filtration

Fill the large wash bottle with distilled water and add 1 ml of 6 N HNO_3. Place a clean test tube in the suction flask so that the stem of the filter funnel will enter the test tube when the funnel is in place. Attach a sintered or Gooch crucible to the filtering apparatus and apply suction. Transfer a small amount of supernatant to the filter as shown in Figure 5-5 and collect this portion in the test tube. If the solution in the test tube is turbid, the crucible may be faulty. If the solution is clear, test it for completeness of precipitation by adding 1 ml of silver nitrate solution. If no turbidity appears, remove the test tube and complete the filtration. Try to keep as much of the precipitate as possible in the

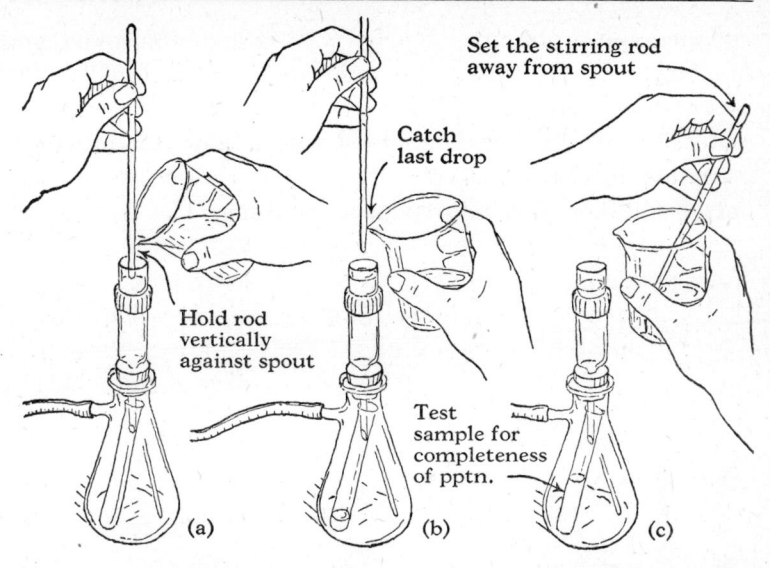

FIG. 5-5. Quantitative decantation of a liquid in the filtering process; collecting a test sample of the filtrate.

beaker while transferring the solution to the filter. Should a turbidity appear, draw the solution into the test tube and wash the crucible with several small portions of water. Transfer the solution and washings from the test tube to the beaker. In this case, the calculation of the amount of solution, the concentration of the silver nitrate, or the weight of the sample is in error. Check the calculation and the weight of sample to determine how much additional silver nitrate must be added. If the concentration appears to be in error, consult the instructor.

After the supernatant has been transferred, add an estimated 10-15 ml of acidified wash water, using a directed stream from the wash bottle to remove the precipitate from the stirring rod and the walls of the beaker. Stir the precipitate in this wash and allow it to settle. Decant the wash water through the filter, leaving the precipitate in the beaker, again using the stirring rod to prevent loss of material to the outside of the beaker. Wash the precipitate three times in this fashion.

Transfer the precipitate to the filter as shown in Figure

58 INTRODUCTORY QUANTITATIVE ANALYSIS • Chapter 5

5-6. Lay the stirring rod across the beaker with the end extending about one inch beyond the spout. Bring the beaker into the position shown and systematically play a stream of water around the inside to wash the precipitate into the filter. Do not attempt to scrape this or any other precipitate out of a beaker with a stirring rod.

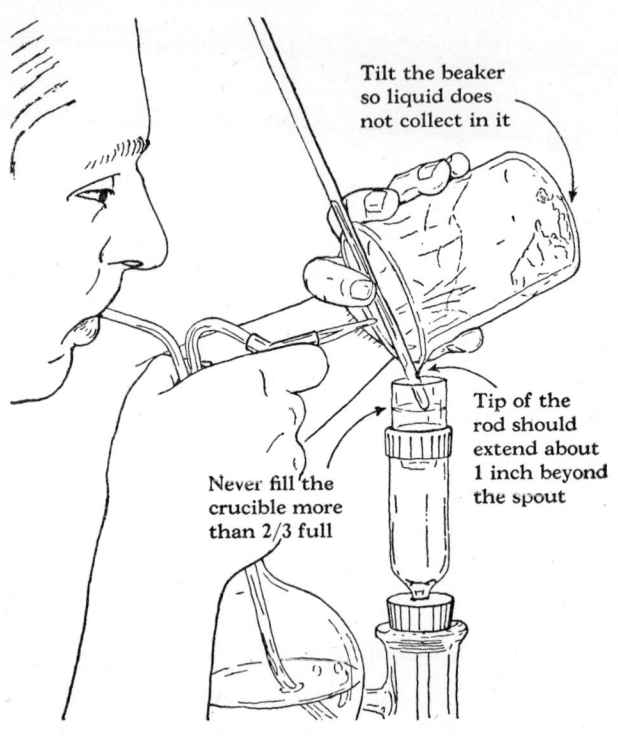

FIG. 5-6. Washing a precipitate into a filtering crucible.

Use a policeman to loosen the traces of precipitate that adhere to the beaker and the stirring rod as shown in Figure 5-7. Rinse particles of precipitate from the policeman into the beaker and set the policeman aside. Use the stirring rod as before to transfer the remaining precipitate to the filter. Do not use the policeman for this purpose. Continue the operation of policing until no visible particles of silver chloride remain.

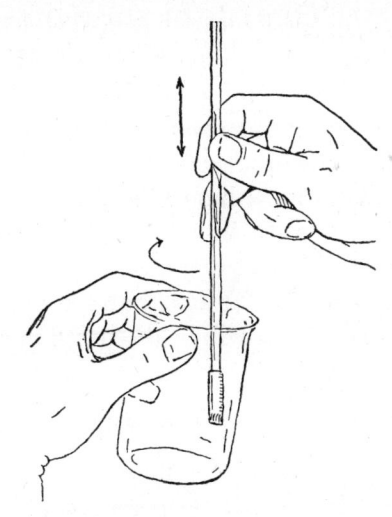

FIG. 5-7. Any adhering precipitate is loosened from the beaker by gently rubbing the sides and bottom of the vessel with an edge of a rubber policeman mounted on a stirring rod.

Washing

After all of the precipitate has been transferred to the filter, remove the rubber stopper and empty the suction flask. Insert a test tube in the flask as shown previously in Figure 5-5. Apply suction and direct a gentle stream of the acidified wash water around the upper part of the crucible. Be careful not to strike the precipitate directly and spatter it. Take the test tube containing this wash and test for silver ion by adding a few drops of 6 N HCl. If no precipitate is produced, discontinue washing. If a cloudiness appears, continue washing, testing each wash separately until no precipitate is observed.

Place the crucibles in their proper beakers and dry them in the oven for at least one hour. Cool the crucibles in the desiccator and weigh them. Repeat the heating and weighing operations until constant weight is obtained. Calculate the percent potassium chloride in the sample. An agreement within five parts per thousand between the two determinations indicates satisfactory work.

THE CONTROL OF SOLUBILITY

In quantitative applications of precipitation, such as the preceding determination of chloride, the precipitates employed, and the conditions used must be critically selected. Specifically, the following factors must be considered:
1. Solubility losses must be negligible.
2. The precipitate must be quantitatively pure.
3. Losses in mechanical separation must be negligible.

Solubility losses and the factors that are of practical value in the control of solubility will be discussed in the subsequent sections of this chapter.

Effect of Temperature on Solubility

The solubility of a substance may be changed by altering the temperature. Heat may be regarded as a product of a reaction when it is evolved and as a reactant when it is absorbed. It then follows from the mass action law that salts which absorb heat when they dissolve become more soluble and those which evolve heat when they dissolve become less soluble as the temperature is increased. Most inorganic precipitates are in the first group and so their solubilities decrease with a decrease in temperature. In aqueous solutions, the available temperature range is from about 0° C to 100° C. The change in solubility that can be effected is not very great and there are only a limited number of cases in which this factor is of practical value.

Effect of the Composition of the Solution on Solubility

The slightly soluble inorganic salts of analytical importance are, to a first approximation, completely dissociated into their constituent ions in aqueous solution. The solubility of such salts in water represents the establishment of an equilibrium between the solid and a very dilute solution of the ions derived from it. This solubility can be changed by the addition of substances to the solution which react with the ions of the salt. The most important way to *decrease* the solubility of a salt is to add a substance that provides one of the ions derived from the salt. This is called the **common**

ion effect. The most practical way to *increase* the solubility is to add substances that react with the ions derived from the salt. The formation of weak acids or bases by the addition of hydrogen or hydroxyl ions and the formation of complex ions fall into this category.

The solubility of inorganic salts may also be decreased by adding water-miscible solvents such as alcohol to change the character of the solvent. This is of value in a few cases but, generally, the quality of the separations obtained is impaired and so the use of solvents other than water in inorganic precipitations is of limited application.

Solubility Losses

Material always is lost through solubility in the precipitation and in the washing and transfer steps. In most cases, the order of magnitude of such losses can be estimated and used as a guide in evaluating a possible procedure.

For example, the solubility of silver chloride is about 0.19 mg per 100 ml of water at 25° C. The procedure previously given required the use of 200 to 300 ml of a dilute nitric acid solution for the transfer and washing of the precipitate. Since dilute nitric acid contains no ions that combine with silver or chloride ions, there will be no marked effect on the solubility of silver chloride. If we assume that the solution has time to become saturated with silver chloride during transfer and washing, the estimated solubility loss is $\frac{200 \text{ to } 300}{100} \times 0.19$ or 0.3 to 0.5 mg. For a precipitate weight of 0.3-0.5 g, this is a possible error of one part in a thousand and should not be serious. Even in this case, however, the total transfer and washing volume should be kept small.

The solubility loss of silver chloride in the precipitation step also must be considered. In this case, the effect of a common ion (silver) on the solubility must be estimated by the use of the solubility product of silver chloride. The calculation of solubility products and the calculation of the common ion effect will be discussed separately in the following sections.

Estimation of Solubility Products from Solubility Data

In a saturated solution of silver chloride, the following equilibrium is maintained.

$$AgCl_{(s)} = Ag^+ + Cl^-$$

The corresponding solubility product, as discussed in Chapter 4, is:

$$K_{sp} = [Ag^+][Cl^-]$$

The solubility of silver chloride in water is 0.19 mg per 100 ml and so the solubility in moles per liter is:

$$\frac{\text{moles AgCl dissolved}}{\text{liters used}} = \frac{\frac{0.19 \times 10^{-3}}{143.3}}{\frac{100}{1000}} = 1.3 \times 10^{-5}$$

The dissolved silver chloride is present as silver and chloride ions and so we can describe the solution in the following way:

1.3×10^{-5} moles of AgCl dissolve per liter
$[AgCl_{(s)}]$ in the solution = 0
$[Ag^+]$ in the solution = $1.3 \times 10^{-5} M$
$[Cl^-]$ in the solution = $1.3 \times 10^{-5} M$

Therefore, the numerical value of the solubility product is:

$$K_{sp} = [Ag^+][Cl^-] = [1.3 \times 10^{-5}][1.3 \times 10^{-5}] = 1.7 \times 10^{-10}$$

It is important to realize that the concentrations of the silver and chloride ions are not necessarily equal at equilibrium. They happen to be equal in this particular case because their only source was silver chloride.

The solubility products of more complex salts can be calculated in a similar way from a knowledge of their solubility in water. For example, 33 mg of barium iodate dissolve in 100 ml of water at 25° C. This corresponds to 6.8×10^{-4} moles of barium iodate per liter since the molecular weight is 487.2. To the best approximation, the barium iodate is completely ionized and so the concentration of barium ion is 6.8×10^{-4} M and that of iodate ion is $2 \times 6.8 \times 10^{-4}$ M or 13.6×10^{-4} M. The equilibrium involved is:

$$Ba(IO_3)_{2(s)} = Ba^{++} + 2IO^-_3$$

The corresponding solubility product is:

$$K_{sp} = [Ba^{++}][IO^-_3]^2$$

Again substituting numerical values in the solubility product expression, we obtain:

$$K_{sp} = [6.8 \times 10^{-4}][13.6 \times 10^{-4}]^2 = 1.3 \times 10^{-9}$$

As a final example, suppose the compound A_2B_3 has a molecular weight of 350 g and a solubility in water of 7.0 mg/100 ml. The molar solubility is then 2×10^{-4}. The equilibrium involved is:

$$A_2B_3 = 2A^{+++} + 3B^{--}$$

The corresponding solubility product is:

$$K_{sp} = [A^{+++}]^2[B^{--}]^3$$

Since the dissolved A_2B_3 exists as A^{+++} ions and B^{--} ions, the concentrations are:

$$[A^{+++}] = 2 \times [2 \times 10^{-4}] M$$
$$[B^{--}] = 3 \times [2 \times 10^{-4}] M$$

Substituting these concentrations, we obtain:

$$K_{sp} = [4 \times 10^{-4}]^2[6 \times 10^{-4}]^3 = 3.5 \times 10^{-17}$$

Estimation of the Common Ion Effect

The solubility of silver chloride is 0.19 mg per 100 ml or 1.3×10^{-5} M in water. If we add an excess of silver ion, as we did in the procedure for the determination of chloride, some of this dissolved silver chloride must precipitate to maintain equilibrium and a lower solubility results.

Suppose, for example, that 0.01 mole of silver nitrate is added to one liter of a saturated solution of silver chloride. If we let y represent the moles per liter of silver chloride dissolved in this solution, the resulting silver and chloride ion concentrations are:

$[Ag^+]$ = 0.01 M (from $AgNO_3$) + y M (from $AgCl$)
$[Cl^-]$ = y M (from $AgCl$)

Substituting these values and the calculated solubility product constant into the equilibrium equation, we obtain:

$$(0.01 + y)\, y = 1.7 \times 10^{-10}$$

An exact value of y which can be obtained from this equation by the application of standard mathematical methods for the solution of quadratic equations seldom is justified. A sufficiently good approximate solution can be obtained as follows:

The maximum value that y can have is $1.3 \times 10^{-5}\, M$ corresponding to a saturated solution of silver chloride in water. Since $[Ag^+]$ = 0.01 + y, the maximum $[Ag^+]$ = 0.010013 M and the minimum $[Ag^+]$ = 0.01 M.

These limits of the silver ion concentration correspond to

$$[Cl^-]_{max} = \frac{1.7 \times 10^{-10}}{[Ag^+]_{min}} = 1.7 \times 10^{-8} \text{ and}$$

$$[Cl^-]_{min} = \frac{1.7 \times 10^{-10}}{[Ag^+]_{max}} = 1.698 \times 10^{-8}$$

Obviously, in this case, the difference between the two limits is negligible. Since the percentage change between the maximum value and the minimum value is so small, we can take either limit, or any value between them, and obtain a good approximate value for the chloride ion concentration. The estimated solubility is therefore 1.7×10^{-8} moles of silver chloride per liter.

If we precipitate silver chloride from 100 ml of a solution that is 0.01 M in silver ion, the solubility loss is not 0.19 mg as in 100 ml of water, but 0.00024 mg as calculated below.

$$\frac{100}{1000} \times 1.7 \times 10^{-8} \times 143.34 \times 1000 = 0.00024 \text{ mg}$$

From this result, it is evident that the use of an excess of a common ion can decrease the solubility of a precipitate significantly. This is a practical way to reduce the solubility loss in the precipitation step. It is not generally useful in washing a precipitate because the excess common ion would have to be added in the form of a subsequently volatile compound.

The method of approximation illustrated above is particularly useful in more complex cases. For example, suppose we need to estimate the solubility of barium iodate in a 0.05 M $Ba(NO_3)_2$ solution. In the preceding section, the solubility of barium iodate was given as 33 mg per 100 ml or 6.8×10^{-4} moles per liter and the calculated K_{sp} was 1.3×10^{-9}. If y represents the molar solubility of barium iodate in 0.05 M $Ba(NO_3)_2$, the exact relationships are:

$[Ba^{++}] = 0.05\ M$ (from $Ba(NO_3)_2$) $+ y\ M$ (from $Ba(IO_3)_2$)

$[IO_3^-] = 2y\ M$ (from $Ba(IO_3)_2$)

$K_{sp} = [Ba^{++}][IO_3^-]^2 = [0.05 + y][2y]^2 = 1.3 \times 10^{-9}$

In this case, an exact result would involve the solution of a cubic equation. However, an approximate solution can be obtained simply and checked by the method used before.

$[Ba^{++}] = 0.05 + y$ Max value of $y = 6.8 \times 10^{-4}$

Min $[Ba^{++}] = 0.05$;   Max $[Ba^{++}] = 0.05068$;

Assume $[Ba^{++}] = 0.05\ M$

$[IO_3^-] = 2y = \sqrt{\dfrac{K_{sp}}{[Ba^{++}]_{min}}} = \sqrt{\dfrac{1.3 \times 10^{-9}}{0.05}} = 1.6 \times 10^{-4}$ (max)

y = solubility of $Ba(IO_3)_2 = \dfrac{1.6 \times 10^{-4}}{2} = 8 \times 10^{-5}$ (max)

and the corresponding $[Ba^{++}] = 0.05008$ instead of the assumed value of 0.05.

As in the silver chloride example, the maximum value differs from the minimum value by only a small percentage and so any value in this range may be used.

In this case, the precipitation of barium iodate from a solution that is 0.05 M in barium ion reduces the solubility loss from 33 mg in 100 ml of water to 3.9 mg as shown by the calculation below:

$$\text{Ba}(\text{IO}_3)_2 \text{ lost} = \frac{100}{1000} \times 8 \times 10^{-5} \times 487.2 \times 1000 = 3.9 \text{ mg}$$

In the above examples, the first calculated value differs from the first assumed value by only a small percentage. This is the result of a good first choice. As a case in which the first approximation is less satisfactory, let us calculate the solubility of lead sulfate in 0.0001 M Pb(NO$_3$)$_2$ solution, knowing that the solubility of lead sulfate in water is 4.3 mg per 100 ml.

(a) *Calculation of the Solubility Product*

The given solubility corresponds to 1.4×10^{-4} moles per liter since the molecular weight of PbSO$_4$ is 303. Therefore,

$[\text{Pb}^{++}] = 1.4 \times 10^{-4} M$ and $[\text{SO}_4^{--}] = 1.4 \times 10^{-4} M$ at equilibrium

$K_{sp} = [\text{Pb}^{++}][\text{SO}_4^{--}] = 1.96 \times 10^{-8} \cong 2.0 \times 10^{-8}$

(b) *Estimation of Solubility in 0.0001 M Pb(NO$_3$)$_2$*

Let y = molar solubility of PbSO$_4$ in $1.0 \times 10^{-4} M$ Pb(NO$_3$)$_2$

$[\text{Pb}^{++}] = 1.0 \times 10^{-4} + y$ Max value of $y = 1.4 \times 10^{-4}$

Min $[\text{Pb}^{++}] = 1.0 \times 10^{-4}$ Max $[\text{Pb}^{++}] = 2.4 \times 10^{-4}$

In this example, the maximum and minimum values differ by a large percentage and so a good value to choose is the average, 1.7×10^{-4}.

$$[\text{SO}_4^{--}] = y = \frac{K_{sp}}{(\text{Pb}^{++})} = \frac{2.0 \times 10^{-8}}{1.7 \times 10^{-4}} = 1.2 \times 10^{-4}$$

The corresponding $[\text{Pb}^{++}] = 1 \times 10^{-4} + 1.2 \times 10^{-4} = 2.2 \times 10^{-4}$. This is 20% greater than the assumed value of 1.7×10^{-4}. If a more exact value is desired, a second approximation can be obtained.

Min $[\text{Pb}^{++}] = 1.7 \times 10^{-4}$;   Max $[\text{Pb}^{++}] = 2.2 \times 10^{-4}$

As before, we again choose an average value, 2.0×10^{-4}.

$$[SO_4^{--}] = \frac{2.0 \times 10^{-8}}{2.0 \times 10^{-4}} = 1.0 \times 10^{-4}$$

The corresponding $[Pb^{++}] = 1.0 \times 10^{-4} + 1.0 \times 10^{-4} = 2.0 \times 10^{-4}$. This checks our assumed value of 2.0×10^{-4}. This exact correspondence is, of course, fortuitous.

The solubility loss is then $1.0 \times 10^{-4} \times 303 = 3.0 \times 10^{-2}$ g per liter or 3.0 mg per 100 ml in 0.0001 M $Pb(NO_3)_2$ compared to 4.3 mg per 100 ml in water. The effect is small in this case because the concentrations of lead ion in 0.0001 M $Pb(NO_3)_2$ is of the same order as that in a saturated water solution of lead sulfate.

Effect of Hydrogen Ion on the Solubility of Salts of Weak Acids

Obviously, the method described for the gravimetric determination of chloride cannot be applied directly when other constituents of a sample also can precipitate as insoluble silver salts under the conditions employed.

Since silver chloride is the salt of a strong acid, its solubility will not be changed appreciably by a change in hydrogen ion concentration. On the other hand, if the interfering precipitate is the salt of a weak acid, an increase in the hydrogen ion concentration may prevent it from precipitating.

As an example, we may consider silver acetate, $AgOOCCH_3$, which will be designated as AgAc. Its solubility in water is 0.067 moles per liter. The equilibrium established and the corresponding solubility product at 25° C are:

$$AgAc = Ag^+ + Ac^-$$
$$K_{sp} = [Ag^+][Ac^-] = 4.5 \times 10^{-3}$$

In making this calculation, we assumed that all the acetate ion remained uncombined in solution. This is not strictly true; a very small amount of it must have reacted with hydrogen ion from water to form HAc in order to establish the equilibrium

$$HAc = H^+ + Ac^-$$

for which the dissociation constant is known to be 1.8×10^{-5}

$$\frac{[H^+][Ac^-]}{[HAc]} = K_{HAc}$$

If a strong acid is added, practically all of the acetate ion can be changed to acetic acid. This causes additional silver acetate to dissolve in order to maintain equilibrium.

The extent to which the solubility of a salt of a weak acid can be increased by the addition of hydrogen ion may or may not be significant. It is, therefore, frequently necessary to estimate the effect quantitatively as illustrated by the following examples.

Example 1.—Nitric acid is added to a precipitate of silver acetate until the final concentration of hydrogen ion is $0.1\ M$. Estimate the amount of silver acetate dissolved per liter of this solution.

Equilibria Involved

Solution of AgAc:
$$AgAc_{(s)} = Ag^+ + Ac^- \qquad K_{sp} = [Ag^+][Ac^-]$$

Reaction of H^+:
$$H^+ + Ac^- = HAc \qquad \frac{1}{K_{HAc}} = \frac{[HAc]}{[H^+][Ac^-]}$$

Net effect of H^+:
$$AgAc + H^+ = Ag^+ + HAc \qquad K = \frac{[HAc][Ag^+]}{[H^+]}$$

To show the relationship between the equilibrium constant of the net reaction and the constants of the component reactions, we may rewrite the net reaction without cancelling the acetate ions.

$$\underbrace{\boxed{AgAc}}_{K_{sp} \rightarrow} + \overbrace{\boxed{H^+ + Ac^-}}^{\leftarrow K_{HAc}} = \boxed{Ac^- + Ag^+} + \boxed{HAc}$$

$$K = \frac{[HAc][Ac^-][Ag^+]}{[H^+][Ac^-]} = \frac{K_{sp}}{K_{HAc}}$$

Therefore: $\dfrac{[HAc][Ag^+]}{[H^+]} = \dfrac{4.5 \times 10^{-3}}{1.8 \times 10^{-5}} = 250$

The above relationship illustrates a general principle which can be stated as follows:

If a reaction can be expressed as the sum of two other reactions, the equilibrium constant of the net reaction is the product of the constants for the component reactions.

Concentration Relationships

Since AgAc dissolves to form Ag^+ and a mixture of Ac^- and HAc we can set

$$[Ag^+] = [Ac^-] + [HAc]$$

The relative concentrations of Ac^- and HAc are determined by the equilibrium:

$$\frac{[H^+][Ac^-]}{[HAc]} = K_{HAc} = 1.8 \times 10^{-5}$$

If the final concentration of hydrogen ion is 0.1 M, then

$$\frac{[Ac^-]}{[HAc]} = \frac{1.8 \times 10^{-5}}{0.1} = 1.8 \times 10^{-4}$$

This means that for every 100,000 HAc molecules, there are only 18 Ac^- ions. Therefore, we can neglect the concentration of Ac^- to a first approximation and write

$$[Ag^+] = [HAc] + [Ac^-] \cong [HAc]$$

Approximate Solution

Let y = moles of AgAc dissolved per liter.
$[Ag^+] = y = [HAc]$; final $[H^+] = 0.1$ M

$$\frac{[HAc][Ag^+]}{[H^+]} = K = 250 = \frac{y^2}{0.1}$$
$$y = 5$$

Therefore, the solubility has been increased from 0.067 moles per liter in water to 5 moles per liter in the solution in which the final hydrogen ion concentration is 0.1 M. To produce one liter of such a solution, 5.1 moles of HNO_3 are required since 5 moles are used to form HAc.

Example 2.—Estimate the solubility of barium sulfate in a solution containing a final hydrogen ion concentration of 0.1 M. The solubility product of barium sulfate is 1.0×10^{-10} and the ionization constant of bisulfate ion is 2×10^{-2}.

Equilibria Involved
Solution of $BaSO_4$:
$$BaSO_{4(s)} = Ba^{++} + SO_4^{--} \qquad K_{sp} = [Ba^{++}][SO_4^{--}]$$
Reaction of H^+:
$$H^+ + SO_4^{--} = HSO_4^- \qquad \frac{1}{K_{HSO_4^-}} = \frac{[HSO_4^-]}{[H^+][SO_4^{--}]}$$
Net effect of H^+:
$$BaSO_{4(s)} + H^+ = Ba^{++} + HSO_4^- \qquad K = \frac{[Ba^{++}][HSO_4^-]}{[H^+]}$$

Proceeding as in Example 1, we obtain a value for K as follows:

$$\underline{|BaSO_4|} + |H^+ + SO_4^{--}| \xleftarrow{K_{HSO_4^-}} |SO_4^{--} + Ba^{++}| + |HSO_4^-|$$

$$\xrightarrow{K_{sp}}$$

$$K = \frac{[HSO_4^-]\;[SO_4^{--}]\;[Ba^{++}]}{[H^+][SO_4^{--}]} = \frac{K_{sp}}{K_{HSO_4^-}} = 5 \times 10^{-9}$$

Concentration Relationships

$BaSO_4$ dissolves to form Ba^{++} and a mixture of SO_4^{--} and HSO_4^-. Therefore:

$$[Ba^{++}] = [SO_4^{--}] + [HSO_4^-]$$

The ratio of sulfate to bisulfate in a 0.1 M H^+ solution is

$$\frac{[SO_4^{--}]}{[HSO_4^-]} = \frac{K_{HSO_4^-}}{[H^+]} = \frac{2 \times 10^{-2}}{0.1} = 0.2$$

In other words, there are about 5 HSO_4^- ions for each SO_4^{--} ion. If we neglect the $[SO_4^{--}]$ and set $[Ba^{++}]$ = $[HSO_4^-]$, the approximation is good to about 20%.

Approximate Solution

Let y = moles of $BaSO_4$ dissolved per liter
$$[Ba^{++}] = y = [HSO_4^-]; \text{ final } [H^+] = 0.1 \ M$$
$$\frac{[HSO_4^-][Ba^{++}]}{[H^+]} = 2 \times 10^{-8} = \frac{y^2}{0.1}$$
$$y = 2.2 \times 10^{-5}$$

Although the formation of bisulfate ions causes barium sulfate to be twice as soluble in this solution as in water, the effect is unimportant since the solubility in water is only $1 \times 10^{-5} \ M$.

The marked quantitative difference in the effect of hydrogen ion on the solubilities of silver acetate and barium sulfate is due to a choice of relatively extreme cases. In the case of each salt, the change in solubility due to hydrogen ion is dependent on the actual solubility of the salt as well as the strength of the weak acid formed. Since these two factors must be considered, there are many exceptions to the qualitative listing shown in Table 5-1 concerning the effect of hydrogen ion on the solubility of salts.

Effect of Complex Ion Formation on Solubility

An increase in solubility due to the formation of complex ions or, less frequently, undissociated salts is closely related in principle to the effect of hydrogen ion on the solubility of salts of weak acids. For example, lead sulfate can be dissolved in ammonium acetate due to the formation of undissociated lead acetate molecules. Similarly, copper hydroxide can be dissolved in ammonium hydroxide due to the formation of cupric tetrammine ions, $Cu(NH_3)_4^{++}$.

To illustrate the quantitative estimation, we may consider the effect of the formation of silver diammine ions on the solubility of silver chloride in a one molar ammonium hydroxide solution. The designation, one molar ammonium hydroxide, means only that one mole of NH_3 gas is dissolved per liter of reagent and that we can refer to the dissolved substance as $NH_{3(aq)}$ or NH_4OH as convenience dictates.

Equilibria Involved

Solution of AgCl:

$$AgCl_{(s)} = Ag^+ + Cl^- \qquad K_{sp} = [Ag^+][Cl^-]$$

Reaction of $NH_{3(aq)}$:

$$Ag^+ + 2\,NH_{3(aq)} = Ag(NH_3)_2^+ \qquad K_1 = \frac{[Ag(NH_3)_2^+]}{[Ag^+][NH_3]^2}$$

Net effect of $NH_{3(aq)}$:

$$AgCl_{(s)} + 2NH_{3(aq)} = Ag(NH_3)_2^+ + Cl^- \qquad K = \frac{[Ag(NH_3)_2^+][Cl^-]}{[NH_3]^2}$$

The value of K can be calculated from the K_{sp} and K_1 by the scheme used in the preceding "weak acid" examples as follows:

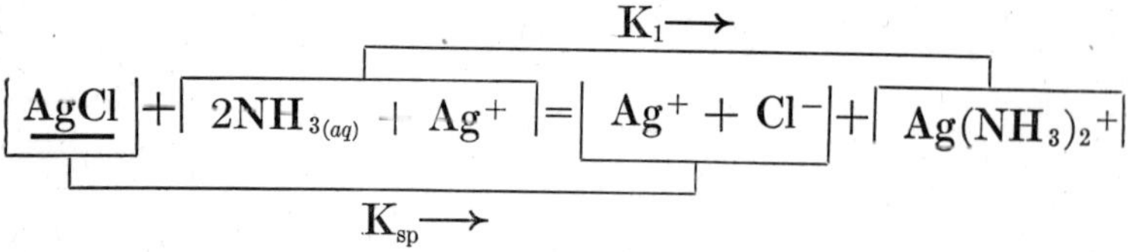

$$\underbrace{\boxed{AgCl} + \boxed{2NH_{3(aq)} + Ag^+}}_{K_{sp} \rightarrow} = \overbrace{\boxed{Ag^+ + Cl^-} + \boxed{Ag(NH_3)_2^+}}^{K_1 \rightarrow}$$

$$K = \frac{[Ag(NH_3)_2^+][Ag^+][Cl^-]}{[NH_3]^2[Ag^+]} = K_{sp} \cdot K_1$$

$$K = 1.7 \times 10^{-10} \times 1.7 \times 10^7 = 2.9 \times 10^{-3}$$

Concentration Relationships

AgCl dissolves to form Cl^- and a mixture of Ag^+ and $Ag(NH_3)_2^+$

Therefore: $[Cl^-] = [Ag^+] + [Ag(NH_3)_2^+]$ = solubility of AgCl

$$\frac{[Ag(NH_3)_2^+]}{[Ag^+][NH_3]^2} = 17,000,000$$

TABLE 5-1
Qualitative Effect of Hydrogen Ion on the Solubility of Common Salts

Salts	Weak Acids Formed	Remarks
Perchlorates...............	none	No Specific Effect
Nitrates..................	none	
Halides (except fluorides)....	none	
Iodates, bromates, chlorates..	none	
Sulfates	HSO_4^-	Limited effect
Fluorides	HF	
Carbonates.......	HCO_3^- and H_2CO_3	Salts of these acids are seldom insoluble in moderately concentrated to concentrated acid solutions.
Chromates.......	$HCrO_4^-$ and $Cr_2O_7^{--}$	
Sulfides..........	HS^- and H_2S	
Oxalates.........	$HC_2O_4^-$ and $H_2C_2O_4$	
Phosphates (Arsenates)....	HPO_4^{--}, $H_2PO_4^-$, and H_3PO_4	
Salts of many organic acids...	Corresponding organic acids	

Therefore, the $[Ag^+]$ must be very small compared to $[Ag(NH_3)_2^+]$, provided the final NH_3 concentration is not very small. As a result we may write:

$$[Cl^-] = [Ag(NH_3)_2^+]$$

Each $Ag(NH_3)_2^+$ formed requires two NH_3 molecules and since the original concentration of $NH_{3(aq)}$ was $1\ M$ the final concentration is:

$$[NH_3] = 1 - 2\,[Ag(NH_3)_2^+] = 1 - 2\,[Cl^-]$$

Approximate Calculation

$$\frac{[Ag(NH_3)_2^+]\,[Cl^-]}{[NH_3]^2} = 2.9 \times 10^{-3}$$

Let y = moles of AgCl dissolved per liter

$[Cl^-] = y = [Ag(NH_3)_2^+]$
$[NH_3] = 1 - 2\,[Ag(NH_3)_2^+]$

As a first approximation, assume $2\,[Ag(NH_3)_2^+]$ is small compared to 1.

$$\frac{y^2_{max}}{[NH_3]^2_{max}} = 2.9 \times 10^{-3} \quad ; \quad y_{max} = 5.25 \times 10^{-2} \times 1$$

The $[NH_3]$, therefore, must lie between 1.0 as a maximum and $1.0 - 2 \times 5.25 \times 10^{-2}$ or 0.895 as a minimum. As a second approximation, we may use the average $(1.0 + 0.895)/2$ or 0.95 as the assumed value. This leads to the result:

$$y = 5.38 \times 10^{-2}\,[NH_3] = 5.1 \times 10^{-2}$$

The value for the $[NH_3]$ is now known to lie between 0.95, the assumed value and $1.0 - 2 \times 5.1 \times 10^{-2}$ or 0.90, the corresponding calculated value. If a more exact result is required, further approximations can be made but it is evident that the value 5.1×10^{-2} for the molar solubility of silver chloride is reasonably correct.

In this case, the solubility of silver chloride has been increased from $1.3 \times 10^{-5}\,M$ in water to $5.1 \times 10^{-2}\,M$ in $1\,M$ NH_4OH, a factor of 4000.

Problems

1. (a) Write the expression for the solubility product in each of the following reactions:

$$AgBr = Ag^+ + Br^-$$
$$Ag_2CrO_4 = 2Ag^+ + CrO_4^{--}$$
$$PbCrO_4 = Pb^{++} + CrO_4^{--}$$
$$Pb_3(PO_4)_2 = 3Pb^{++} + 2PO_4^{---}$$

(b) Let s represent the solubility in moles per liter of each of the above substances. Write the expression for the solubility product in terms of s.

2. 100 milliliters of water dissolve 0.19 mg of AgCl at 25° C. Write expressions for (a) the molarity of the AgCl solution, (b) the solubility product of AgCl.

3. From the data in Problem 2, estimate the volume of 0.01 M HNO_3 that can be used to wash a AgCl precipitate without exceeding a loss of 0.1 mg of chloride ion. Assume that the solution becomes saturated with AgCl during the washing. *Ans.* **211 ml.**

4. In the gravimetric chloride determination, what must be the Ag^+ concentration after precipitation of the AgCl so that the loss of chloride ion does not exceed 0.01 mg in 300 ml of this solution? Use the data given in Problem 2.
Ans. **1.8×10^{-4} M.**

5. One hundred milliliters of a solution contain 0.7456 g of KCl. To this solution, 2.000 g of $AgNO_3$ are added. What is the final concentration of Ag^+, of Cl^-? The solubility product of AgCl is 1.7×10^{-10}.
Ans. **$Ag^+ = 3.95 \times 10^{-2}$ M.**
$Cl^- = 4.3 \times 10^{-9}$ M.

6. The solubility product of Ag_2CrO_4 is 1.1×10^{-12}. Calculate (a) the CrO_4^{--} concentration, (b) the Ag^+ concentration, (c) the solubility of Ag_2CrO_4 in g/100 ml in a saturated aqueous solution.
Ans. (a) **6.5×10^{-5} M;**
(b) **1.30×10^{-4} M;**
(c) **2.16×10^{-3} g/100 ml.**

7. What volume of 0.1 M AgNO$_3$ must be added to: (a) 1 liter, (b) 50 ml of 0.001 M K$_2$CrO$_4$ solution so that a precipitate of Ag$_2$CrO$_4$ just begins to form?

Ans. (a) .105 ml; (b) 0.0053 ml.

8. (a) Calculate the solubility of AgIO$_3$ in g/100 ml in a 0.0001 M AgNO$_3$ solution. The solubility product for AgIO$_3$ is 5.3×10^{-8}. (b) How many milliliters of 0.1 M AgNO$_3$ must be added to the solution so that the loss of AgIO$_3$ will not exceed 0.1 mg/100 ml of solution?

Ans. (a) 5.3 mg; (b) 17.6 ml.

9. Three hundred milliliters of a solution contain 0.1699 g of AgNO$_3$. What weight of K$_2$CrO$_4$ must be added so that the weight of Ag$^+$ in solution does not exceed 1.0 mg? The solubility product is given in Problem 6.

Ans. 0.1630 g.

10. Outline a possible method for the determination of chloride ion in a solution that contains the following substances: (a) sodium acetate, (b) ammonium hydroxide, (c) potassium chromate.

11. (a) The solubility product for CaSO$_4$ is 6×10^{-5}. Calculate the solubility in g/liter. (b) The ionization constant for the reaction

$$HSO_4^- = H^+ + SO_4^-$$

is 10^{-2}. Calculate the solubility of CaSO$_4$ in g/liter if the final hydrogen ion concentration is 1 M.

Ans. (a) 1.054 g/l; (b) 10.54 g/l.

12. The solubility product for BaF$_2$ is 1.7×10^{-6} and the ionization constant for HF is 7.2×10^{-4}. Calculate the solubility of BaF$_2$ if the final hydrogen ion concentration is 0.1 M.

Ans. 0.202 M.

13. The solubility product for ZnS is 4.5×10^{-24} and for the reaction:

$$H_2S = 2H^+ + S^{--}$$

$K = 1 \times 10^{-22}$. Calculate the solubility of ZnS in a solution

GRAVIMETRIC TECHNIQUES AND THE CONTROL OF SOLUBILITY 77

where the final hydrogen ion concentration is 0.3 M.

Ans. 6.37×10^{-2} M.

14. The solubility product for CuS is 4×10^{-38} and for the reaction
$$H_2S = 2H^+ + S^{--}$$
$K = 1 \times 10^{-22}$. What must be the hydrogen ion concentration to make the solubility of copper sulfide 10^{-7} moles/liter?

Ans. 5.0 M.

15. For AgCl $K_{sp} = 1.7 \times 10^{-10}$ and for the reaction
$$Ag(NH_3)_2{}^+ = Ag^+ + 2NH_{3(aq)}$$
$K = 6 \times 10^{-8}$. Calculate the solubility of AgCl in g/liter in a solution where the initial concentration of ammonia is 1.0 M.

Ans. 14.2 g/l.

16. For CuS $K_{sp} = 4 \times 10^{-38}$ and for the reaction
$$Cu(NH_3)_4{}^{++} = Cu^{++} + 4NH_{3(aq)}$$
$K = 4.56 \times 10^{-14}$. Calculate the volume of 10 M ammonia that is required to dissolve 1 mg of CuS.

Ans. 1.12×10^4 liters.

Chapter 6

GRAVIMETRIC DETERMINATION OF SULFATE
PHYSICAL CHARACTER AND PURITY OF PRECIPITATES
GRAVIMETRIC DETERMINATION OF IRON

•

GRAVIMETRIC DETERMINATION OF SULFATE

General Discussion

The gravimetric determination of sulfate by precipitation as barium sulfate is similar in method to the preceding chloride determination. The only significant difference in technique is the use of filter paper in place of a filter crucible to collect the precipitate. This permits transfer of the precipitate to an ordinary crucible in which the paper can be removed by burning it. The technique frequently is employed to handle precipitates that must be heated to high temperatures in order to establish a fixed composition.

Variations in the acidity, temperature, manner of precipitant addition, and time of digestion markedly affect the filterability of barium sulfate precipitates and the extent to which various foreign ions are coprecipitated.

Foreign anions such as nitrate, chlorate and chloride are coprecipitated as the corresponding barium salts and the ignited precipitate contains the salt or oxide in addition to the precipitated barium sulfate. The coprecipitation of chloride can be decreased by the slow addition of barium chloride to the solution. Nitrate and chlorate, however, interfere seriously even at low concentrations and so they should be removed from the solution before precipitation.

Foreign cations such as ferric iron, calcium and, to a lesser extent, the alkali metals are coprecipitated as the sulfates.

The ignited barium sulfate then yields a low result for the percent sulfate in the sample. The magnitude of the error depends upon the difference between the weight of the foreign sulfate or oxide and an equivalent amount of barium sulfate. While dilution of the solution prior to precipitation decreases this error, it cannot be avoided entirely except by the removal of the interfering ions. Precipitates can often be purified by reprecipitation but this is not practical in the case of barium sulfate.

The particular conditions employed are experimentally known to yield results of the desired accuracy for alkali sulfate samples but they are not necessarily the best conditions to use for other samples. In this, as in most determinations, the final details of a method rest upon trial and error because there still are many gaps in our fundamental knowledge of the phenomena involved.

The technique is somewhat more complex than in the chloride determination and so careful attention to detail is more critical. There also is a greater possibility of accidental loss of a determination. For these reasons, the samples should be run in triplicate using one determination to become familiar with specific difficulties.

General Preparations

Most of the following operations can and should be completed while the preceding determination is in progress. Operations requiring the greatest time should be started first.

Wash three 400-600 ml beakers, three large watch glasses, and four stirring rods with cleanser rather than with cleaning solution. Rinse them thoroughly with tap water followed by distilled water. Number the beakers on the ground area for identification. Cover each beaker with a watch glass and store the equipment until needed.

Wash and rinse three 10 ml crucibles, again using cleanser rather than cleaning solution. Identify each crucible by means of existing differences or consult your instructor if it appears necessary to make identifying marks on them. Support a crucible on its side in the wire triangle as shown in Figure 6-1.

Adjust a Bunsen burner to give a non-luminous flame with a full gas supply and place it under the crucible so that the tip of the flame cone is just below but not touching the crucible. Ignite each crucible at red heat in this way for 10 to 15 minutes. Allow it to cool in air for 2 to 3 minutes after removing the flame and place the crucible in the desiccator to cool to room temperature. Weigh the crucibles accurately and store them in the desiccator until needed. After the first weighings, the crucibles should be reignited and reweighed until successive weighings agree within 0.1 to 0.2 mg. Actually, a single ignition usually establishes a reproducible weight. The safest procedure is to reignite and reweigh, but a choice in the matter is justifiable.

Transfer the sulfate unknown to a clean, dry weighing bottle and dry it at 105 to 110° C in the oven for at least one hour. Store the dried sample in the desiccator until it has cooled to room temperature. Use the technique described in the chloride determination to weigh and transfer a 0.3-0.4 g sample into each of the three beakers. Dissolve each sample in a convenient amount of distilled water, add 5 ml of 6 N HCl and dilute to 200 to 300 ml. Cover the beakers and store them until it is convenient to proceed with the determination.

Precipitation

Heat the sample solution and keep it just below the boiling point. It is undesirable to keep the solution boiling because of possible loss due to spattering but it is necessary to keep the temperature around 90° C to facilitate formation of large filterable particles and to minimize coprecipitation of foreign ions.

Calculate, within one ml, the volume of 5% $BaCl_2$ solution required to precipitate the sulfate in your sample, assuming that it is pure sodium sulfate (a 1 g sample requires about 29 ml). Measure the calculated amount of reagent in a graduate and add *one* or *two* drops of it to the hot solution

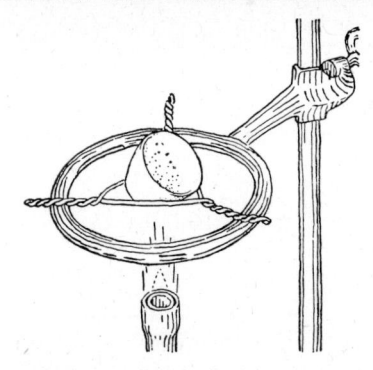

FIG. 6-1. Position of the crucible in ignition operations. The size of the flame and the placement of the burner depend on the specific process involved.

from the end of a clean stirring rod. *Stir, without further addition of barium chloride*, until the solution becomes cloudy due to precipitate formation. After observing the first cloudiness, slowly pour all of the barium chloride from the graduate into the stirred solution. Poor results frequently are obtained when the barium chloride is added too rapidly. Continue stirring for a short time and allow the precipitate to digest in the hot solution for at least one half hour. When the supernatant is free of precipitate, add about 1 ml of barium chloride solution and carefully note whether any additional precipitate forms. If it does form, check your volume calculations. If your calculated volume is not in error, consult your instructor.

Filtration should not be started until you have enough time available (about one hour) to complete the filtration and the washing in unbroken sequence. In this particular case, the precipitate may be allowed to stand in contact with the supernatant indefinitely.

Filtration and Washing

Clean three funnels by pouring cleaning solution through them. Rinse thoroughly and wipe the mouth of each funnel dry to facilitate fitting the paper.

Take a piece of 9-cm quantitative paper and prepare a filter as shown in Figure 6-2.

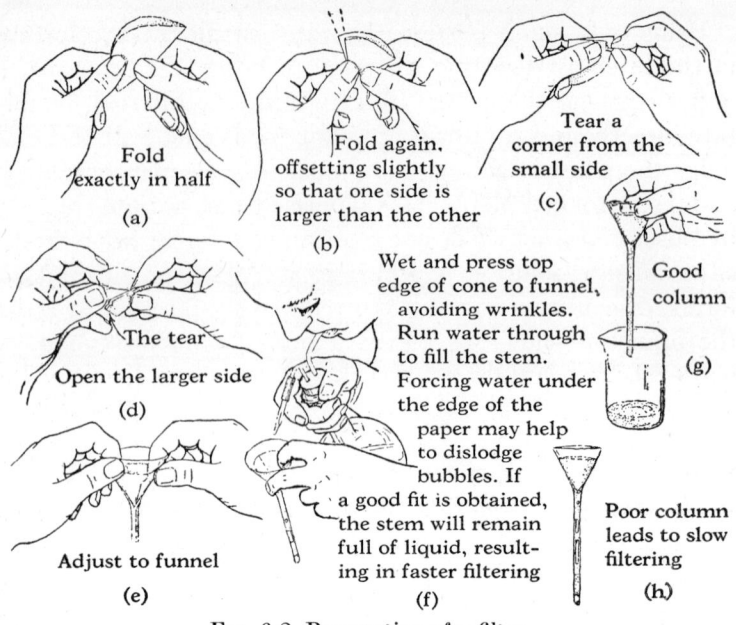

FIG. 6-2. Preparation of a filter.

(a) Fold exactly in half
(b) Fold again, offsetting slightly so that one side is larger than the other
(c) Tear a corner from the small side
(d) Open the larger side — The tear
(e) Adjust to funnel
(f) Wet and press top edge of cone to funnel, avoiding wrinkles. Run water through to fill the stem. Forcing water under the edge of the paper may help to dislodge bubbles. If a good fit is obtained, the stem will remain full of liquid, resulting in faster filtering
(g) Good column
(h) Poor column leads to slow filtering

Support the prepared funnels in funnel holders or in iron rings and place numbered, 400-600 ml receivers under them. Heat the water in the large wash bottle for subsequent washing operations. Loosen the stopper of the bottle before heating it.

It is not necessary, but it is more efficient to filter the barium sulfate from a hot solution, since the speed of filtration is greater at the higher temperature and the solubility loss is not significant. Using the technique described for the chloride determination, decant the supernatant through the filter and wash the precipitate in the beaker with three 10 to 30 ml portions of hot water from the wash bottle. Empty the receivers at this point and then transfer the precipitate to the filter. Use a policeman in connection with the hot water washing to remove any adhering particles from the beaker. The precipitate tends to creep up the thin film of water on the beaker walls and so the last portions of it can be more efficiently transferred by use of alcohol. A 50 ml wash bottle filled with methyl alcohol is useful for this purpose.

Using only small portions of water, wash the precipitate in the filter by directing a stream of hot water around the upper edges of the paper. Be careful not to hit the precipitate directly and spatter it or to hit the funnel wall and dislodge the paper. Each washing must be collected separately and tested for complete removal of the excess barium chloride by observing whether or not a precipitate forms when dilute silver nitrate solution is added to it. When no precipitate forms, discontinue washing and remove the filter paper from the funnel as shown in Figure 6-3. If it is inconvenient to ignite the precipitate at this point, the crucibles may be kept in covered beakers as long as desired.

Ignition

Two important sources of error in the ignition are mechanical loss and chemical reduction. Material may be lost mechanically if water and volatile compounds in the paper are vigorously evolved by a too rapid initial heating and by loss of some of the small ignited particles due to sudden air currents or by faulty manipulation of the crucible. At moderately high temperatures barium sulfate is reduced to barium sulfide by reaction with carbon and organic compounds derived from the paper and the flame. It, therefore, is necessary to maintain free access of air to the crucible during

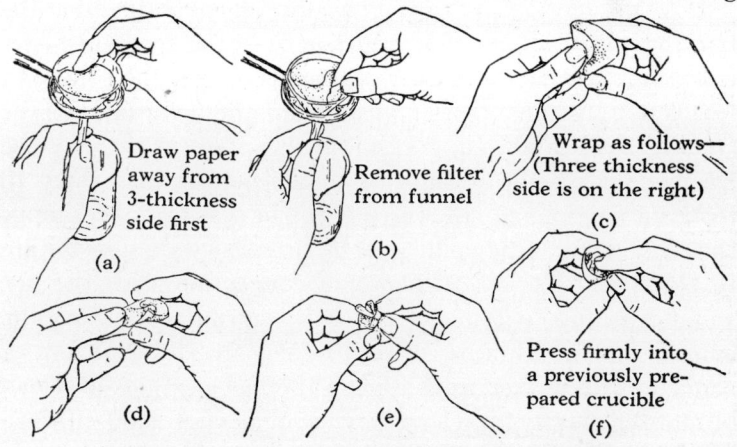

Fig. 6-3. Preparation of a filtered sample for ignition.

ignition, to use a non-luminous flame which is kept away from the crucible mouth, and to burn the carbon at the lowest practical temperature. If the crucible is strongly heated while an appreciable amount of carbon is present, a significant portion of the sulfate usually is reduced to sulfide.

Place the crucible on its side in a triangle with its mouth across an apex as shown previously in Figure 6-1. Adjust the burner to give a non-luminous flame with a very limited gas supply and place it under the bottom end of the crucible. By varying the flame intensity and the height of the crucible above the burner, keep the crucible hot enough to volatilize the water steadily. Increase the temperature, when necessary, to maintain a visible evolution of volatile compounds from the paper after the water has been driven off. Try to avoid igniting these volatile compounds but, if they do ignite, simply remove the flame until burning ceases and then continue the heating. As soon as the paper has been charred, increase the temperature until the carbon begins to glow. It may be necessary to turn the crucible in order to bring isolated portions of carbon closer to a hot wall. Do this as sparingly and as carefully as possible. As soon as all the carbon has been removed, use the full gas supply and raise the burner so that the point of the luminous flame is just below, but not in contact with, the base of the crucible. Ignite at this maximum temperature for 5 to 10 minutes. Allow the crucible to cool in air for 2 to 3 minutes after removing the flame and then place it in the desiccator to cool to room temperature. This single ignition usually establishes a constant weight but, again, the only safe technique is to re-ignite and reweigh to demonstrate a constancy of 0.1 to 0.2 mg in the weight. Report the results to your instructor as percent sodium sulfate in the sample. Ideally, all three determinations should agree within five parts per thousand. Practically, any two results which agree that closely may be considered acceptable.

The crucibles together with the precipitates should be saved until the results have been checked. To clean the crucibles, the bulk of the residue may be lifted or knocked out of the crucible. Scrubbing with cleanser will remove the remainder as effectively as any of the common laboratory reagents.

PHYSICAL CHARACTER AND PURITY OF PRECIPITATES

In Chapter 5, the conditions for precipitation were discussed solely from the solubility point of view. We now wish to consider the physical character of a precipitate. This includes such attributes as particle size, colloid formation, and flocculation—qualities which are important in the mechanical separation of a precipitate as well as in its purity. The discussion must be partially based upon a set of empirical generalizations because a satisfactory theory has not yet been developed.

Particle Size and Separation

When a compound precipitates from solution, there must be a growth of the precipitate from its component ions to form progressively larger units until mechanically separable particles or agglomerates are obtained. The size of the particles and the type of agglomerates which result depend upon the nature of the compound and upon the conditions employed during and after the precipitation. In discussing these small particles, it is convenient to use the units:

micron, μ, = 10^{-4} cm and millimicron, $m\mu$, = 10^{-7} cm

The particle-size range of some suspension groups and the associated problem of mechanical separation for these groups are indicated below.

Approx. Size	Suspension Group	Mechanical Separation
1 $m\mu$	Solutions of simple ions	Essentially impossible
1 – 100 $m\mu$	Colloidal dispersions of inorganic salts	Impractical. Requires ultra-filters or ultra-centrifuges.
100 $m\mu$ – 10μ	"Fine" suspensions	Undesirable. Requires very fine filters.
Larger than 10μ	"Coarse" suspensions	Filterable with medium to coarse paper or filter crucibles.

Particle Size and Area

The specific surface of a solid is defined as the area per unit weight of a substance. It depends upon the density of the material and upon the size and shape of the particles. The increase of specific area with a decrease of particle size is important in connection with the coprecipitation of impurities, the formation of colloids, and solubility. To illustrate this increase, let us, for simplicity, assume cubical particles of edge length, e, and calculate the specific surface corresponding to a size in each suspension group mentioned above. Suppose, furthermore, that one gram of the solid occupies one-third of a cubic centimeter. The number of particles, N, in one gram is then:

$$N = \frac{1}{3e^3}$$

The area of each cube is $6e^2$ since there are six faces, each face having an area e^2. The specific area, A, is therefore:

$$A = 6e^2 \cdot \frac{1}{3e^3} = \frac{2}{e}$$

We then obtain the following results for uniform cubical particles:

Nature of Suspension	"Coarse"	"Fine"	Colloidal
Length of edge	10μ	1μ	$10m\mu$
No. of particles/g	3×10^8	3×10^{11}	3×10^{17}
Specific surface (cm²/g)	2×10^3	20×10^3	2000×10^3

Particle Size and Solubility

Assume that one gram of the solid contains 3×10^{17} particles, 10 mμ on an edge. Is there any reason to expect these particles to grow by recrystallization and to appear as a smaller number of larger particles; for example, as 3×10^{11} particles, 1μ on an edge? From the preceding tabulation, it is seen that if this growth occurs, the surface area decreases by 1980×10^3 cm² (from 2000×10^3 cm² to 20×10^3 cm²). If this decrease in surface results in a more stable arrange-

```
    ~ — ~ Solution ~ —
  ┌─────┐   ┌─────┐                    ┌──────────┐
  │Solid│   │Solid│    Growth          │  Solid   │
  │  A  │   │  B  │   ────────▶        │    AB    │
  └─────┘   └─────┘                    └──────────┘
```

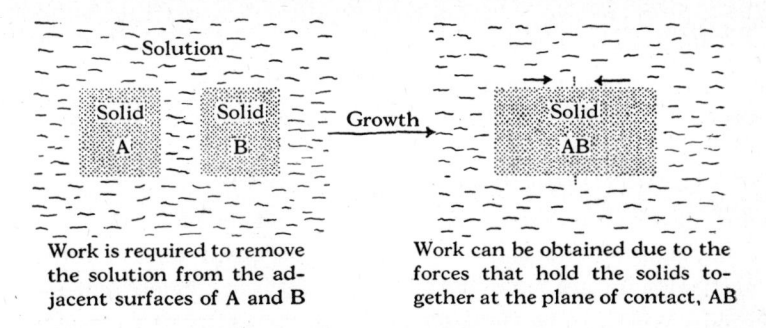

Work is required to remove the solution from the adjacent surfaces of A and B

Work can be obtained due to the forces that hold the solids together at the plane of contact, AB

FIG. 6-4. Schematic growth of a solid.

ment, work can be obtained and so the process can occur spontaneously. There are various ways in which growth can occur but, regardless of the path, the net effect can be pictured in terms of two particles coalescing as shown above.

In general, the cohesive forces between the molecules or ions of the solid are much greater than the forces between the molecules in the solution and those in the surface of the solid. Principally because of this fact, the work that can be obtained is greater than that required to free the surface from solvent and so the suspension tends to decrease in specific surface by growth to larger particles. This tendency to minimize the specific surface results in a greater solubility for small particles than for large ones. The difference in solubility depends upon the nature of the solid and the composition of the solution in contact with it. It is of practical importance only when the particles are so small that a small absolute change in size causes a large change in specific surface. For example, in the preceding tabulation, a growth of 0.99μ from 10 mμ to 1μ particles decreases the specific surface by 1980×10^3 cm^2. However, a growth of 9μ (9 times as much) from 1μ to 10μ particles decreases the specific surface by 18×10^3 cm^2 (only 100th as much). For this reason, the effect of particle size on solubility is of most significance for particles smaller than a few microns.

After a precipitate has been formed, the rate of growth to large particles is limited by the rate of solution of the small particles. For sparingly soluble materials at room temperature, this rate is slow. To increase the rate, precipitates frequently are digested at elevated temperatures. The value of such a digestion must be experimentally evaluated in each case.

The Formation and Flocculation of Colloidal Suspensions

By a *colloidal suspension*, we shall mean one in which the particles are smaller than about 100 mμ. Such particles are too small to be separated by ordinary filtration. Because of the small size, these suspensions sometimes appear to be clear solutions. The *agglomeration* of such particles into filterable units and the steps that can be taken to avoid the formation of colloidal suspensions are of primary interest.

Various ions and molecules in a solution may be *adsorbed* on the surface of a precipitate because strong forces of attraction exist between them and the components of the solid lattice. Since work is required to remove such adsorbed substances, it follows from the preceding discussion that the tendency of very small particles to disappear by recrystallization will be decreased. The adsorbed substances also may decrease the rate of solution of the small particles. Regardless of the relative importance of these two factors, adsorption serves to inhibit the disappearance of small particles by recrystallization. In addition, adsorption is a critical factor in connection with the agglomeration of small particles into loosely bound, but filterable units.

The factors of general significance in the formation and *flocculation* of colloidal suspensions of inorganic precipitates can be illustrated by considering the specific case of silver chloride.

Primary Adsorption.—The silver and chloride ions that are found alternately in the surface of a silver chloride particle exert forces that act on all the ions and molecules in a solution. Lattice ions in solution will be most strongly adsorbed because the same forces that result in the formation of the precipitate itself act to bind them to the surface. In the absence of an excess of one of the lattice ions in the solution, those ions which form the least soluble compounds with the lattice ions are most strongly adsorbed. Thus, if silver chloride is precipitated by the addition of an excess of potassium chloride to a dilute silver nitrate solution, there is a *primary adsorption* of chloride ions on the surface of the silver chloride particles. These primarily adsorbed ions are essentially a part of the solid.

Counter Ions.—Each of the above silver chloride particles acquires a net negative charge by primary adsorption of excess chloride ions in the solution. Because of this charge, all positive ions are subject to a force of attraction and all negative ions are subject to a force of repulsion as they come near the charged particle. As a result, the concentration of negative ions is increased in a region of the solution immediately surrounding the particle. The total electrical charge due to the excess of positive over negative ions in this *counter-ion region* is equal to the total negative charge on the silver chloride particle. The ions of increased concentrations in this region are called the *counter ions*. The relation between the primarily adsorbed ions and the counter ions in the example we have been using is shown in Figure 6-5.

Chloride ions in excess are directly adsorbed on the surface of the crystal lattice. These negative ions attract positive ions from the body of the solution

Counter ion region in which the positive ion concentration is greater than, and the negative ion concentration is less than, that in the body of the solution

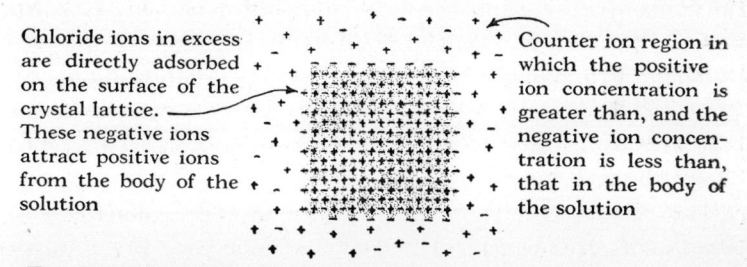

FIG. 6-5. Relationship of the primarily adsorbed ions to the counter ion region.

When particles of silver chloride approach each other, cohesive forces act at very small distances to hold the particles together. If these same particles acquire negative charges by primary adsorption of chloride ions, there is an electrical repulsion between them that opposes agglomeration. The counter ions around a charged particle act to limit the electric field to a small region close to its surface. If the field is limited sufficiently, the charged particles can approach closely enough to be loosely united as an agglomerate. When the counter-ion region is too diffuse, a sufficiently close approach is prevented by electrical repulsion and therefore the

Jagged lines indicate the region in which cohesive forces act strongly to hold particles together

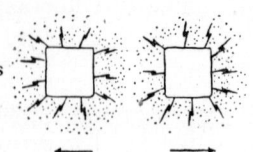

Here the counter ions are diffuse and the electrical repulsions between the particles prevent agglomeration

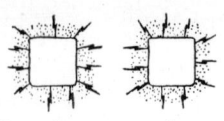

Agglomeration →

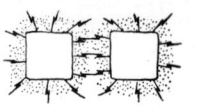

When the counter-ion region is compressed, the particles can approach closely enough so that cohesive forces can hold them together

Loosely bound agglomerates are formed due to the cohesive forces

FIG. 6-6. Diagram showing the effect of the counter ions on the flocculation of a colloid.

particles remain dispersed. The extent to which the field around a charged particle is compressed is determined by the concentrations and the kinds of counter ions present. An increase in concentration of a given counter ion compresses the field, although the effect is not linear. When the ions are varied, it is found that the ratio of charge to radius is an index of the ability of a counter ion to compress the field. Thus, the order of increasing effectiveness of some of the cations is K^+, H^+, Ba^{++}, La^{+++}; among the anions SO_4^{--} is more effective than NO_3^-.

Effect of Temperature.—If the temperature is increased, the kinetic energy of the colloidal particles is increased, and so electrical repulsion is less effective in keeping the fast moving particles apart. An increase in temperature also will affect the primary adsorption process, the rate of growth of the particle, and the distribution of counter ions, so that a simple picture of the overall effect cannot be given. In general, the net effect of an increase in temperature is an increased rate of flocculation.

Flocculation and Peptization.—In practical applications of precipitation, a primary adsorption of one of the lattice ions seldom can be avoided since we must use an excess of one of them to obtain complete precipitation. Certain precipitates, such as the silver halides, the heavy metal hydroxides and sulfides are almost invariably obtained as colloids. The preceding empirical generalizations furnish a useful guide for choosing the conditions under which the colloid will flocculate to form agglomerates of filterable size, and the conditions for preventing the redispersion of the flocculated colloid, a process which is called *peptization*.

A practical illustration of the above processes is shown in the following example:

Formation of the Colloid.—Equal volumes of 0.01 M $AgNO_3$ and 0.011 M KCl are mixed and a colloidal dispersion of silver chloride is obtained. Primary adsorption of an excess lattice ion, chloride in this case, inhibits the growth of the particles and makes flocculation very slow because of the resultant electrical repulsion between the charged particles. The concentration of the only available counter ion, K^+, is only 0.005 M and so the counter-ion region is diffuse.

Flocculation.—The solution is made 0.1 M in nitric acid. This provides a more effective counter ion (H^+ is very much smaller than K^+) and also a much higher concentration (0.1 M instead of 0.005 M). As a result, the fields around the negatively charged silver chloride particles are greatly compressed and so the particles flocculate as agglomerates of filterable size.

Prevention of Peptization.—When the precipitate is washed with water, the concentration of the counter ions is greatly decreased. The electrical field becomes much more diffuse and so some of the flocculated silver chloride is peptized. To avoid loss of the precipitate in this way, a counter ion is added to the wash water in the form of a subsequently volatile compound. The most obvious choice in this case is nitric acid.

Adsorption and Purity

Because of adsorption, various foreign ions ordinarily will be found in any precipitate. In accordance with the previous discussion of the dependence of specific area on particle size, the amount of the impurities adsorbed on a given weight of precipitate increases as the average particle size decreases. For this reason, contamination resulting from adsorption usually is greatest for flocculated colloids. When a precipitate is washed, some, but not all, of the adsorbed ions (primarily adsorbed ions as well as the counter ions) can be removed. Insofar as possible, conditions which favor the formation of large particles must be used in order to reduce the amount of adsorbed impurities.

Very often, the contamination of a precipitate by adsorption can be reduced by choosing conditions that favor the adsorption of subsequently volatile compounds. Thus, if silver chloride is precipitated by adding excess potassium chloride to silver nitrate, the precipitate contains primarily adsorbed chloride ions with potassium ions as the counter ions. Any potassium chloride which remains after washing is not volatilized when the precipitate is dried. However, if nitric acid is added in the precipitation step and used during the washing, potassium ion is replaced by hydrogen ion as the counter ion. Any nitric acid adsorbed is then volatilized when the silver chloride is dried. For the same reason, ferric hydroxide often is washed with ammonium nitrate solution, since any adsorbed ammonium compounds will be volatilized during the ignition of the precipitate.

Contamination by Occlusion

As a precipitate forms and grows, substances adsorbed on the surface of small particles may be entrapped by subsequent growth and agglomeration and these substances will no longer be exposed on the accessible surface of the precipitate. Such *occluded substances* are a serious source of contamination since they cannot be removed by subsequent washing. The precipitate must recrystallize in order to expose the occluded substances to the solution. Precipitates commonly are digested at elevated temperatures to promote recrystallization and thereby reduce the amount of occluded impurities. The value of this procedure must be tested experimentally in a given case.

When occlusion occurs to a serious extent, as it frequently does, the most generally effective method of reducing contamination is reprecipitation. Thus, the ammonium hydroxide precipitation of ferric hydroxide in the presence of appreciable amounts of zinc and nickel ions should yield a clean separation since zinc and nickel ions form very stable ammonia complexes. Actually, the precipitate usually is contaminated by significant amounts of zinc and nickel that cannot be removed by subsequent washing. The precipitate, separated from the mother liquor, can be dissolved in acid to yield a solution in which the concentrations of the zinc and nickel ions are much less than in the original solution. *Reprecipitation* of the ions from this solution, therefore, reduces the contamination by these ions. Contamination by adsorption and occlusion is common to all precipitates although there is a wide variation in the detailed behavior of specific substances.

Solid Solution or Mixed Crystal Formation

The formation of *solid solutions* and the phenomenon of post precipitation are important but are of less general occurrence than adsorption and occlusion. If a sodium sulfate solution is added slowly to a solution containing barium and lead ions, we might expect that barium sulfate would be precipitated first, leaving the lead in solution because lead sulfate is one hundred times as soluble as barium sulfate. However, if the experiment is tried, it is found that lead ions frequently take the place of the barium ions in the barium sulfate crystal lattice and that the barium sulfate solid acts essentially as a solvent for lead sulfate. The amount of lead that coprecipitates in this way can be influenced by the precipitation conditions but it cannot be made negligible unless the concentration of lead ion is made very small. The lead ions tend to distribute themselves between the solid and the liquid so as to establish an equilibrium between the two phases. Prolonged digestion serves only to change the initial contamination to such an equilibrium value.

Post Precipitation

If hydrogen sulfide is passed into a 0.01 M solution of zinc ion in 0.1 M HCl, no zinc sulfide is precipitated over a long period of time, although the solution is supersaturated with respect to zinc sulfide. However, if the solution also contains substances such as cupric or mercuric ions, cupric and mercuric sulfides will precipitate first and they, in turn, will induce the precipitation of zinc sulfide. Although some zinc sulfide forms during the precipitation of the other sulfides, most of it precipitates after the other compounds have formed. This phenomenon is termed *post precipitation* and represents a case of less frequent occurrence than solid solution formation. Post precipitation is important in connection with some of the sulfide separations and in the separation of calcium from magnesium by oxalate precipitation.

Effect of Conditions of Precipitation on Size and Purity

In the preceding discussion, it has been indicated that a precipitate will increase in average particle size and, in general, become more pure if it is given an opportunity to recrystallize during a period of digestion. Unfortunately, the extent to which such recrystallization occurs is limited. It usually is more important to use conditions of precipitation which favor the direct growth to large particles and thus minimize the occlusion and adsorption of non-volatile impurities. Many exceptions to any generalizations that are made can be found because the relative importance of the various factors involved depends not only upon the compound being precipitated but also upon the other substances which are present in the solution. Recognizing this limitation, the following general picture is given to serve as a useful guide in choosing the conditions for precipitation.

Primary Particles.—The initial step in precipitation must be the aggregation of a sufficient number of the constituent ions to form a regular lattice arrangement that has essentially the properties of the solid. Just how large these initial particles must be is not yet clear, nor is the mechanism of formation of these initial particles understood. It is quite possible that other lattice arrangements such as the walls of the vessel and various foreign solid particles in the solution serve as centers upon which initial deposition of the ions occurs. In any case, we may refer to these ill-defined initial units of the precipitate as primary particles or nuclei. It also is reasonable to suppose that the number of such particles formed in the first stages of a precipitation increases with an increase in the initial concentration of the constituent ions of the precipitate. Once these primary particles exist, further precipitation can occur by the deposition of ions on their surfaces. This, in general, is faster than the formation of additional primary particles. It is, therefore, desirable to keep the initial concentration of the ions low so as to form a small number of nuclei to serve as centers for the deposition of the remaining ions. The use of dilute solutions should lead to a small number of large particles rather than a large number of small particles.

When we speak of a dilute solution, we mean that the concentrations should be compared with the solubility of the compound under the conditions employed. Thus, Von Weirmarn has presented the thesis that the initial relative supersaturation is a critical factor in determining the size of the particles of the precipitate. If Q is the concentration of material initially present in the solution, and if S is the solubility of coarse particles, the relative supersaturation, RS, is defined as:

$$RS = \frac{Q - S}{S}$$

The use, therefore, of elevated temperatures, acidity regulation, etc., to increase the solubility of a precipitate during its initial formation, is generally desirable in securing precipitates of large particle size. It is, of course, difficult to distinguish experimentally between the effects which an in-

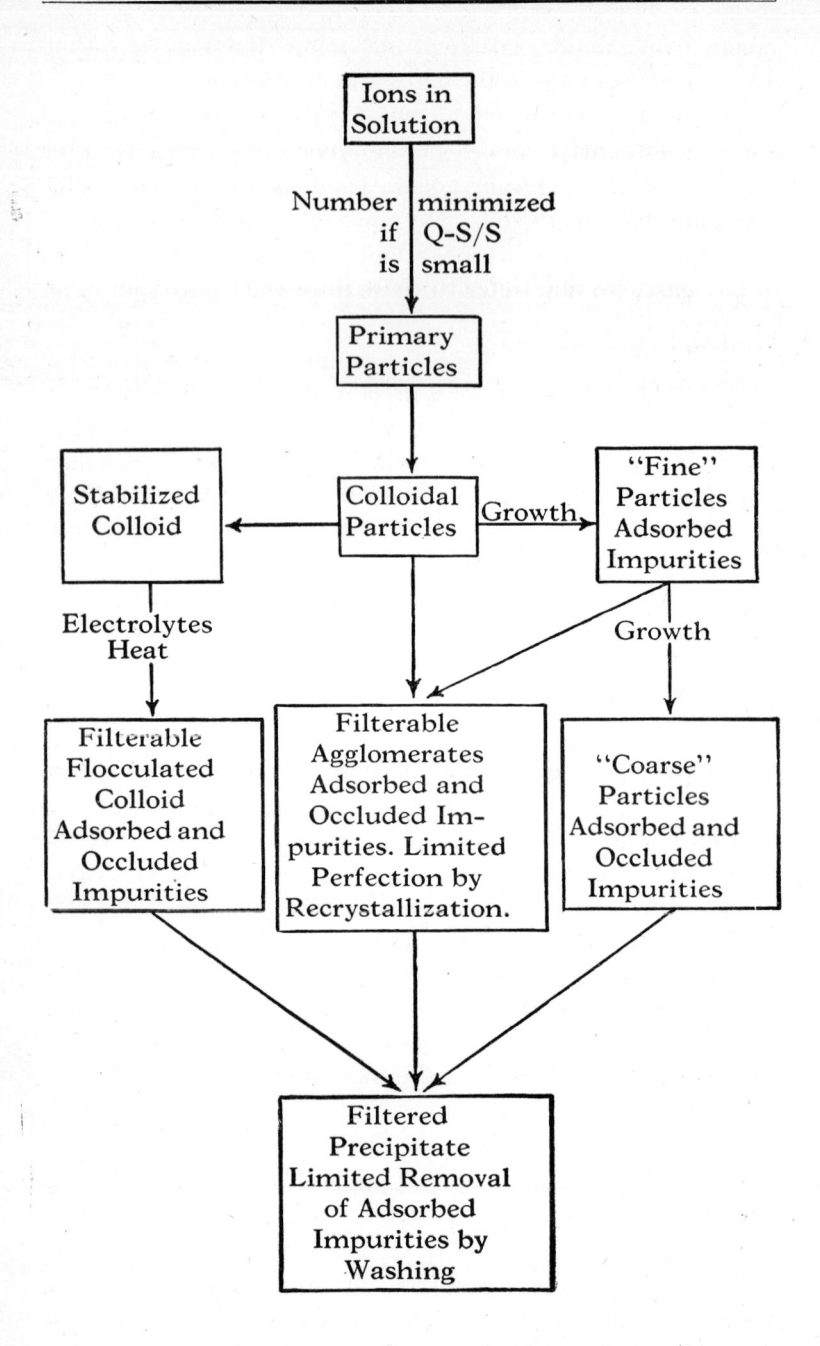

```
                    ┌──────────────┐
                    │  Ions in     │
                    │  Solution    │
                    └──────────────┘
                    Number │ minimized
                       if  │ Q-S/S
                       is  │ small
                           ▼
                    ┌──────────────┐
                    │  Primary     │
                    │  Particles   │
                    └──────────────┘
                           │
                           ▼
┌────────────┐      ┌──────────────┐            ┌──────────────┐
│ Stabilized │◄─────│  Colloidal   │  Growth    │   "Fine"     │
│  Colloid   │      │  Particles   │───────────►│  Particles   │
│            │      │              │            │  Adsorbed    │
│            │      │              │            │  Impurities  │
└────────────┘      └──────────────┘            └──────────────┘
    │ Electrolytes         │                           │ Growth
    │ Heat                 │                           │
    ▼                      ▼                           ▼
┌────────────┐      ┌──────────────┐            ┌──────────────┐
│ Filterable │      │  Filterable  │            │  "Coarse"    │
│ Flocculated│      │ Agglomerates │            │  Particles   │
│  Colloid   │      │ Adsorbed and │            │  Adsorbed and│
│ Adsorbed and│     │  Occluded Im-│            │  Occluded    │
│  Occluded  │      │ purities. Limited│        │  Impurities  │
│ Impurities │      │ Perfection by│            │              │
│            │      │Recrystallization.│        │              │
└────────────┘      └──────────────┘            └──────────────┘
      │                    │                           │
      └────────────────────┼───────────────────────────┘
                           ▼
                    ┌──────────────┐
                    │   Filtered   │
                    │  Precipitate │
                    │Limited Removal│
                    │  of Adsorbed │
                    │ Impurities by│
                    │   Washing    │
                    └──────────────┘
```

crease of solubility has upon the initial particle formation and upon its subsequent rate of recrystallization.

The qualitative considerations which have been suggested as of general importance are summarized in the schematic picture, on the opposite page, of the formation of simple inorganic precipitates.

GRAVIMETRIC DETERMINATION OF IRON (Optional)

General Discussion

A sample containing iron is dried, weighed, and dissolved in hydrochloric acid. Any ferrous ion present is oxidized to ferric ion. Ammonium hydroxide is then added in slight excess to precipitate hydrous ferric oxide. The precipitate is filtered, washed, ignited and weighed as Fe_2O_3.

Hydrous ferric oxide is very insoluble; the solubility product, expressed as $[Fe^{+++}][OH^-]^3$, is approximately 10^{-36}. It precipitates as very small particles which agglomerate to form gelatinous aggregates that are difficult to filter because they tend to plug the holes in the filtering media. Sometimes macerated filter paper is added to the solution to decrease this difficulty. The filterability of the precipitate can be improved by keeping the solution near the boiling point during, and for a short time after, precipitation. Prolonged boiling causes the precipitate to become slimy and more difficult to filter.

The precipitate consists of agglomerates of very small particles and so it has a great tendency to coprecipitate many substances by adsorption and occlusion, as discussed in the previous sections of this chapter. Cations that form insoluble hydroxides and anions that form insoluble ferric salts, under the conditions employed, must be absent. Precipitation is carried out in the presence of a high concentration of ammonium ion to minimize the interference by other cations and to reduce the adsorption and occlusion of non-volatile impurities.

Hydrous ferric oxide can be quantitatively precipitated when the hydroxyl ion concentration is as small as

$10^{-8} - 10^{-9}$ M. The presence of ammonium ion represses the ionization of ammonium hydroxide and prevents a large increase in hydroxyl ion when a small excess of the hydroxide is added. By controlling the hydroxyl ion concentration in this way, the precipitation of hydroxides such as those of magnesium and manganese can be prevented. The presence of ammonium ion also serves to decrease coprecipitation of non-volatile compounds in two ways: first, by keeping the hydroxyl ion concentration low, the primary adsorption of hydroxyl ions is decreased which in turn decreases the coprecipitation of cations as counter ions; and second, the presence of a high concentration of ammonium ion tends to decrease the primary adsorption of other cations. Both of these effects favor the coprecipitation of volatile ammonium compounds.

Precipitation near the boiling point in the presence of ammonium ion serves only to decrease the coprecipitation problem, not to eliminate it. Frequently, the amount of coprecipitation that occurs still is very large. In such cases, the precipitate can be dissolved in hydrochloric acid to obtain a solution in which the concentration of the interfering substances is much smaller than in the original solution. Reprecipitation from this solution then yields a precipitate of higher purity.

General Preparations

Transfer the iron sample to a clean, dry weighing bottle and dry it at 105-110° C for at least one hour. Store the dried sample in the desiccator until needed.

Weigh three 0.50-0.70 g portions of the sample into clean 400-600 ml beakers. Dissolve each portion in 10 ml of 6 N HCl, heating on a steam bath if necessary. When solution is complete, add 250 ml of water. Oxidize any ferrous ion which may be present by adding bromine water or hydrogen peroxide in slight excess. If bromine water is used, an excess can be detected by the color of bromine in solution. If hydrogen peroxide is used, touch the tip of a dry stirring rod to the solution and transfer a small drop of it to a spot plate that contains a drop of dilute potassium dichromate. A blue color shows an excess of hydrogen peroxide.

Precipitation

Heat the sample nearly to boiling and add 6 N NH_4OH slowly from a graduated cylinder until a slight excess of ammonia is present as indicated by the odor of the solution. Do not inhale directly over the beaker. Sweep the vapor to your nose by passing a cupped hand over the beaker. Remove the beaker from the flame and allow the precipitate to settle. It should be noted that the desired ammonium ion is obtained in the neutralization of the acid originally present.

Filtration and Washing

Do not begin the filtration unless at least two hours are available to filter and wash in unbroken sequence.

Prepare filters as described in the gravimetric sulfate determination, using a more porous paper. Decant the supernatant liquid through the filter leaving as much precipitate as possible in the beaker. Wash the precipitate with three or four 50-100 ml portions of hot water, decanting after each addition, and discard the washings. Place the beaker containing the precipitate under the funnel. Pour 10 ml of 6 N HCl slowly over the filter to dissolve any precipitate that has been transferred as well as that remaining in the beaker. Wash the filter three or four times with hot water. When the last washing has been caught in the beaker, add 200 ml of water to the solution, heat it, and precipitate with ammonium hydroxide as before. Transfer the hydrous ferric oxide to the filter by the method described in the gravimetric chloride determination. Particular care must be exercised in dislodging all particles of precipitate from the walls of the beaker with a policeman. Wash the precipitate on the filter with hot water until the washings are free from chloride ion, as shown by testing them with silver nitrate after acidifying with nitric acid. The precipitate must be washed as soon as possible after filtration has been completed. If hydrous ferric oxide is allowed to dry, the surface of the precipitate cracks. It then is difficult to wash the precipitate thoroughly because the water channels through the cracks. Should such cracking occur, the precipitate must be redissolved in hydrochloric acid and reprecipitated. After thorough washing, the precipitate may advantageously be allowed to dry in the funnel.

Ignition

Remove the filter paper from the funnel, transfer it to a crucible, and ignite as described in the sulfate determination. The temperature must be kept as low as possible until the carbon has been oxidized, to prevent any reduction of ferric oxide to ferro ferric oxide, Fe_3O_4. For the same reason, the flame from the burner must not be permitted to enter the mouth of the crucible. After the carbon has been burned, heat the crucible at the maximum temperature of the burner for 15 to 30 minutes. Cool the crucible in air for a few minutes and then cool it in the desiccator until room temperature is established. Weigh it, and repeat the ignition and weighing until a constant weight is found. Calculate the percent iron in the sample.

Problems

1. Equal volumes of 0.007 M $AgNO_3$ and 0.006 M KCl are mixed.
    a. What ions are primarily adsorbed on the precipitate?
    b. What are the counter ions?
    c. Would flocculation be a slow or a rapid process?
    d. If the H^+ concentration is made 0.1 M, what effects does this have on the precipitate?
2. a. A solid having a density of 2.0 consists of cubical

particles of 100 mμ edge length. Calculate the number of particles per gram and the specific area of the solid.

    b. What is the decrease in specific area of the solid if these particles grow to cubes having an edge length of 1μ?

    c. What general precautions are taken to minimize the specific area of a precipitate?

Ans. (a) 5×10^{14} particles/g; 3×10^5 cm^2/g
(b) 2.7×10^4 cm^2/g

3. In the sulfate determination, 5 ml of 6 N HCl are added prior to the precipitation of barium sulfate.

    a. What is the probable effect of the acid on the particle size of the barium sulfate precipitate?

    b. What is the probable effect on the purity of the ignited barium sulfate?

4. In the determination of barium by precipitation as barium sulfate, it was found that 0.5000 g of the ignited precipitate contained 4.2 mg of sodium sulfate. Calculate the percent error in the determination.

Ans. **0.8%**

5. In a sulfate determination, 0.5000 g of the ignited barium sulfate precipitate was found to contain 3.2 mg of Fe$_2$O$_3$. Does this produce a low or a high result? Calculate the percent error in the determination.

Ans. **2.2% low**

6. In the gravimetric determination of sulfate, how will the size of the particles precipitated be affected by the following changes in conditions:

    a. The barium sulfate is precipitated at room temperature rather than at 90-100° C?

    b. The initial concentrations of barium ion and sulfate ion are 1 M instead of 0.05 M?

7. In the gravimetric determination of chloride, why must the silver chloride be washed with dilute nitric acid while in the sulfate determination, the barium sulfate is washed with water?

Chapter 7

EVALUATION OF ANALYTICAL DATA

Significant Figures

Every measurement involves a determination of the magnitude of some physical quantity such as the weight of an object, the volume of a solution, the length of a balance beam, etc. The number of figures used to express the value of such a quantity should be limited by the reproducibility of the measurement. These figures are known as *significant figures* if they are not zeros inserted merely to locate a decimal point. Thus, if the weights of four different objects are reported as 2.5 kg, 102 g, 0.07813 g, and 1.1200 g, we find that there are two, three, four and five significant figures respectively, indicating that different degrees of reproducibility were obtained in the weighing of the four objects.

In the absence of a more explicit estimate of the reproducibility, e.g., 102 ± 3 g, it is customary to assume that the variation in the value is limited to one unit in the last digit. The values reported for the four objects above, therefore, should be interpreted to mean that the respective weights have been found to lie consistently between 2.4 and 2.6 kg, 101 and 103 g, 0.07812 and 0.07814 g, and 1.1199 and 1.1201 g.

In the preceding example, the zeros in 1.1200 are significant because they are not used to locate the decimal point and, therefore, must have been specified to show the reproducibility of the measurement. The zeros in 0.07813 are not significant because they are needed only to locate the decimal point. If the value is expressed in a smaller unit, such as 78.13 mg, the zeros disappear. If the weight of an object is reported as 2,500 g, there is no way to decide whether or not the zeros are significant unless some qualifying statement is made. The zeros are needed to specify the correct magnitude of the quantity but they also may have been needed to show the reproducibility that was obtained. This ambiguity can readily be avoided by changing the units or by using a factor of 10^x where x specifies the order of magnitude; 2,500 g then becomes 2.5 kg or 2.5×10^3 g to indicate only two significant figures.

Best Value of a Single Quantity

If some variation is apparent in a series of measurements of a quantity, several questions arise:

1. What is the best value to use?
2. May any of the measurements be rejected?
3. What uncertainty is attached to the best value?

It is not our purpose to derive the theories upon which the answers to such questions are based, but rather to illustrate how conclusions from these theories can be applied.

If a large number of observations are made of a single quantity and if we plot the number of times a given value occurs against the value itself, we obtain curve II in Figure 7-1.

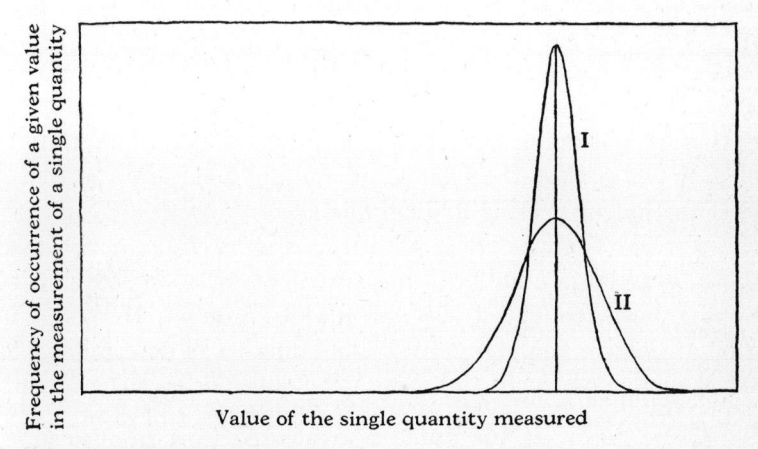

FIG. 7-1. Error distribution curves, where the precision of measurements in (II) is less than that in (I).

If a series of more precise measurements of the same quantity are made by using more care, better methods, or more sensitive equipment, the scattering is less and a sharper curve such as I in Figure 7-1 is obtained. The term *precision* denotes the difference between the value of an observation and the *arithmetic mean*, A, of all the observations of the quantity. *Accuracy* is defined as the difference between the average value of the measurements and the true value of a quantity. Actually, we never know the true value of any physical quantity. The best we can obtain is the average of values that have been determined by various competent observers using techniques that have been carefully corrected for errors. These errors can be grouped into two classes:

1. The systematic or corrigible errors.
2. The random or indeterminate errors.

The first group of errors primarily affects the accuracy by producing a shift in the curve as a whole as shown in Figure 7-2. For example, a gram weight may be 0.995 g or a meter stick may not be exactly one meter long. The second group of errors is responsible for distribution about the line A and is due to poor judgment, temperature fluctuation—accidental variations of all kinds. These errors are reflected in the precision of the measurements.

An examination of one of the distribution curves shows that it is symmetrical about the arithmetic mean. In other words, the chance of obtaining a high result is the same as that of obtaining one that is low by the same amount. It shows also that the chance of making a large error is less than that of making a small one.

Curves such as those shown in Figure 7-1 are obtained if a very large number of measurements of a single quantity have been made; actually, an infinite number. However, in quantitative analysis, only a small number of determinations are made ordinarily and so we must consider how the Theory of Errors can be applied to such a limited set of data.

Let us suppose that four determinations of the weight of a crucible, as shown in the first column, have been made and

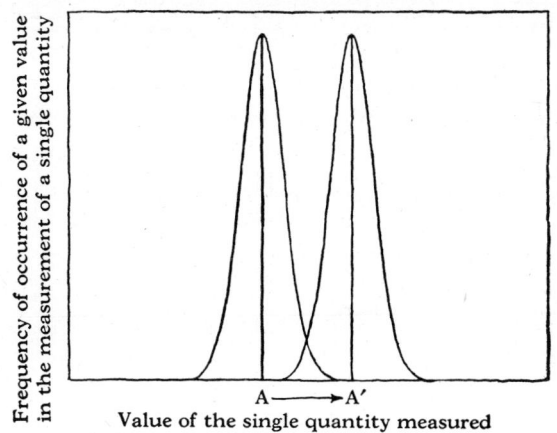

FIG. 7-2. Shift of the error distribution curve by a systematic or corrigible error.

that no determination involves a known error.

Weight	Deviation	Weight	Deviation
12.6303	0.0006	....	0.0008
12.6313	0.0004	12.6313	0.0002
12.6310	0.0001	12.6310	0.0001
12.6311	0.0002	12.6311	0.0000
Ave.12.6309	0.0003	12.6311	0.0001

The average or arithmetic mean of the four weighings is 12.6309. The deviations from this average are listed in the second column. The average deviation is 0.0003. The average value therefore should be written as 12.6309 ± 0.0003.

Rejection of an Observation.—The next question that arises upon examining the results more closely is whether or not the first weighing differs sufficiently from the other three to permit us to discard it. To decide this point, take the average of the remaining weighings and calculate all the deviations from the new average as shown in the last column. Since the deviation of the first weighing is more than four times the average deviation of the other three, we are justified in rejecting the observation because the theory states that there is less than one chance in 100 of the determination being valid. The average value then is 12.6311 ± 0.0001 g.

Best Value for the Sum of Several Quantities

So far, we have considered only the value of a single physical quantity. Next, consider the reproducibility in the sum of several such quantities. For example:

$$\begin{array}{r} 14.64 \pm 0.01 \\ 1.523 \pm 0.001 \\ \underline{0.3675 \pm 0.0001} \\ 16.5305 \pm ? \end{array}$$

From what has been said in the preceding paragraphs, the uncertainty introduced by 14.64 makes the sum also uncertain in the second decimal place even though all the numbers are given to four significant figures. The sum then should be rounded off to 16.53. In a case like this, where the uncertainty of one figure in the column is so much larger than the others, the uncertainty of the sum (or difference) is simply the largest uncertainty, i.e., ± 0.01. However, if the numbers in a sum have approximately the same uncertainty, the resultant uncertainty is equal to the square root of the sum of the squares of the individual uncertainties, Thus,

$$\begin{array}{r} 16.4385 \pm 0.0004 \\ \underline{15.9763 \pm 0.0003} \\ 0.4622 \pm \sqrt{(4 \times 10^{-4})^2 + (3 \times 10^{-4})^2} \\ = 0.4622 \pm \sqrt{25 \times 10^{-8}} \\ = 0.4622 \pm \phantom{\sqrt{2}} 0.0005 \end{array}$$

The square root of the sum of the squares is used because we do not know whether the uncertainty in a given determination is positive or negative. If, in the example above, we had assumed that they were both of the same sign, the uncertainty in the answer would have been ± 0.0007. On the other hand, if we had assumed that they were of opposite signs, the uncertainty would have been ± 0.0001. The first is too large an estimate and the second is too small—the square root of the sum of the squares gives the most likely answer.

Best Value of a Product or Quotient

In multiplication or division, it is the relative or percent uncertainty and not the absolute value of the uncertainty in the factor that affects the result. Whenever the relative uncertainty of one factor is much greater than that of any other factor, the resultant uncertainty in the product or quotient can be estimated as shown in the following example:

$$(13.72)\ (0.0082)\ (1.547) = 0.174043688$$

13.72 has a precision of 1 part in 1,372
0.0082 has a precision of 1 part in 82
1.547 has a precision of 1 part in 1,547

One factor (0.0082) has an uncertainty (1 part in 82) that is much greater than those in the other factors. The precision of the answer must therefore be about 1 part in 82 or $0.174 \times \frac{1}{82}$ and so the result should be written as 0.174 ± 0.002.

When two or more of the least precise factors have relative uncertainties of the same order of magnitude, the most probable relative uncertainty in the result is given by the relation:

$$E = \sqrt{e_1^2 + e_2^2 + e_3^2}$$

where E is the relative or percentage uncertainty in the result and e_1, e_2, etc. are the relative or percentage uncertainties in the individual factors. As in addition and subtraction, the sum of the squares is used to avoid overestimating (by addition of the uncertainties) or underestimating (by subtraction of the uncertainties) the magnitude of the uncertainties. As an example consider the following:

$$(5.56)\ (0.735)\ (0.365) = 1.4916090$$

Factor	Relative Uncertainty	% Uncertainty
5.56	1 part in 556	$\dfrac{100}{556} = 0.18$
0.735	1 part in 735	$\dfrac{100}{735} = 0.14$
0.365	1 part in 365	$\dfrac{100}{365} = 0.27$

Since the orders of magnitude of the relative uncertainties are the same, the extended calculation of the uncertainty in the product is required.

$$E \text{ (in percent)} = \pm \sqrt{(0.18)^2 + (0.14)^2 + (0.27)^2} = \pm 0.35$$

$$\text{Absolute value of } E = \frac{0.35}{100} \times 1.492 = \pm 0.005$$

Result should be reported as 1.492 ± 0.005.

Propagation of Errors in Calculations

For a calculation involving additions or subtractions as well as multiplications or divisions, the additions and subtractions can conveniently be done first. For example:

$$\left[\frac{(0.438)(79.6 - 4.31)}{(237 - 214)}\right]^2$$

$$79.6 - 4.31 = 75.3 \pm 0.1$$
$$237 - 214 = 23 \pm 1.4$$

$$= \left[\frac{(0.438 \pm 0.001)(75.3 \pm 0.1)}{(23 \pm 1.4)}\right]^2$$

Since the result cannot be more closely defined than the factor (23 ± 1.4), the expression becomes:

$$\left[\frac{(0.44)(75)}{23 \pm 1.4}\right]^2 = 2.0 \pm 0.2$$

Example 1.—Apply the Theory of Errors to the determination of the percent chlorine in some sample using the gravimetric method of analysis, assuming that each weight can be determined to ± 0.0003 g, and that errors in atomic weights are negligible.

Numerical Solution.—

Wt. weighing bottle
 + sample.......... 16.3569 ± 0.0003
Wt. weighing bottle... 16.1013 ± 0.0003

Wt. sample.......... $0.2556 \pm \sqrt{(3 \times 10^{-4})^2 + (3 \times 10^{-4})^2}$
 $= 0.2556 \pm 0.0004$

Wt. crucible + ppt.... 12.6051 ± 0.0003
Wt. crucible.......... 12.0843 ± 0.0003
Wt. ppt............. $0.5208 \pm \sqrt{(3 \times 10^{-4})^2 + (3 \times 10^{-4})^2}$
 $= 0.5208 \pm 0.0004$

Uncertainty in wt.
 of sample...... $= \dfrac{0.0004}{0.2556} \times 100 = 0.16\%$

Uncertainty in wt.
 of ppt.......... $= \dfrac{0.0004}{0.5208} \times 100 = 0.08\%$

$E = \sqrt{(0.16)^2 + (0.08)^2}$
 $= 0.18$

Therefore, the quotient is equal to $2.038 \pm (2.038)(0.18\%)$ or 2.038 ± 0.004.

Percent chlorine $= \dfrac{35.46}{143.34} \times 100 \; (2.038 \pm 0.004)$
 $= 50.4 \pm 0.1$

Example 2.—Calculate the uncertainty in the standardization of a 0.1 M AgNO$_3$ solution, using pure sodium chloride as the primary standard. Again suppose that each weight can be determined to ± 0.0002 g and that each volume reading can be estimated to 0.02 ml. Neglect errors in the atomic weights.

Numerical Solution.—

Wt. weighing bottle
+ sample.......... 17.4453 ±0.0002
Wt. weighing bottle... 17.2111 ±0.0002
Wt. sample.......... $0.2342 \pm \sqrt{(2\times10^{-4})^2 + (2\times10^{-4})^2}$
= 0.2342 ±0.0003

Final buret reading   40.57 ±0.02
Initial buret reading   0.45 ±0.02

Vol. AgNO$_3$......... $40.12 \pm \sqrt{(2\times10^{-2})^2 + (2\times10^{-2})^2}$
= 40.12 ±0.03

Uncertainty in wt.
of sample...... = $\dfrac{0.0003}{0.2342} \times 100 = 0.13\%$

Uncertainty in
AgNO$_3$ volume. = $\dfrac{0.03}{40.12} \times 100 = 0.07\%$

$E = \sqrt{(0.13)^2 + (0.07)^2}$
= .15

Therefore, the weight volume ratio is equal to 0.005837 ± (0.005837 ± 0.000008).

Normality of AgNO$_3$ = $\dfrac{10000}{58.45} \times (0.005837 \pm 0.000008)$
= 0.0999 ±0.0001

In the above examples, the uncertainty of a single determination has been calculated from the uncertainty limits in the separate steps. If a number of determinations of the same quantity have been made, the overall precision can be calculated by the procedure given in the second section in this chapter. If the two methods of calculating the precision do not agree, the chemistry of the procedure might profitably be examined.

Problems

1. Four determinations of the weight of a weighing bottle were made involving no known error. The weights are:

> 17.3461
> 17.3463
> 17.3452
> 17.3460

What is the best value to use? May any result be rejected?

2. Determine the following sums using the correct number of significant figures.

> (a) 15.65   (b) 0.13752   (c) 1.7654   (d) 117.3
>   1.376   0.0008   11.61   1.4762
>   0.0134   0.3146

Ans. (a) **17.03**, (b) **0.1383**, (c) **13.39**, (d) **119.1**

3. Calculate the percent uncertainty in weight of the following samples:

> (a) Wt. weighing bottle + sample......17.6542 ± 0.0002
>   Wt. weighing bottle..............16.8371 ± 0.0002

> (b) Wt. weighing bottle + sample......17.7755 ± 0.0005
>   Wt. weighing bottle..............17.6671 ± 0.0005

Ans. (a) **0.035%** (b) **0.65%**

4. Determine the following products using the correct number of significant figures:

> (a) (12.72) (0.045)
> (b) (0.1734) (44.1) (0.86)
> (c) (0.515) (0.464)
> (d) (0.776) (0.808) (0.691)

Ans. (a) **0.57**, (b) **6.58**, (c) **0.2389**, (d) **0.433**

5. In the following examples calculate the percent un-

certainty in the results:

(a) $\dfrac{(0.1374)\,(8.64 - 0.376)}{1136 - 1088}$

(b) $\dfrac{(7.362)\,(273.1 + 18.6)}{(6.896)\,(273.1 - 238.9)}$

Ans. (a) **2.9%**, (b) **0.42%**

6. The density of a sample is 2.5. Its weight can be determined to 0.1%. Assuming that the density of air is 0.0012 g/ml and that the density of brass is 8.4 g, calculate the buoyancy correction and compare it to the uncertainty of the weighing.

Ans. **Buoyancy correction = 0.03%**

7. Estimate the uncertainty in the standardization of a sodium hydroxide solution using pure potassium acid phthalate as the primary standard. (See Chap. 10). Assume that each weight can be determined to 0.0002 g and that each volume reading can be estimated to 0.02 ml.

Wt. weighing bottle + sample........ 19.9837 ± 0.0002
Wt. weighing bottle.................. 19.2369 ± 0.0002

Wt. sample...........................

Final buret reading.................. 41.36 ± 0.02
Initial buret reading................ 0.24 ± 0.02

Volume NaOH.......................

Ans. **0.08%**

8. Assuming that in the gravimetric determination of a sulfate, each weight can be determined to 0.0001 g and that there is no error in the atomic weights, estimate the percent uncertainty in the following analysis:

EVALUATION OF ANALYTICAL DATA 113

Wt. weighing bottle + sample .... 18.6532 ± 0.0001
Wt. weighing bottle .... 18.2166 ± 0.0001
Wt. sample ....
Wt. crucible precipitate .... 7.3364 ± 0.0001
Wt. crucible .... 6.7420 ± 0.0001
Wt. BaSO₄ ....

Ans. **0.04%**

9. In the gravimetric chloride determination the following results were obtained:
Wt. sample 0.2500   0.5000   0.3200
% Cl 65.45   65.35   65.51
a. What value should be reported?
b. Calculate the average deviation.
c. How do these results compare with the precision to be expected in the laboratory if the maximum uncertainty due to each weighing is 0.2 mg?

10. In the gravimetric determination of an iron ore, four analyses on a sample yielded the following results:
Wt. sample 0.2500   0.5000   0.7500   0.4000
% Fe₂O₃ 35.87   35.54   35.63   35.48
a. What value should be reported?
b. Calculate the average deviation.
c. How do these results compare with expected laboratory precision if the maximum uncertainty due to each weighing is 0.2 mg?

Chapter 8

VOLUMETRIC APPARATUS

The most frequent measurements in volumetric analysis involve *burets*, *pipets*, and *volumetric flasks*. It is not difficult to achieve precise measurements with these instruments but careful attention to details must be exercised. Thus a change in temperature will change the volume of a solution, and to a lesser extent, the volume of the apparatus. Specific details in regard to these instruments are discussed in subsequent sections of this chapter.

The Effect of Temperature on Volumetric Measurements

The volume of a dilute aqueous solution does not change uniformly with the temperature, but at room temperature, where most measurements are made, an increase of one degree causes the volume of the solution to expand approximately 0.02%. This expansion decreases the molarity of the solution and so a given *weight* of a sample requires a larger volume of solution to react with it as will be evident in the following example. Twenty ml of 0.2500 M AgNO$_3$ are required to react with 0.2923 g of sodium chloride. If the 0.2500 M AgNO$_3$ was prepared at 20° C and used for the reaction at 30° C, the solution would have expanded by approximately 0.2%. Therefore, the 0.2500 moles of AgNO$_3$ originally distributed throughout 1000 ml at 20° C are now distributed throughout 1002 ml at 30° C. The molarity of the solution, i.e., the moles per 1000 ml, no longer is 0.2500 but 0.2500 × 1000/1002 and so 20.04 ml of the solution are required.

If the sample of an unknown is present in the form of a solution, the correction due to thermal expansion will cancel under certain conditions. Thus, if 5.845 g of pure sodium chloride are dissolved in enough water to make 1000 ml of a 0.1000 M solution at 20° C, 50 ml of this solution measured at 20° C will require exactly 20 ml of 0.2500 M AgNO$_3$ likewise prepared and measured at 20° C. If these solutions are permitted to warm up to 30° C, 50 ml of the sodium chloride solution again will require exactly 20 ml of the silver nitrate solution. This is due to the fact that both expand at the same percentage rate and so the concentrations of both solutions decrease in the same ratio.

The following example illustrates a case in which the reactants are present as solutions and one in which a temperature correction must be applied. Suppose a 0.1000 M NaCl solution was prepared at 25° C and on a subsequent day a 0.2500 M AgNO$_3$ solution was prepared at 20° C. If these solutions are compared by reaction at any temperature a correction for the difference in temperature of preparation must be made. This can be done by correcting the concentration of both solutions to a common temperature which may be chosen arbitrarily. If we choose 25° C, the silver nitrate solution becomes 1000/1001 × 0.2500 M; if we choose 20° C, the sodium chloride solution becomes 1001/1000 × 0.1000 M.

The Buret

The buret is used to *deliver* a variable but known volume of liquid. This volume is calculated from the position of the meniscus at the beginning and at the end of the titration.

Cleaning and Greasing the Buret.—A buret which is exposed to the atmosphere gradually acquires a film of grease. Such a film prevents aqueous solutions from draining freely—small drops remain behind—and so the volume of the solution delivered by the buret is not accurately calculated from the meniscus data. Sometimes films like manganese dioxide are deposited on the buret walls. Such material may react with, and change the concentration of, some reagent. Care, therefore, must be used to see that the buret is clean before using it as a measuring device.

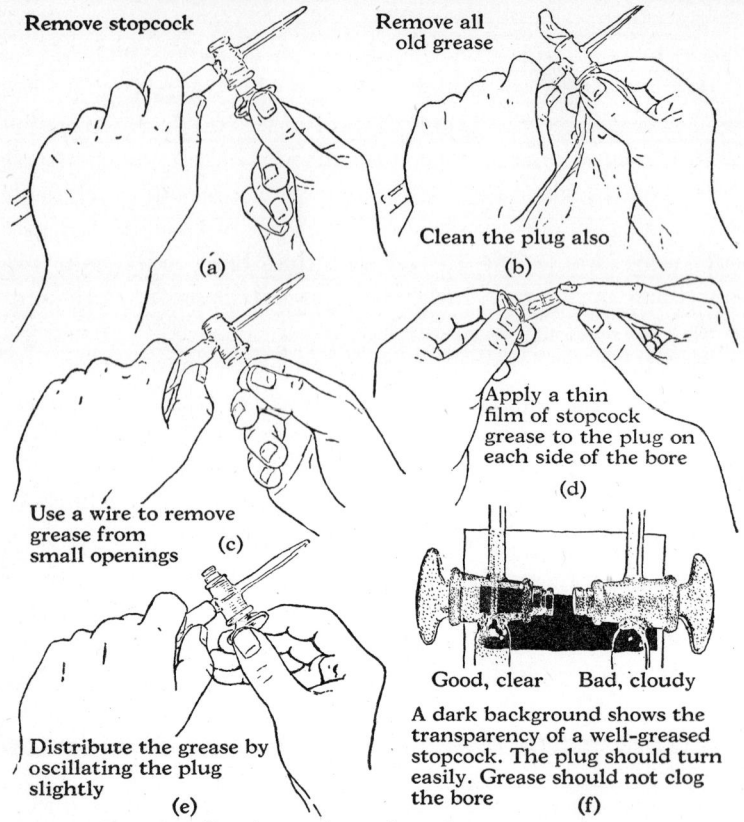

116   INTRODUCTORY QUANTITATIVE ANALYSIS • Chapter 8

Remove stopcock (a)

Remove all old grease / Clean the plug also (b)

Use a wire to remove grease from small openings (c)

Apply a thin film of stopcock grease to the plug on each side of the bore (d)

Distribute the grease by oscillating the plug slightly (e)

Good, clear   Bad, cloudy

A dark background shows the transparency of a well-greased stopcock. The plug should turn easily. Grease should not clog the bore (f)

FIG. 8-1. Cleaning and greasing a buret stopcock.

If the buret is free from a brown deposit, clean the stopcock and regrease it as shown in Figure 8-1.

After the stopcock has been greased properly, clean the buret as shown in Figure 8-2.

Rinse the barrel of the buret with several portions of tap water by partially filling it, drain a small portion through the tip, and pour the bulk of the rinse from the top of the barrel while rotating the buret. If any drops of water collect on the walls when the rinse is poured from the buret, the cleaning is unsatisfactory and must be repeated. Rinse the buret with two or three portions of distilled water and then fill it to the top with distilled water. Clamp it in position and cover the top with a test tube or small beaker to minimize

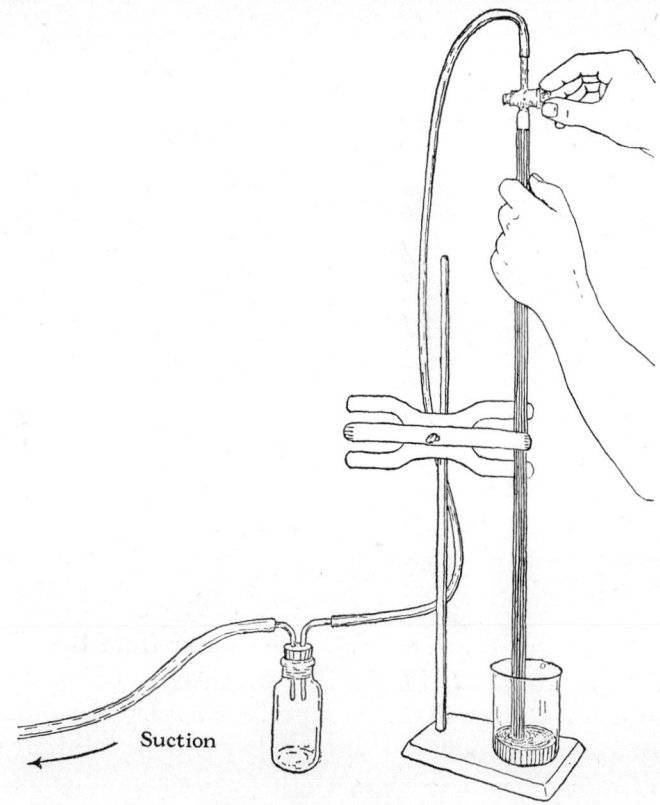

Fig. 8-2. To clean a buret, draw cleaning solution into it up to level shown, controlling the suction with the stopcock. Let stand several minutes. Disconnect the tubing and allow the buret to drain.

the entrance of grease or other dirt into the barrel. The buret may be used without further cleaning so long as solutions drain without the formation of observable drops on the walls.

If a brown deposit is present on the buret walls, it probably is due to manganese dioxide. This can conveniently be removed by adding a small quantity of concentrated hydrochloric acid which can be distributed over the walls of the buret by tilting and rotating it. If the deposit is black, it probably is due to finely divided silver. This can be removed with concentrated nitric acid. After such removal the buret *must* be well rinsed with water, regreased and cleaned as outlined above.

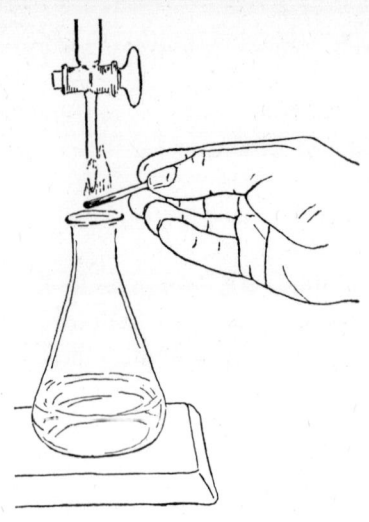

Fig. 8-3. If the tip of the buret clogs with grease, open the stopcock, gently warm the tip with a match, until the grease melts and is forced out by the liquid.

Preparation for Use.—Pour the water from the buret, add about 10 ml of the solution which is to be used, distribute it over the walls of the buret, drain some of it through the stopcock and pour out the remainder. Repeat this operation two or three more times so that the composition of the liquid retained on the buret walls and in the tip does not differ appreciably from the bulk of the solution to be used. Fill the buret with the solution. Open the stopcock wide to flush out any air bubbles that may be entrapped in the tip. If difficulty is experienced in removing the last bubble, apply suction to the tip to increase the rate of flow of the liquid. Drain the solution until the meniscus is in the graduated region but not necessarily on a graduation mark.

Whenever possible, solutions should be poured directly into the buret from a bottle. If the bottle is large, it should rest on the table during the pouring operation. Sometimes it is less hazardous to pour the approximate amount of solution into a small, clean beaker and then to pour from this into the buret. If the beaker is wet, it must first be rinsed with the solution to be used. This procedure is preferable to the use of a small funnel. If, however, a funnel is used, care must be exercised to avoid flooding and the funnel must be removed before making a volume reading. If flooding has occurred, the outside of the buret must be carefully wiped free of any liquid to prevent the solution from draining into the titration flask. Mount the buret vertically so that the liquid level is parallel to the graduations.

Occasionally, a piece of grease will break loose at the stopcock and will plug the tip of the buret. An easy method of removing this plug is illustrated in Figure 8-3.

Manipulation of the Buret.—In operating the buret, the stopcock is manipulated as shown in Figure 8-4.

This permits a positive control of the liquid flow at all times. It frequently is desirable to add liquid volumes less than that contained in a single drop. This can be accomplished by splitting drops as shown in Figure 8-5.

Reading the Buret.—The amount of liquid delivered by the buret is measured by the change of position of the meniscus. If the buret graduations are correct, any error in the

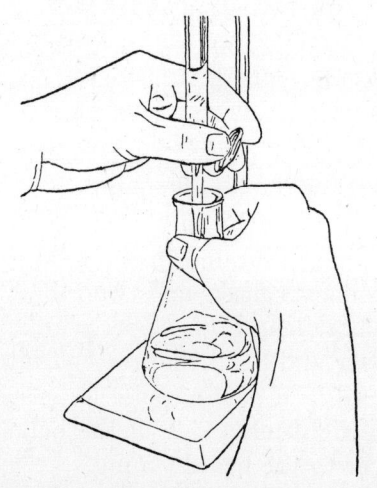

FIG. 8-4. The stopcock is manipulated with one hand maintaining a very slight pull on the plug in order to keep it seated. The flask is swirled with the other hand while the solution is being added. The tip of the buret extends well into the flask to prevent spattering. If any drops of solution remain on the flask walls, they should be washed down with a small amount of distilled water.

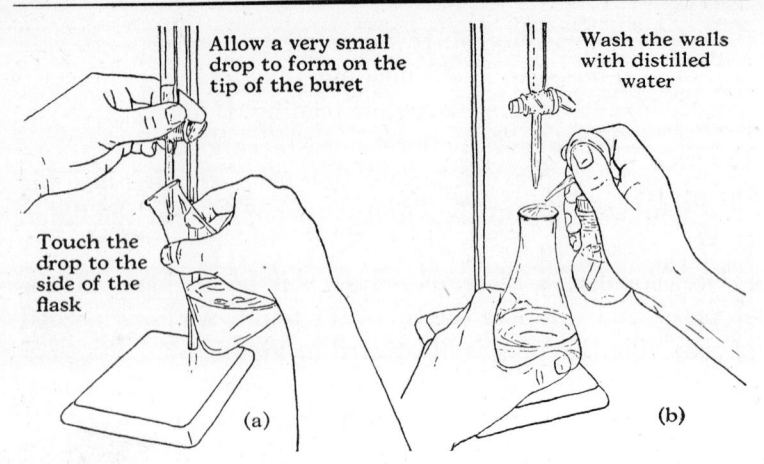

FIG. 8-5. Method of approaching the end-point of a titration by splitting a drop.

volume must come from errors in the meniscus readings. To minimize these errors, the meniscus should be level with the eye to avoid parallax as shown in Figure 8-6.

If the buret contains a transparent liquid, the position of the meniscus can be clarified by mounting a piece of black paper on a white card and holding it in back of the buret as shown in Figure 8-6. This permits the meniscus position in an ordinary 50 ml buret to be estimated to 0.01 ml. If a highly colored liquid is used, it is convenient to read the position of the top of the liquid column.

Calibration.—Unless the burets supplied have been certified, they should be calibrated in the following way. Select two 125 ml Erlenmeyer flasks and two rubber stoppers to fit them. Wrap a short length of copper wire around the neck of one Erlenmeyer and bend the free end into a hook. This flask is to be used as a counterpoise by suspending it from the hook on the right-hand side of the balance. Weigh the other Erlenmeyer to the nearest 5 mg.

Fill the buret with distilled water that has been previously brought to room temperature, and record the temperature of this stock supply of water. Drain the liquid slowly until the meniscus is approximately on the zero mark. It is desirable but not essential that the initial reading be zero. Touch the tip of the buret to the side of a beaker to remove the drop hanging from the tip. Read the position of the meniscus after allowing one minute for drainage. Deliver 10 ml of water in a slow stream into the weighed Erlenmeyer, being careful to prevent spattering. Touch the tip of the buret to the inside of the flask. Immediately stopper the flask. Again allow one minute for drainage and read the meniscus position. As soon as this operation has been completed, fill the buret with distilled water. Weigh the Erlenmeyer to 5 mg. Repeat the above operations using 0-20, 0-30, etc., volumes.

In order to calculate the volume of water delivered from the observed weights, two important corrections must be applied. One is due to the fact that the weighings are performed in air which exerts different buoyancy effects on the weights and on the material being weighed. Thus, at 20° C, one ml of air weighs approximately 0.0012 g; one gram of water occupies a space of about one ml; one gram of brass occupies a space of 1/8.4 ml. The effect of air buoyancy, therefore, is to make the weighing of one ml of water too light by 0.0012 (1-1/8.4) g = 0.00105 g. We have neglected

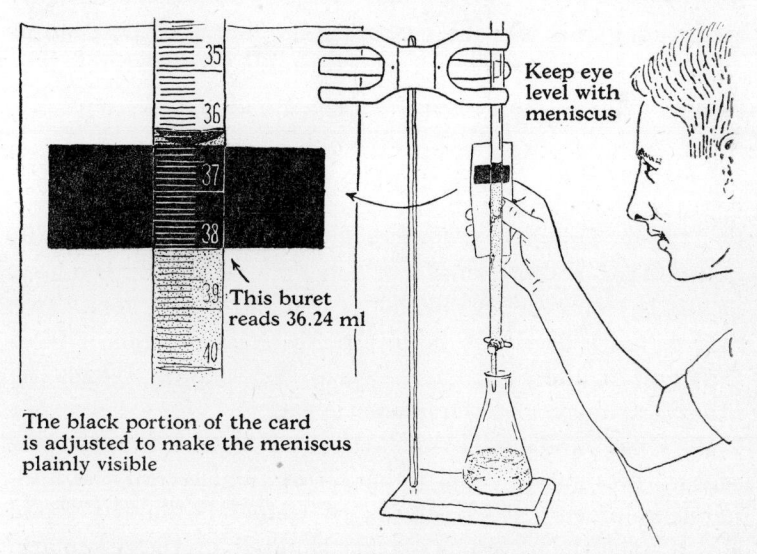

FIG. 8-6. Reading a buret with the aid of a black strip on a white card.

this correction in all previous work because the densities of the materials that have been weighed have been large enough to make such corrections small.

The other correction is due to the fact that one ml of water weighs one gram only at 4° C. For example, the density of water at 20° C is 0.99823 and so the volume of water that weighs one gram in vacuum is equal to $1.00000/0.99823 = 1.00177$ ml. For convenience, these two corrections have been combined in order to calculate the true volume as shown in Table 8-1.

TABLE 8-1

VOLUME PER GRAM OF WATER WHEN WEIGHED AT THE INDICATED TEMPERATURE, USING BRASS WEIGHTS

Temp. °C	Corr. ml	Temp. °C	Corr. ml
15	1.00208	22	1.00320
16	1.00220	23	1.00340
17	1.00234	24	1.00360
18	1.00248	25	1.00384
19	1.00264	26	1.00406
20	1.00282	27	1.00430
21	1.00300	28	1.00456

The actual volume of water delivered by a buret is equal to the weight of the water multiplied by the factor as given in Table 8-1. The use of Table 8-1 is shown by the following example:

Data.—Temperature = 22.6° C
Indicated volume = 10.01 ml
Weight H_2O = 9.945 g

Calculation of Correction.—Linear interpolation of the correction factor = $0.6 \times .00020 = 0.00012$

$$1.00320 + .00012 = 1.00332$$

True volume = $9.945(1.00332) = 9.945(1) + 9.945(0.00332)$

$$= 9.945 + 0.033 = 9.978 \text{ ml}$$

Therefore, at the 10 ml mark, the correction is 9.98 − 10.01 = −0.03 ml. Typical data for a calibration are shown in Table 8-2.

TABLE 8-2
Calibration of 50 ml Buret

Temperature........	22.6	22.9	23.0	23.1	23.1
Initial Reading......	0.00	0.00	0.01	0.00	0.02
Final Reading.......	10.01	19.99	30.00	40.00	50.00
Indicated Volume....	10.01	19.99	29.99	40.00	49.98
Weight Erlenmeyer..	2.295	2.240	2.175	2.445	2.385
Weight Erl. + H_2O...	12.240	22.175	32.125	42.360	52.270
Wt. H_2O	9.945	19.935	29.950	39.915	49.885
Buoy. and Dens. Corr.	0.033	0.068	0.102	0.137	0.171
True Volume........	9.978	20.003	30.052	40.052	50.056
Buret Corr..........	−0.03	+0.01	+0.06	+0.05	+0.08

In order to establish the reliability of the calibration, check the 30 and 40 ml points. Duplicate results should agree within 0.02 ml.

The Pipet

A pipet is used to deliver a fixed, known volume of solution. The most frequent errors in the volume of solution delivered involve faulty adjustment of the meniscus to the graduation mark and variations in the amount of drainage permitted.

Cleaning.—A pipet must be so clean that only a thin continuous film of solution is left on the wall when it drains. Ordinary cleaning solution is the reagent usually used to accomplish this. Drawing such solutions into a pipet by mouth is dangerous and should be avoided. If a tall cylinder of cleaning solution in which the pipet can be immersed is not available, a rubber tube should be connected by way of a trap to an aspirator or suction line, and the cleaning solution drawn into the pipet from a beaker as shown in Figure 8-7.

The rubber tubing should not be slid on to the pipet but

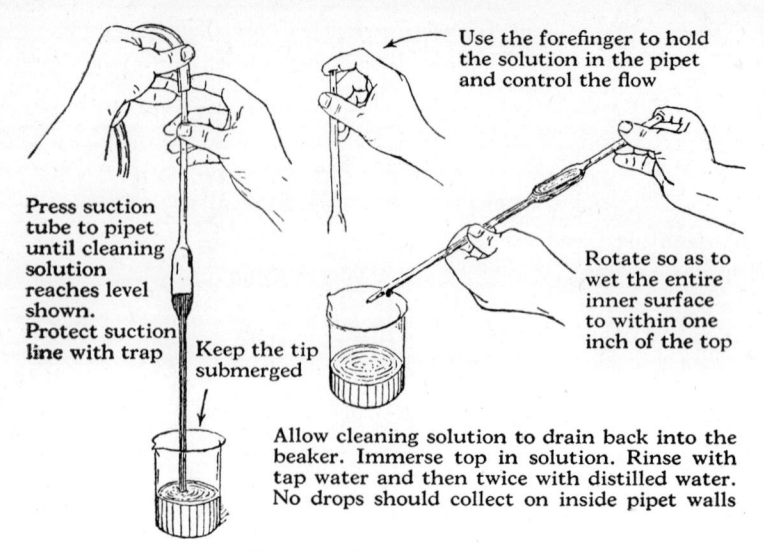

FIG. 8-7. Cleaning a pipet.

merely placed firmly against the end in order to facilitate removal at the proper time. Follow through the sequence of operations as shown in Figure 8-7. Rinse the pipet with several portions of tap water. Repeat the treatment with cleaning solution until only a thin continuous water film remains on the walls with no evidence of the formation of droplets. Finally, rinse the pipet with two or three portions of distilled water.

Use.—A pipet must be rinsed with the solution to be used since it is not feasible to dry the inside as a common practice. Pour a small amount of the liquid to be used into a clean, dry beaker. Wipe the outside of the pipet to avoid introducing water into the solution. Draw some of the solution into the pipet from the beaker so as to fill about one-fourth of the barrel, rotate it in a horizontal position to rinse all of the wall to within one inch of the top, and let the solution drain out of the tip. Repeat this operation two more times. To pipet a sample, follow the procedure illustrated in Figure 8-8.

Calibration.—Weigh a rubber-stoppered 125 ml Erlenmeyer flask to the nearest 5 mg, using a counterpoise as de-

VOLUMETRIC APPARATUS

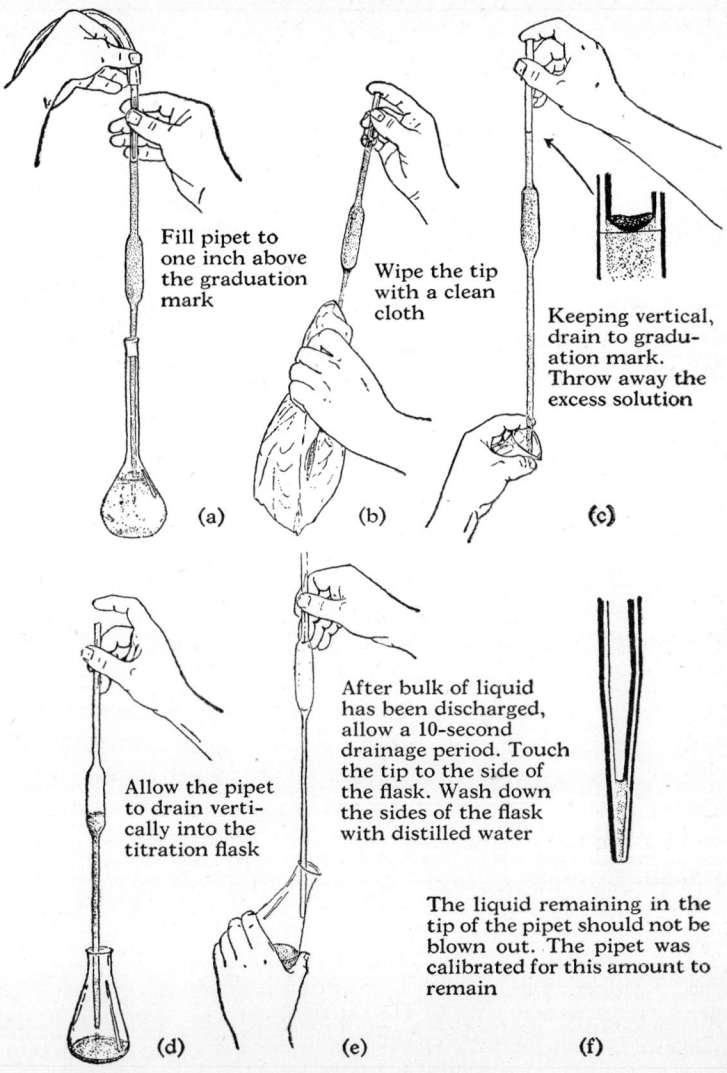

(a) Fill pipet to one inch above the graduation mark

(b) Wipe the tip with a clean cloth

(c) Keeping vertical, drain to graduation mark. Throw away the excess solution

(d) Allow the pipet to drain vertically into the titration flask

(e) After bulk of liquid has been discharged, allow a 10-second drainage period. Touch the tip to the side of the flask. Wash down the sides of the flask with distilled water

(f) The liquid remaining in the tip of the pipet should not be blown out. The pipet was calibrated for this amount to remain

FIG. 8-8. Use of the pipet.

scribed previously. If the pipet drains cleanly, fill it with distilled water at room temperature, recording the temperature of the water at the time of pipetting. Then follow the technique shown in Figure 8-8 to measure and to transfer the water. Again weigh the flask to the nearest 5 mg. Repeat the procedure to obtain duplicate results which should agree within one part per thousand. A larger deviation probably is due to faulty technique in pipetting. A greater precision than this is easily obtainable with pipets larger than 10 ml.

The Volumetric Flask

Solutions of accurately known final volume are prepared by use of a volumetric flask.

Cleaning.—Use a small amount of cleaning solution to clean the flask, rinse with several portions of tap water, followed by two or three portions of distilled water. It is very desirable that the walls above the graduation mark in the neck be so clean that no drops of liquid adhere.

Use.—The transfer of known volumes of solution to the flask by means of a pipet or buret is straightforward. A similar transfer of a known weight of solid is more difficult and frequently is required. If the solid is readily wetted by, or soluble in, the water or solution to be added, and is not in the form of large pieces, it may be weighed directly into a small funnel inserted in the mouth of the flask as shown in Figure 8-9. The material can then be washed into the flask, the funnel rinsed and removed. Where this simple technique is not feasible due to the particular solid involved, the weighed amount of solid can be dissolved in a small beaker. This solution is then carefully transferred to the flask by the same technique used in transferring a precipitate to a filter.

Add enough distilled water to half fill the flask and agitate it carefully to obtain a uniform solution. Further water is added until the level of the solution is 1-2 cm below the graduation mark. The remaining water is carefully added dropwise from a pipet or a small wash bottle until the bottom of the meniscus coincides with the graduation mark. If a pipet is used for this purpose, the last drop or fraction of a drop can easily be added by placing a finger tightly on the upper end of the partially filled pipet and warming the bulb with the other hand, thus forcing the liquid out slowly. The temperature of the final solution when diluted to the mark should be within two or three degrees of the temperature at which the flask has been calibrated. If the flask had been

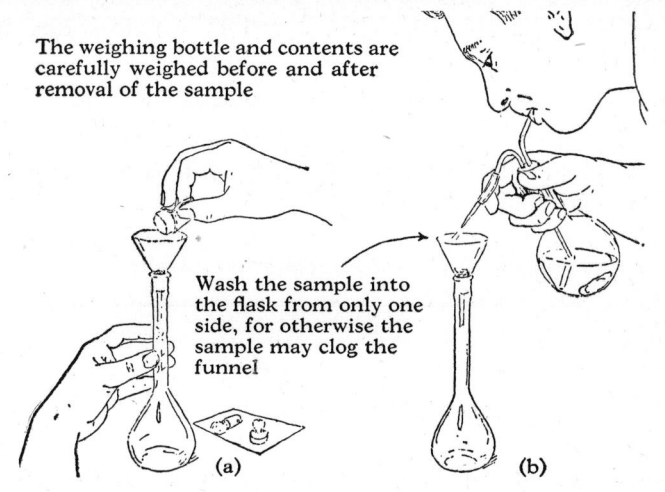

FIG. 8-9. Transfer of a weighed sample to a volumetric flask.

calibrated at 20° C and the solution was prepared at 30° C, an error of approximately 0.2% will be introduced when the solution has cooled to 20° C. At this point, stopper the flask and mix the contents *thoroughly*. Shaking or swirling the filled flask is of little value since the solution is so well confined that little agitation results. It is necessary to tilt the stoppered flask back and forth. This agitates the solution as the air in the flask is forced back and forth through it. The removal of any solution before thorough mixing will alter the concentration and therefore the solution must be discarded.

Calibration.—Since volumetric flasks are seldom in error by more than one part per thousand and since balances will be required that can sustain larger loads than ordinary analytical balances are able to do, no procedure for the calibration of volumetric flasks is presented.

Problems

1. A 0.1000 M NaCl solution was prepared at 25° C. The

solution was used several days later at 18° C in a volumetric determination of silver in a solid sample.

(a) Is the solution more or less concentrated at 25° C?

(b) What percentage error is introduced if the solution is used at the lower temperature and no correction is made?

2. What volume of 0.1000 M NaCl is required to react with 50.00 ml of 0.1000 M AgNO$_3$ at 20° C in each of the following cases?

(a) Each solution was prepared at 20° C.

(b) The 0.1000 M AgNO$_3$ was prepared at 20° C and the 0.1000 M NaCl was prepared at 28° C.

(c) The 0.1000 M AgNO$_3$ was prepared at 25° C and the 0.1000 M NaCl was prepared at 15° C.

3. The density of potassium acid phthalate is 1.6; the density of brass is 8.4. Calculate the correction due to buoyancy that should be applied to a 0.7000 g sample of potassium acid phthalate. *Ans.* +0.4 mg.

4. The density of platinum is 21.45; the density of brass is 8.4. Calculate the correction due to buoyancy that should be applied to a 15.0 g sample of platinum. *Ans.* −1.1 mg.

5. If 0.7000 g of potassium acid phthalate was weighed using platinum weights, what would be the correction due to buoyancy? *Ans.* +0.4 mg.

6. Calculate the volume of 1 g of water in each of the following cases:

(a) Temp. H$_2$O = 28° C; density H$_2$O = 0.9963

(b) Temp. H$_2$O = 12° C; density H$_2$O = 0.9995

(c) Temp. H$_2$O = 40° C; density H$_2$O = 0.9922

Ans. (a) **1.0037**; (b) **1.0005**; (c) **1.0079**

7. Calculate the buoyancy correction at room temperature for 50 g of water in each of the following cases:

(a) Brass weights were used; density = 8.4
(b) Platinum weights were used; density = 21.45
(c) Aluminum weights were used; density = 2.70
   Ans. (a) **44.1 mg;** (b) **47.7 mg;** (c) **31.0 mg.**

8. Calculate the correct volume delivered by a pipet in each of the following examples, assuming that brass weights having a density of 8.4 were used.
 (a) Temp. H_2O = 21.5° C; Wt. H_2O = 19.975 g
 (b) Temp. H_2O = 26.5° C; Wt. H_2O = 49.845 g
 (c) Temp. H_2O = 36.0° C; density of H_2O at 36.0° C is 0.99371; Wt. H_2O = 39.650 g
   Ans. (a) **20.037 g;** (b) **50.053 g;** (c) **39.936 g.**

Chapter 9

INTRODUCTION TO VOLUMETRIC PRINCIPLES

General Considerations

In volumetric methods, a substance that undergoes a known reaction with the constituent to be determined is added in the form of a solution of known concentration—that is, a *standard solution*. The process of determining the amount of standard solution required exactly to react with the constituent is called a *titration*. The solution added in a titration frequently is referred to as the *titrant*. Ordinarily, the volume of standard solution is measured, although in some very precise analyses its weight is determined.

Standard solutions can be prepared by two general methods. The direct method consists in dissolving a definite amount of a substance of known purity in some solvent, usually water, and diluting the resulting solution to a known final volume. The substance of known purity is called a *primary standard*. Primary standards should be easily obtainable in known and reproducible purity. They should have a high equivalent weight so as to minimize weighing errors.

While the direct method of preparing standard solutions is preferable, the nature of the material frequently makes it necessary to have recourse to an indirect method. Thus, solid sodium hydroxide contains a variable and unknown amount of sodium carbonate. It likewise is very hygroscopic. A standard solution of sodium hydroxide therefore usually is prepared by dissolving the solid in water and then standardizing that solution by reacting it with a known amount of acid. Such solutions are known as *secondary* or *derived* standards. Other physical methods of preparing standard solutions are known, but they will not be discussed here.

Any errors in the standard are reflected in all the determinations based upon it. Consequently great care must be exercised in preparing, storing, and handling such a solution.

The *equivalence-point* in a titration is reached when the amount of reagent added is just equivalent chemically to the amount of constituent present. Depending upon the reaction used and the conditions employed, the changes of concentrations of the reacting species expressed as percentages are greatest near the equivalence-point. Various properties of the solution, such as the color, the electrical conductivity, etc., consequently may change abruptly in this region. The point at which an abrupt change in an observable property is taken to mark the equivalence-point is called the *end-point*. The essential problem in all volumetric methods is to select reactions and provide conditions where a clearly defined end-point coincides with, or is reproducibly related to, the equivalence-point. The general approach to the solution of this problem is illustrated in this chapter in connection with volumetric applications of the precipitation of silver chloride and silver thiocyanate.

Stoichiometry

Before discussing the problem of detecting the equivalence-point, the basic stoichiometric calculations involved in volumetric methods will be reviewed. In the following examples, it is assumed that a practical method of detecting the equivalence-point is available. Two methods, which differ only in the choice of moles or millimoles as the units of calculation, are illustrated.

Example 1.—If 30.16 ml of 0.1016 M $AgNO_3$ are used to titrate the chloride ion obtained from a sample, calculate the grams of potassium chloride that may be in the sample.

Basis of Solution.—The reaction involved is:

$Ag^+ + Cl^- = AgCl\ (s)$ and so at the equivalence-point

the moles of Cl^- originally present must be equal to the moles of Ag^+ added.

a) Solution in Terms of Moles

$$\text{Moles } Ag^+ \text{ added} = M \times V_{\text{liters}} = 0.1016 \times \frac{30.16}{1000}$$

$$\text{Moles KCl} = \text{Moles Cl}^- = \text{Moles Ag}^+ \text{ added}$$

$$g \text{ KCl} = \text{Moles KCl} \times \text{M.W. KCl}$$

$$\text{KCl present} = 0.1016 \times \frac{30.16}{1000} \times 74.56 \text{ g.}$$

b) Solution in Terms of Millimoles

$$M = \frac{\text{No. Moles}}{\text{No. liters used}} = \frac{\text{No. Millimoles}}{\text{No. milliliters used}}$$

$$\text{mmoles Ag}^+ \text{ added} = M \times V_{\text{ml}} = 0.1016 \times 30.16$$

$$\text{mmoles KCl} = \text{mmoles Cl}^- = \text{mmoles Ag}^+ \text{ added}$$

$$g \text{ KCl} = \text{mmoles KCl} \times \frac{\text{M.W. KCl}}{1000}$$

$$\text{KCl present} = 0.1016 \times 30.16 \times \frac{74.56}{1000} \text{ g}$$

Example 2.—40.00 ml of $AgNO_3$ are required to titrate the chloride in 0.3781 g of pure KCl. Calculate the molarity of the $AgNO_3$.

a) Solution in Terms of Moles

$$M \text{ AgNO}_3 = \frac{\text{Moles of Ag}^+ \text{ present}}{\text{liters used}}$$

$$\text{Moles Ag}^+ \text{ added} = \text{Moles Cl}^- = \text{Moles KCl}$$

$$\text{Moles KCl in 0.3781 g} = \frac{0.3781}{74.56}$$

$$\text{Moles Ag}^+ \text{ in 40.00 ml} = \frac{0.3781}{74.56}$$

$$M \text{ AgNO}_3 = \frac{\frac{0.3781}{74.56} \times 1000}{40.00} = \frac{0.3781}{74.56} \times \frac{1000}{40.00}$$

Example 3.—30.16 ml of a chloride solution require 40.15 ml of 0.0489 M $AgNO_3$ for titration. Calculate the molarity of the chloride ion.

a) Solution in Terms of Millimoles

$$M \text{ Cl}^- = \frac{\text{mmoles Cl}^- \text{ present}}{\text{ml used}}$$

mmoles Cl⁻ in 30.16 ml = mmoles Ag⁺ in 40.15 ml of 0.0489 M AgNO₃

mmoles Ag⁺ = 0.0489 × 40.15

$$M \text{ Cl}^- = \frac{0.0489 \times 40.15}{30.16}$$

b) Short-Cut Method

It takes 40.15 ml of the silver nitrate to react with 30.16 ml of the chloride solution. In the reaction, one mole of Ag⁺ is equivalent to one mole of Cl⁻. Consequently, the chloride solution must be *more* concentrated than the silver nitrate and the corresponding molarity must be:

$$M \text{ Cl}^- = 0.0489 \times \frac{40.15}{30.16}$$

The three examples given above are representative of the main types of stoichiometric calculations encountered in volumetric analysis. The details of such calculations may become more complicated when more complex reactions are considered, but the methods of approach just given always are applicable.

Titration Curves

In order to understand the various methods used to obtain end-points, it is necessary to know the approximate concentrations of the reacting substances at the equivalence-point and how they vary in its immediate neighborhood. A plot of the concentration of one or more of the reacting substances as a function of the amount of titrant added is called a *titration curve*. Such data show the significant concentration changes that may be used to obtain an end-point.

To illustrate the construction of a typical titration curve, consider the titration of 50.00 ml of 0.1000 M KCl with 0.1000 M AgNO₃. In this case, the only equilibrium that needs to be considered during the course of the titration is that between solid silver chloride and its ions. This equilibrium was discussed in detail in Chapter 6. The essential concentration relationships involved in the calculation of the concentrations of the chloride and silver ions in the present application are shown in Figure 9-1. We have used a value of 1×10^{-10} for the solubility product of silver chloride instead of the more exact value of 1.7×10^{-10} in order to divorce the method from the arithmetic details.

A tabulation of the silver and chloride ion concentrations during the course of the titration is shown in Table 9-1. In making these calculations, we have used the relationships given in Figure 9-1 but have assumed a *constant volume of 100 ml for the entire titration*. This has been done because the changes in concentration, very near the equivalence-point where the volume (100 ml) is essentially a constant, are of most concern. A more precise calculation taking the actual volume at each point into account is considered in Chapter 10.

TABLE 9-1

THE CONCENTRATIONS OF SILVER AND CHLORIDE IONS DURING THE TITRATION OF 50 ML OF 0.1 M CL$^-$ WITH 0.1 M AG$^+$ IN A CONSTANT VOLUME OF 100 ML

$AgNO_3$ (ml)	$[Ag^+]$ M	$[Cl^-]$ M	
0	0	5×10^{-2}	
10	2.5×10^{-9}	4.0×10^{-2}	
20	3.3×10^{-9}	3.0×10^{-2}	
40	1×10^{-8}	1×10^{-2}	
49.50	2×10^{-7}	5×10^{-4}	
49.90	1×10^{-6}	1×10^{-4}	
49.95	2×10^{-6}	5×10^{-5}	Note that the greatest percentage rate of change of $[Ag^+]$ and $[Cl^-]$ occurs near the equivalence-point.
50.00	1×10^{-5}	1×10^{-5}	
50.05	5×10^{-5}	2×10^{-6}	
50.10	1×10^{-4}	1×10^{-6}	
50.50	5×10^{-4}	2×10^{-7}	
55.00	5×10^{-3}	2×10^{-8}	

INTRODUCTION TO VOLUMETRIC PRINCIPLES 135

1 ml before Equivalence point

49.00 ml of 0.1 M AgNO$_3$

50.00 ml of 0.1 M KCl

↓

99 ml of solution. 1 ml of 0.1 M Cl$^-$ in excess plus small amounts of Cl$^-$ and Ag$^+$ from solubility of AgCl

AgCl

↓

$[Cl^-] \simeq \dfrac{1}{99} \times 0.1$

$\simeq 10^{-3} M$

$[Ag^+] = \dfrac{K_{sp}}{[Cl^-]} \simeq \dfrac{10^{-10}}{10^{-3}}$

$\simeq 10^{-7} M$

Equivalence point

50.00 ml of 0.1 M AgNO$_3$

50.00 ml of 0.1 M KCl

↓

100 ml of solution. No excess of either Cl$^-$ or Ag$^+$. $[Ag^+] = [Cl^-]$

AgCl

↓

$[Ag^+] = [Cl^-] = \sqrt{K_{sp}}$

$\simeq 10^{-5} M$

1 ml after Equivalence point

51.00 ml of 0.1 M AgNO$_3$

50.00 ml of 0.1 M KCl

↓

101 ml of solution. 1 ml of 0.1 M Ag$^+$ in excess plus small amounts of Ag$^+$ and Cl$^-$ from solubility of AgCl

AgCl

↓

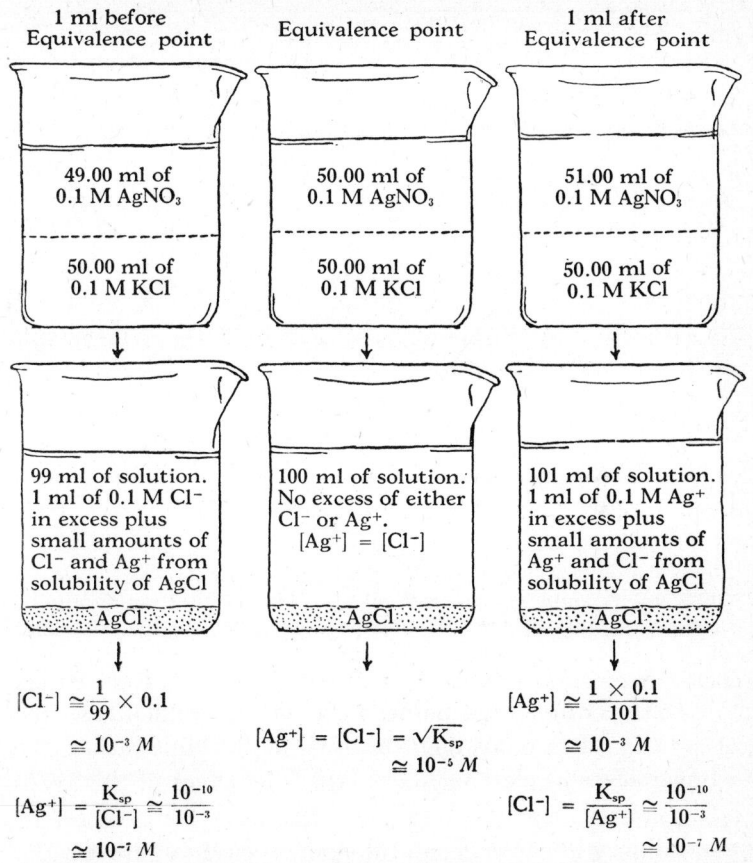

$[Ag^+] \simeq \dfrac{1 \times 0.1}{101}$

$\simeq 10^{-3} M$

$[Cl^-] = \dfrac{K_{sp}}{[Ag^+]} \simeq \dfrac{10^{-10}}{10^{-3}}$

$\simeq 10^{-7} M$

FIG. 9-1. The essential concentration relationships in the vicinity of the end-point in a titration of chloride ions with silver nitrate.

The characteristic features of the data given in Table 9-1 are best shown graphically but it is almost impossible to do this satisfactorily on the usual type of linear plot shown in Figure 9-2.

It can readily be seen that the main graph gives a very inadequate picture of the concentration changes near the equivalence-point, which is the region of most interest, unless we magnify the scale tremendously as pictured in the insert of this figure. The difficulty is due to the great range of concentrations involved—the chloride ion concentration decreases by a factor of 5000 from the beginning of the titra-

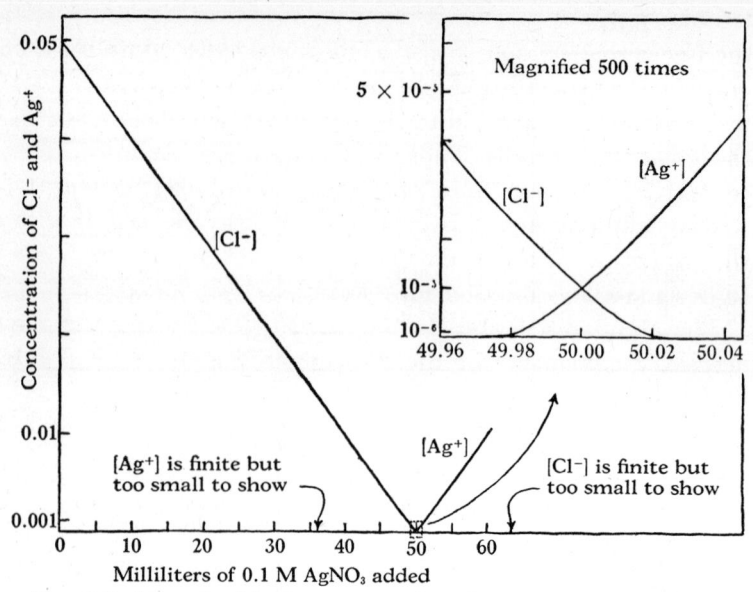

FIG. 9-2. A graph of ionic concentrations in the titration of 50 ml of 0.1 M Cl$^-$ with 0.1 M Ag$^+$. The volume is assumed to be 100 ml throughout.

tion to the equivalence-point. To avoid this difficulty in representation, it is convenient to use a logarithmic rather than a linear scale in plotting such data. The effect of this transformation is indicated in Figure 9-3. The line x represents the ordinary linear scale, and the points on it might represent the concentrations. The line y is the logarithmic scale where each point on the line x is assigned a point according to the relation, $y = \log x$. The dotted lines show the correspondence between representative points on the two scales.

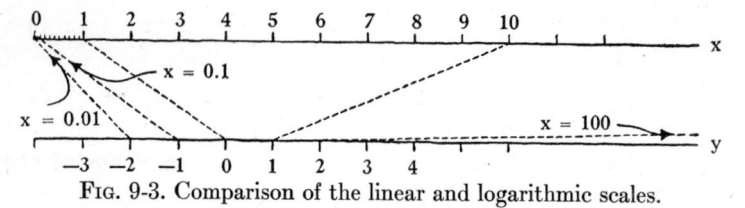

FIG. 9-3. Comparison of the linear and logarithmic scales.

It can be seen from Figure 9-3 that the logarithmic transformation greatly expands the region from zero to one on the linear scale which is just what is needed to simplify the graphical representation of the titration curve. When this transformation is applied to the concentration of substances, the logarithm usually comes out negative since most concentrations are less than one molar. To avoid constantly writing minus signs, it is customary to use the negative of the logarithm of a concentration, and to use the symbol p to designate this relationship. Thus $pCl^- = -\log[Cl^-]$.

The above discussion is illustrated below by making the necessary conversion of the data given for the 5 ml point in Table 9-1.

$$[Ag^+] = 2.2 \times 10^{-9}$$

$$\log[Ag^+] = \log 2.2 + \log 10^{-9} = 0.35 - 9 = -8.65$$

$$pAg^+ = -\log[Ag^+] = +8.65$$

$$[Cl^-] = 4.5 \times 10^{-2}$$

$$\log[Cl^-] = \log 4.5 + \log 10^{-2} = 0.65 - 2 = -1.35$$

$$pCl^- = -\log[Cl^-] = +1.35$$

It should be noted that solubility product calculations may be made very simply in these terms. Thus:

$$pAg^+ + pCl^- = pK_{sp} = 10$$

In the above case if $pAg^+ = 8.65$

$$pCl^- = 10 - 8.65 = +1.35$$

When the data in Table 9-1 are converted to this more convenient notation, the titration curve shown in Figure 9-4 is obtained. The curve clearly shows the marked rate of change of the logarithms of the concentrations of silver and chloride ions close to the equivalence-point. In this connection, it should be noted that the change in logarithm of the concentration is equivalent to the percent change in concentration. This method of representing titration curves is generally employed and is particularly useful in the discussion of acid-base reactions in Chapter 10.

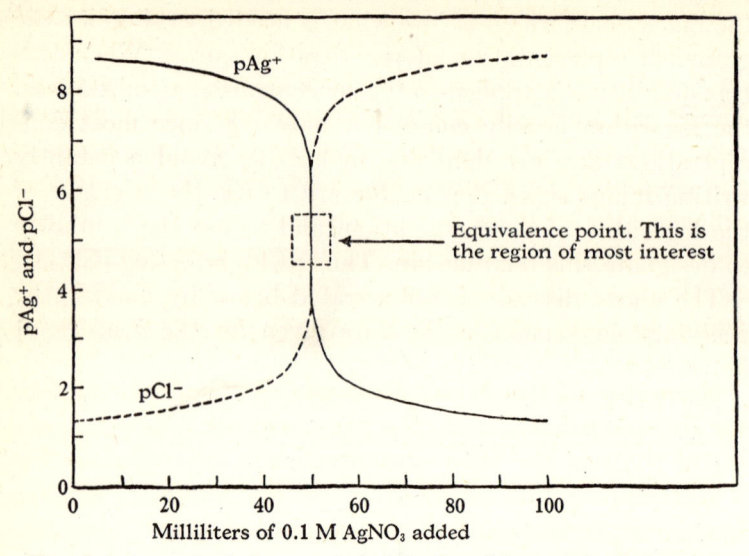

FIG. 9-4. A graph of the negative of the logarithms of the ionic concentrations (pCl⁻ and pAg⁺) in the titration of 50 ml of 0.1 M Cl⁻ with 0.1 M Ag⁺. The volume is assumed to be 100 ml throughout.

End-Point Detection

In the titration of 50.00 ml of 0.1000 M KCl with 0.1000 M AgNO₃, the previously calculated data show the following changes in the concentration of the reacting ions near the equivalence-point.

Vol. $AgNO_3$ ml	$[Ag^+]$ M	$[Cl^-]$ M
49.90	1×10^{-6}	1×10^{-4}
49.95	2×10^{-6}	5×10^{-5}
50.00	1×10^{-5}	1×10^{-5}
50.05	5×10^{-5}	2×10^{-6}
50.10	1×10^{-4}	1×10^{-6}

In order to obtain an end-point which coincides within two parts per thousand of the equivalence-point, it is necessary to use some property of either silver or chloride ions that shows an observable change as the concentrations vary within the above limits.

There are many physical properties—electrode potential, electrical conductivity, light absorption, refractive index, etc.—that depend upon the concentration of the reacting species and may show an abrupt change near the equivalence-point of a titration. An understanding of the magnitude of the concentration changes to expect and the factors that influence the changes is fundamental to the use of such physical methods of end-point detection. However, we will restrict our consideration of methods of determining end-points to those based primarily upon the use of chemical properties of the reacting ions.

Principle of the Mohr Method.—In the Mohr method for the determination of chloride, chromate ions are added to the solution and their concentration is controlled so that a visible precipitate of red silver chromate appears within a few parts per thousand of the equivalence-point. Since the solubility product of silver chromate is known to be 1×10^{-12}, we can estimate the chromate ion concentration that should be employed in the following way:

$$[CrO_4^{--}][Ag^+]^2 = 1 \times 10^{-12} \qquad [CrO_4^{--}] = \frac{1 \times 10^{-12}}{[Ag^+]^2}$$

$AgNO_3$ ml	$[Ag^+]$ M	$[CrO_4^{--}]$ to form Ag_2CrO_4 (s) M
49.95	2×10^{-6}	0.25
50.00	1×10^{-5}	0.01
50.05	5×10^{-5}	0.0004

From these calculations, we find that, in principle, any concentration of chromate ion from 0.0004 to 0.25 M should result in the appearance of a silver chromate precipitate within one part per thousand of the equivalence-point. However, the calculations refer only to the point at which precipitation begins, and ignore the practical fact that a measurable amount of precipitate must form before it can be seen. Experimentally, it is found that about 10^{-4} moles of precipitate must be formed per liter of solution in order to be clearly visible to the average eye. For this reason, it is desirable to use a chromate concentration near the upper limit in order to minimize the amount of excess silver required to produce a visible precipitate. On the other hand, the chromate ion is colored and an increase in concentration makes it more difficult to clearly recognize the end-point. In practice, a concentration of 0.02 M CrO_4^{--} proves to be a good compromise. With experience, under optimum conditions, the Mohr method yields precise results which are only negligibly high.

Limitations of the Mohr Method.—The Mohr method can be used only in a limited range of acidity—from about 10^{-6} to 10^{-10} M H^+. The hydrogen ion concentration must be greater than 10^{-10} M to prevent a possible precipitation of silver hydroxide. On the other hand, at acidities above 10^{-6} M H^+, most of the added chromate is converted to dichromate ions and a satisfactory end-point cannot be obtained. Chromate ion forms the weak acid $HCrO_4^-$ (K about 10^{-7}) which dimerizes as shown by the reaction:

$$2CrO_4^{--} + 2H^+ = (2HCrO_4^-) = Cr_2O_7^{--} + H_2O$$

Actually, the Mohr method is no longer of great practical importance because of the acidity limitations just discussed and because the end-point is not so sharp as that provided by adsorption indicators, particularly in the titration of those solutions which are more dilute than 0.1 M. In addition, a larger number of ions such as lead, barium, and copper form insoluble chromates and so if these ions are present this method cannot be used. The method has been discussed in detail to illustrate the general factors that are involved in obtaining an end-point that is a suitably precise designation of the equivalence-point. It should be recognized that the provision of a satisfactory end-point in any titration is partially a theoretical and partially an empirical problem. If the application of equilibrium considerations shows that there is a marked change in concentration of the reacting species within a few parts per thousand of the equivalence-point, a suitable end-point *may* be possible. However, in utilizing such a theoretical possibility, various limitations have to be experimentally explored; ideas that look very good on paper may be of limited value.

Adsorption Indicators

The use of adsorption indicators in the titration of chloride with silver gives a sharper end-point over a wider range of concentrations of reactants than does the Mohr method, although the range of acidity that can be used still is quite limited.

The adsorption of various components of a solution on the surface of a solid was discussed in connection with the formation and purity of precipitates in Chapter 6. In certain cases, such adsorption is accompanied by an observable color change and can be used to detect an end-point when the adsorption occurs at or very near the equivalence-point. For example, fluorescein and many of its derivatives are adsorbed on silver chloride.

Fluorescein, which we shall designate as HFl, behaves as a weak acid with a dissociation constant of about 10^{-8}, and so in solution the equilibrium, $HFl = H^+ + Fl^-$ is established. Actually, it is the ion, Fl^-, which is adsorbed on silver chloride. Hence, it is necessary to keep the hydrogen ion concentration below 10^{-7} M in order that a significant fraction of the fluorescein be present as the adsorbable ion. Adsorption of the Fl^- occurs close to the equivalence-point because of the following factors:

a. Silver, chloride, and Fl^- ions can be primarily adsorbed on a precipitate of silver chloride, but of these Fl^- is the least strongly adsorbed.

b. As silver is added to a chloride solution, chloride ions are in excess and they are primarily adsorbed in preference to the Fl^-. Since the resultant silver chloride particles are negatively charged, the Fl^- cannot act as counter-ions.

c. After the equivalence-point is reached, further addition of silver yields an excess of silver ions in solution, that is primarily adsorbed by the precipitate. When this happens, Fl^- either are adsorbed or are incorporated into the lattice. Adsorption changes the structure of these ions and so the characteristic greenish-yellow fluorescence of the dissolved ion is changed sharply to the rather brilliant pink color of the adsorbed ion. Experimentally, it is found that this change occurs within 1-2 parts per thousand of the equivalence-point in the titration of 0.01 to 0.1 M solutions.

The adsorption equilibria involved in such methods are rather obscure and so the optimum condition to use in a given case must be experimentally determined. One general factor, however, should be noted. The color change occurs on the surface of the precipitate—not in the body of the solution. It is very desirable, therefore, to maintain the precipitate as a colloidal dispersion in order to provide a large surface and to have the color change appear to occur throughout the body of the solution. In the case of silver chloride, substances such as dextrin and gum arabic frequently are added in order to stabilize the precipitate as a colloid. A high concentration of electrolytes favors the flocculation of the colloid and interferes with the visibility of the end-point.

As previously indicated, fluorescein can be used only if the hydrogen ion concentration is less than about 10^{-7} M because HFl is a weak acid with an ionization constant of about 10^{-8}. Dichlorofluorescein, which behaves similarly as far as adsorption is concerned, is a stronger acid. As a consequence, it can be used in the presence of hydrogen-ion concentrations up to about 10^{-4} M.

Adsorption indicators are used in a limited number of titrations based upon precipitation reactions. Such applications depend primarily upon specific properties rather than upon the application of general principles.

The Volhard Method

It has been shown that neither the Mohr method nor the adsorption-indicator method can be applied to the determination of chloride in strongly acid solutions. The Volhard method, however, can be so applied, and it is of interest at this point because it illustrates a general method of applying volumetric methods where direct titrations are impossible.

The essential titration in this case is based upon the precipitation of silver thiocyanate (AgSCN). The solubility product of silver thiocyanate is about 10^{-12}. A titration curve similar to that in Figure 9-4 shows a marked change in the logarithms of the concentrations of silver and thiocyanate ions within a few parts per thousand of the equivalence-point. When a suitable concentration of ferric ions is established in the solution, a sharp end-point can be obtained in this titration due to the formation of red ferric thiocyanate complex ions. Neither the ferric nor the thiocyanate ions react with hydrogen ion. Hence, the titration can be carried out in strongly acid solutions. In fact, it must be done in solutions more acid than 0.01 M H^+ to prevent hydrolysis of the ferric ion.

The Volhard method of determining chloride or other anions that form insoluble silver salts is performed as follows. An excess of a standard solution of silver nitrate is added to the solution to precipitate the chloride present. In principle, or in fact, this precipitate is separated from the supernatant liquid and the total amount of excess silver is then determined by titration with a standardized solution of thiocyanate. Subtraction of the determined excess of silver from the known total amount then gives the amount of silver required to precipitate the chloride ion in the sample. This process is called a *back titration* or an *indirect titration* and is used in many cases where a direct titration is impractical.

When a very insoluble silver salt such as silver iodide is determined in this way, it is not necessary to filter before titration with thiocyanate because there is no significant conversion of the precipitate to silver thiocyanate when the titration is performed. For a precipitate like silver chloride which is somewhat more soluble than silver thiocyanate, this is not true. The solubility product of silver chloride is about 10^{-10} and that of silver thiocyanate is about 10^{-12}. At the equivalence-point, in the back titration, some of the precipitated silver chloride dissolves to form thiocyanate, and so the amount of thiocyanate used in the back titration is too great. This difficulty is avoided by separating the precipitated chloride before the thiocyanate titration or by coating the precipitate with some substances to make its rate of solution very slow. One of the substances frequently used for this purpose is nitrobenzene.

Application of Precipitation Methods

The primary purpose of the preceding discussion in this chapter is to illustrate the general principles upon which volumetric methods are based. Volumetric methods which depend upon precipitation are of limited direct application because it is difficult to provide suitable methods of end-point detection, and because many precipitations occur slowly. When the latter is true, no sharp end-point can be obtained, since it is necessary to wait for variable periods of time after each addition of reagent before observing some property that marks the equivalence-point.

Volumetric Determination of Chloride Using Dichlorofluorescein Indicator

Using the adsorption indicator method, a silver nitrate solution is standardized by titration against a standard sodium chloride solution. The latter is directly prepared by dissolving a known weight of the pure salt in a known volume of solution. The percent chloride in the unknown sample is determined by titration with the standardized silver nitrate using the adsorption indicator method. In addition, the Volhard method is used to extend the range of experience even though it is better analytical practice to titrate the unknown by the method used in the standardization. Inaccuracies arising from inherent errors of a particular method and the subjective element in determining a particular end-point are minimized by using the same method for standardization and determination.

Standardization of Silver Nitrate.—Obtain a liter of approximately 0.1 N $AgNO_3$ in a clean, but not necessarily dry, brown bottle and shake the solution thoroughly to insure uniform concentration.

Place 4−5 g of pure sodium chloride in a clean weighing bottle and dry it in the oven for at least one hour. Accurately weigh 4 — 4.5 g of the pure salt into a clean, short-stemmed funnel seated in the mouth of a 500 ml volumetric flask. Carefully wash the solid into the flask with distilled water. Rinse and remove the funnel, dissolve the solid, and dilute to volume as described in Chapter 8. *Mix the solution thoroughly.* Calculate the molarity of the solution.

Rinse a clean buret with two or three small portions of the silver nitrate solution and fill it. Drain until the liquid level falls within the graduated portion and record the initial volume reading. Pipet 25 ml of the sodium chloride solution into a 250 ml Erlenmeyer flask, add 0.3 — 0.5 ml of 0.1% dichlorofluorescein solution and an estimated 0.1 g of dextrin. Keep the solution well mixed by swirling the flask, and add the silver nitrate solution rapidly until a pink-tinged area persists around the point where the silver nitrate enters. Add the silver nitrate more and more slowly as it becomes increasingly difficult to restrict the pink color to a small area near the point of entrance of the silver nitrate, finally adding it a drop at a time. At this point, wash the walls of the flask with a stream of water. The end-point is reached when one drop produces a permanent pink on the colloidally dispersed particles. Since silver chloride darkens on exposure to light, such exposure should be minimized.

Repeat the determination until a precision of one to two parts per thousand in the ratio of titration volumes is obtained. In the subsequent determinations, the first result may be used to estimate the amount of silver nitrate required, permitting the end-point to be approached much more rapidly. Calculate the molarity of the silver nitrate solution.

Determination of Chloride in the Unknown.—Transfer the unknown sample to a clean, dry, weighing bottle and dry it for at least one hour. Prepare a solution by weighing the bulk of the sample into a 250 ml volumetric flask as described in the preparation of the standard sodium chloride solution. Titrate 25 ml aliquots of the unknown solution, using dichlorofluorescein indicator as in the standardization until a precision of one to two parts per thousand is attained. Calculate the percent chloride from these results.

Volhard Method

Potassium Thiocyanate Standardization.—Obtain approximately 250 ml of 0.1 M KSCN in a clean bottle. Rinse and fill a buret with the potassium thiocyanate solution. Deliver 30 – 40 ml (accurately measured) of silver nitrate from another buret into a 250 ml Erlenmeyer, add 10 ml of 6 N HNO$_3$ and 1 ml of 0.5 M Fe^{+++}. Add the potassium thiocyanate with *vigorous* swirling of the solution until one drop produces a faint but permanent reddish-brown tinge. If the end-point is passed, additional silver nitrate may be added and the end-point redetermined until a satisfactory observation is made. Repeat the titration until the ratio of titration volumes agrees within one to two parts per thousand.

Titration of the Unknown.—Pipet 25 ml of the sample solution into a 250 ml Erlenmeyer flask. Add 10 ml of 6 N HNO$_3$ and 1 ml of the ferric solution. Record the initial reading of the buret containing the potassium thiocyanate solution. Add approximately 0.5 ml of potassium thiocyanate to produce a red color in the solution.

Titrate by adding silver nitrate from the other buret until the red color disappears. Then add approximately 5 ml more of the silver nitrate solution. Filter through coarse filter paper into a clean Erlenmeyer flask to remove the precipitate. Wash the original container and the precipitate to avoid loss of the excess silver ion. Titrate the filtrate plus washings with the potassium thiocyanate solution as in the thiocyanate standardization. From the total volume of potassium thiocyanate required, the volume of silver nitrate added in excess is calculated. Subtract this volume from the total volume of silver nitrate added to obtain the volume required for titration of the 25 ml sample. Repeat the determination until an agreement is obtained. Calculate the percent of chloride in the sample from the data.

Titrate two more 25 ml samples as above by adding silver nitrate until the red color just disappears. Instead of adding more silver nitrate and removing the precipitate by filtration, add potassium thiocyanate solution dropwise until a faint but permanent reddish-brown color just appears. Do not use any distilled water to wash the sides of the flask because the final volume must be known.

The concentration of thiocyanate ion necessary to produce a distinguishable reddish-brown color under the above conditions has been determined experimentally to be approximately 2×10^{-5} M. The difference between the amount of thiocyanate used for the back titration in the presence of the precipitate and in the absence of the precipitate is a measure of the amount of silver chloride that has been converted to silver thiocyanate. Use this fact, the total volume of solution, and the concentration of thiocyanate needed to give a visible ferric thiocyanate color to estimate the solubility product of silver thiocyanate.

Problems

1. A sample of pure potassium chloride weighing 0.746 g reacts quantitatively with 33.3 ml of a silver nitrate solution. What is the concentration of the silver nitrate solution?
Ans. **0.300 M**

2. A sample of pure barium chloride dihydrate weighing 0.611 g reacts quantitatively with 45.4 ml of a silver nitrate solution. What is the concentration of the silver nitrate solution?
Ans. **0.1102 M**

3. A sample of pure barium chloride dihydrate weighing 0.611 g reacts quantitatively with 30.2 ml of a sulfuric acid solution. What is the concentration of the sulfuric acid solution?
Ans. **0.0828 M**

4. If 31.50 ml of 0.100 M $AgNO_3$ are used to titrate the bromide ion in a sample, calculate the weight of potassium bromide that may be in the sample. *Ans.* **0.3749 g KBr**

5. If 42.50 ml of 0.500 M AgNO$_3$ are used to titrate the chloride ion in a sample, calculate the weight of sodium chloride that may be in the sample. *Ans.* **0.1242 g NaCl**

6. If 32.45 ml of 0.1000 M AgNO$_3$ react with 25.0 ml of a potassium chloride solution, what is the concentration of the chloride solution? *Ans.* **0.1298 M**

7. If 37.3 ml of 0.205 M AgNO$_3$ react with 50.0 ml of an unknown bromide solution, what is the bromide ion concentration of the solution? *Ans.* **0.1529 M**

8. If 47.5 ml of 0.0150 M AgNO$_3$ react with 50.0 ml of an unknown thiocyanate solution, what is the thiocyanate ion concentration? *Ans.* **0.01425 M**

9. Calculate the molarity of a potassium thiocyanate solution if 44.50 ml are required to titrate 0.6796 g of pure silver nitrate. *Ans.* **0.0899 M**

10. A silver ore weighing 1.7166 g is dissolved in nitric acid and titrated using the Volhard method. It is found that 15.85 ml of 0.1000 M KCNS are required for the titration. Calculate the percent silver in the ore. *Ans.* **9.96%**

11. To 0.500 g of an unknown chloride, 40.0 ml of 0.1000 M AgNO$_3$ are added, the precipitate is removed by filtration, and the clear supernatant is back-titrated with 4.64 ml of 0.1000 M KCNS. Calculate the percent sodium chloride in the sample. *Ans.* **41.3% NaCl**

12. The Volhard method is used to determine bromide. If the thiocyanate concentration in the titration must be 10^{-5} M to produce an observable end-point, what is the concentration of bromide ion at the end-point? K_{sp} for AgCNS = 1×10^{-12}; K_{sp} for AgBr = 3.3×10^{-13}. *Ans.* **3.3×10^{-6} M**

13. In the Mohr method for the determination of chloride, the chromate ion concentration at the end-point is 0.03 M. Estimate the chloride ion concentration. K_{sp} for silver chromate = 1.1×10^{-12}; K_{sp} for silver chloride = 1.7×10^{-10}. *Ans.* **2.8×10^{-5} M**

14. To 100 ml of 0.03 M KCl, 0.340 g of silver nitrate are added. What is the pCl$^-$? the pAg$^+$?
$\qquad$ *Ans.* **pCl$^-$ = 2, pAg$^+$ = 7.77**

15. To 100 ml of 0.03 M BaCl$_2$, 0.340 g of silver nitrate are added. What is the pCl$^-$? the pAg$^+$? the pBa^{++}?
$\qquad$ *Ans.* **pCl$^-$ = 2.40, pAg$^+$ = 7.37, pBa^{++} = 2.50**

16. To 50 ml of 0.015 M KI, 50 ml of 0.010 M AgNO$_3$ are added. The K$_{sp}$ for AgI is 1.5×10^{-16}. Calculate pK$_{sp}$, pAg$^+$, and pI$^-$. *Ans.* **pK$_{sp}$ = 15.82, pI$^-$ = 2.60, pAg$^+$ = 13.22**

17. To 50 ml of 0.015 M K$_2$CrO$_4$, 50 ml of 0.010 M AgNO$_3$ are added. The K$_{sp}$ for Ag$_2$CrO$_4$ is 1.1×10^{-12}. Calculate pK$_{sp}$, pAg$^+$, and pCrO$_4^{--}$.
$\qquad$ *Ans.* **pK$_{sp}$ = 11.96, pCrO$_4^{--}$ = 2.30, pAg$^+$ = 4.83**

18. A 1.000 g sample of an unknown containing chloride and cyanide is titrated with 0.1000 M AgNO$_3$. When 10.3 ml of silver nitrate have been added, the first permanent turbidity appears throughout the solution. This volume is a measure of the amount of cyanide present according to the reaction:
$$Ag^+ + 2CN^- = Ag(CN)_2^-$$
An additional 45.8 ml are required to completely precipitate silver chloride and silver cyanide. Calculate the percent potassium chloride and percent potassium cyanide in the sample. $\qquad$ *Ans.* **KCl = 18.80%, KCN = 6.71%**

Chapter 10

PRINCIPLES AND ANALYTICAL APPLICATIONS OF ACID-BASE REACTIONS

In recent years, the concept of acidic and basic substances has been generalized in order to widen the range of phenomena that can be correlated. For our present purposes, the older concept that an acid is a substance which dissociates in water to yield hydrogen ions and a base is one that dissociates to yield hydroxyl ions is satisfactory. Acid-base reactions are of great practical importance in analysis, not only because of their use in titrating a large number of inorganic and organic substances, but also because the hydrogen ion concentration of a solution often is of great importance in controlling reactions. We are interested, therefore, in the principles that underlie acid-base titrations and in the methods that are commonly used to control the hydrogen ion concentration of solutions.

Stoichiometry

The stoichiometry of all acid-base titrations can be based on the mole as the unit of calculation, as discussed in the preceding chapter. However, it is more convenient to use the concept of the equivalent weight of an acid or a base and thereby reduce the calculations to the most general terms. The following definitions are involved:

1. The equivalent weight of an acid is that weight which yields one mole of hydrogen ions in the reaction employed.

2. The equivalent weight of a base is that weight which reacts with one mole of hydrogen ions in the reaction, $H^+ + OH^- = H_2O$.

ACIDIMETRY AND ALKALIMETRY

3. A *normal solution*, designated by the symbol N, contains one equivalent weight per liter of solution or one milliequivalent per milliliter.

4. At the equivalence-point, the same number of equivalents of acid and base have been added.

The required calculations follow directly from these definitions as shown in the following examples:

Example 1.—How many ml of 0.04 M $Ba(OH)_2$ are required to react with 15 ml of 0.1 M HCl?
The reaction is:
$$H^+ + OH^- = H_2O.$$
1 mole HCl = 1 equivalent (eq) because it yields one mole of H^+.
0.1 M HCl is therefore 0.1 N.
1 mole $Ba(OH)_2$ = 2 eq since it yields 2 moles OH^- and reacts with 2 moles H^+.
0.04 M $Ba(OH)_2$ is therefore 0.04 × 2 or 0.08 N.

0.1 N HCl contains 0.1 eq/liter or 0.1 meq/ml.
In 15 ml of the HCl, there are 15 × 0.1 meq.
0.08 N $Ba(OH)_2$ contains 0.08 eq/liter or 0.08 meq/ml.
At the equivalence-point, meq HCl = meq $Ba(OH)_2$.
Therefore, ml $Ba(OH)_2$ × 0.08 = 15 × 0.1.

Example 2.—How many g of $Ba(OH)_2$ are contained in a solution which requires 25.00 ml of 0.08 N HCl for titration?
meq $Ba(OH)_2$ = meq HCl = 0.08 × 25.00.
Wt. $Ba(OH)_2$ = meq × wt. of one meq.

$$1 \text{ meq } Ba(OH)_2 = \frac{\text{M.W. } Ba(OH)_2}{2 \times 1000} \text{ g.}$$

$$\text{Required wt. } Ba(OH)_2 = 0.08 \times 25.00 \times \frac{\text{M.W. } Ba(OH)_2}{2 \times 1000} \text{ g.}$$

Example 3.—If 50.00 ml of an HCl solution are required to titrate 0.2500 g of pure Na_2CO_3, what is the normality of the HCl solution?
The reaction is:
$$CO_3^{--} + 2H^+ = H_2O + CO_2.$$

1 mole of Na_2CO_3 is 2 eq since it yields 1 mole of CO_3^{--} which reacts with 2 moles of H^+.

$$\text{Eq wt } Na_2CO_3 = \frac{\text{M.W. } Na_2CO_3}{2} = 53 \text{ g.}$$

$$\text{The number of eq of } Na_2CO_3 = \frac{0.2500}{\text{Eq wt}} = \frac{0.2500}{53}.$$

Eq Na_2CO_3 = eq HCl.

$$\text{Eq HCl in 50.00 ml} = \frac{0.2500}{53}.$$

$$\text{Normality HCl} = \frac{\text{no. eq}}{\text{no. liters}}.$$

$$N \text{ HCl} = \frac{\frac{0.2500}{53}}{\frac{50}{1000}} = \frac{0.2500}{53} \times \frac{1000}{50}.$$

The above examples represent the three basic types of required calculation. It is quite important that the principles illustrated be applied to the stoichiometric problems at the end of this chapter until the solutions can readily be set up with confidence.

Titration of Strong Acids with Strong Bases

For the purpose of titration, we can classify an acid or base as strong if its dissociation constant is greater than about 10^{-3}.

Common Strong Acids	Common Strong Bases
$HClO_4$	Alkali Hydroxides
HNO_3	$Ca(OH)_2$
H_2SO_4	$Ba(OH)_2$
Hydrogen Halides	

In such a titration, we need consider only the reaction, $H^+ + OH^- = H_2O$, regardless of the strong acid or base used. Associated with this reaction is the equilibrium $[H^+][OH^-] = K_w = 10^{-14}$.

As in Chapter 9, it is convenient to express concentrations in logarithmic form using the notation, $pH = -\log[H^+]$. The interconversion of $[H^+]$ and pH and the general relations used in calculations are shown in the following examples.

ACIDIMETRY AND ALKALIMETRY

Example 1.—Calculate the $[H^+]$, pH, pOH and $[OH^-]$ in 0.03 N HCl.

(a) $[H^+] = 3 \times 10^{-2}\ M$ in 0.03 N HCl.

(b) Calculation of pH:

$$\log [H^+] = \overline{\log 3 + \log 10^{-2}} = 0.48 - 2 = -1.52$$

$pH = -\log [H^+] = 1.52$.

(c) Calculation of pOH:
$[H^+][OH^-] = K_w = 10^{-14}$
$pH + pOH = 14$.
$pOH = 14 - pH = 14 - 1.52 = 12.48$.

(d) Calculation of $[OH^-]$:
$pOH = -\log [OH^-] = 12.48$.
$\log [OH^-] = -12.48 = -0.48 - 12$.

$$\log [OH^-] = \frac{+1.\quad -1}{0.52\quad -13}$$

Therefore, $[OH^-] = 3.3 \times 10^{-13}\ M$.

This, of course, could have been determined directly from (a) and the ion product of water.

Thus, $[OH^-] = \dfrac{10^{-14}}{3 \times 10^{-2}} = 3.3 \times 10^{-13}\ M$.

Example 2.—Calculate the pOH, pH, and $[H^+]$ in 0.05 N Ca(OH)$_2$.

(a) Calculation of pOH:
$[OH^-] = 5 \times 10^{-2}\ M$ in 0.05 N Ca(OH)$_2$
$\log [OH^-] = \log 5 + \log 10^{-2} = 0.7 - 2 = -1.3$
$pOH = -\log [OH^-] = 1.3$.

(b) Calculation of pH:
$pH + pOH = 14$
$pH = 14 - 1.3 = 12.7$.

(c) Calculation of $[H^+]$:

$$\log [H^+] = -pH = -12.7 = \overline{-0.7 - 12} = 0.3 - 13$$

Therefore, $[H^+] = 2.0 \times 10^{-13}\ M$.

TABLE 10-1

CALCULATION OF THE CONCENTRATIONS OF H^+ AND OH^- IN THE TITRATION OF 50 ML OF A 0.1 N STRONG ACID WITH 0.1 N STRONG BASE

Base ml	Excess in ml Acid	Excess in ml Base	Final Vol. ml	$[H^+]$ M	$[OH^-]$ M	pH
0	50	0	50	10^{-1}	10^{-13}	1.0
5	45	0	55	8.2×10^{-2}	1.2×10^{-13}	1.1
25	25	0	75	3.3×10^{-2}	3.0×10^{-13}	1.5
45	5	0	95	5.3×10^{-3}	1.9×10^{-13}	2.3
49.90	0.10	0	~100	1.0×10^{-4}	1.0×10^{-10}	4.0
49.95	0.05	0	~100	5.0×10^{-5}	2.0×10^{-10}	4.3
50.00	0	0	~100	10^{-7}	10^{-7}	7.0
50.05	0	0.05	~100	2×10^{-10}	5×10^{-5}	9.7
50.10	0	0.10	~100	1×10^{-10}	1×10^{-4}	10.0
55.00	0	5	105	2.1×10^{-12}	4.7×10^{-3}	11.3

In discussing the titration of chloride ion with silver ion, we ignored the change in volume of the resulting solution. We wish now to consider similar calculations in which a change in volume is introduced.

If to a beaker which contains 50 ml of 0.1 M HCl, 25 ml of distilled water are added, the beaker will contain the same number of moles of acid as it did before, but these will be distributed throughout the larger volume. The concentration of acid, therefore, is equal to $0.1 \times 50/75 = 0.0667\ M$. If the experiment is repeated but 25 ml of 0.1 M NaOH are added in place of the 25 ml of distilled water, one half of the acid will be neutralized, the remainder will be distributed throughout the 75 ml. The change in concentration, therefore, is due to two factors and so the concentration will be equal to $1/2 \times 50/75 \times 0.1$ or $0.0333\ M$. If 45 ml of base are added, the final concentration of H^+ becomes $5/50 \times 50/95 \times 0.1$. Beyond the equivalence-point, the calculation is most easily performed by calculating the excess OH^- and the effect of dilution upon this excess. Thus, when 55 ml are

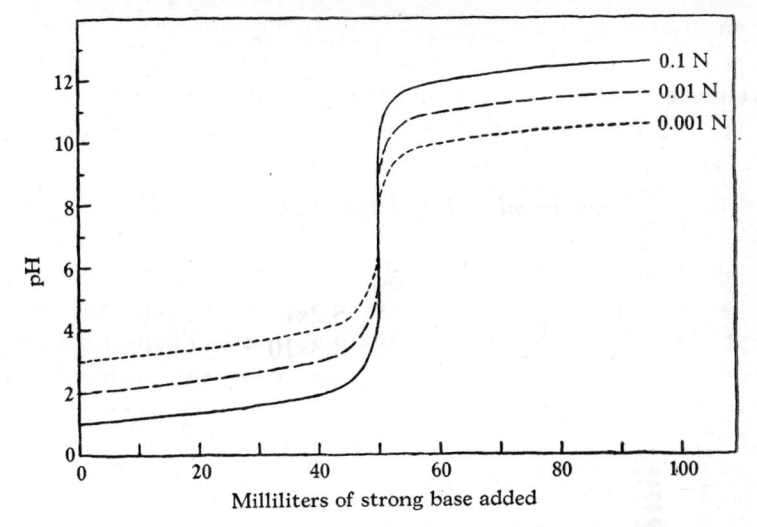

FIG. 10-1. The curves for the titration of 50 ml of a strong acid with a strong base. The concentrations of both the acid and the base are as indicated on the curves.

added, the excess base will be 5 ml and it will be distributed throughout 105 ml and so the OH$^-$ concentration will be $5/105 \times 0.1$. Calculations of the concentrations of H$^+$ and OH$^-$ in the titration of any strong acid with any strong base, taking both these factors into account, are summarized in Table 10-1.

Note that the pH changes from 4.0 to 10.0 within two parts per thousand of the equivalence-point.

In Figure 10-1, we have plotted the data given in Table 10-1 to construct a titration curve. Curves for the titrations of 50 ml of 0.01 N and 0.001 N strong acids with strong bases of the corresponding concentrations likewise have been plotted.

The most significant points to note in Figure 10-1 are, first, the pH at the equivalence-point is 7 regardless of the concentrations used; and, second, the change in pH close to the equivalence-point decreases markedly as the concentrations are decreased. Thus, in the titration of 0.1 N solutions, any observable property of hydrogen or hydroxyl ions that undergoes a marked change from pH 4 to pH 10 will provide an end-point within 0.2% of the equivalence-point. However, in the titration of 0.001 N solutions, the corresponding pH change is only from 6 to 8. The significance of the change in pH near the equivalence-point will be discussed in connection with the use of acid-base indicators.

Acid-Base Indicators

The detection of the end-point in acid-base titrations, is based always upon the observation of a physical or chemical property that depends upon the hydrogen-ion concentration of the solution. Common practice is to employ various weak organic acids and weak organic bases in which the colors of their dissociated forms are different from those of the undissociated forms. These are referred to as *acid-base indicators*.

As an example, we may take the indicator, phenol red, the chemical name of which is phenolsulfonphthalein. In the equilibrium directly involved in the color change, we need consider only that the ion behaves as a weak monobasic acid, which we will designate as HIn.

HIn
The structure shown represents only one of several possible charge distributions of the molecule among which it may resonate. The transmitted color of a solution HIn is yellow.

In$^-$
This structure also is only one of several possible charge distributions which have been altered, by the removal of the hydrogen ion. The transmitted color of a solution of In$^-$ is red.

The color that the average eye perceives in looking at a mixture of colored substances depends upon the relative number of particles of each kind as well as upon the intensity of color of each particle. Thus, if the intensity of the yellow were very weak and that of the red very strong, a mixture that contained only a very small fraction of red particles would be observed as red. If the intrinsic intensity of the two colors is not too different, we can arbitrarily say that if the concentration of one colored form is ten times that of the other, the eye will perceive the mixture as having the color of the form that is predominant. In the intermediate range where the ratio of the two forms changes from ten to one tenth, the eye will perceive a change of color quality or hue. In the limiting case where the intrinsic intensity of a one-colored form approaches zero, i.e., becomes colorless, we obtain a so-called one-color indicator. A change in relative concentrations of the two forms will not produce a change in hue or color but merely a change in the intensity of the color due to the one form. Phenolphthalein is an example of this type of indicator. In such a case, the intensity of color that is observed depends upon the total concentration of the indicator.

The equilibrium established between the two forms of an indicator is determined by the hydrogen-ion concentration of the solution in accordance with the following expression:

$$\frac{[H^+][In^-]}{[HIn]} = K_{HIn} \quad \text{or} \quad \frac{[In^-]}{[HIn]} = \frac{K_{HIn}}{[H^+]}$$

Since the ion, In^-, is red and the acid, HIn, is yellow, the dependence of the color of the solution on the concentration of hydrogen ion can be indicated in the following way:

$$\frac{[\text{red form}]}{[\text{yellow form}]} = \frac{K_{HIn}}{[H^+]}$$

To illustrate the practical significance of this relationship, suppose that C_0 moles of HIn have been added to one liter of solution. To this solution, we will then add enough acid or base to obtain the approximate hydrogen-ion concentrations listed at the top of the next page.

We thus conclude that in general:

1. A two-color indicator shows a "transition" color at a 50-50 mixture of its color forms when $[H^+] = K_{HIn}$.

$[H^+]$	$[HIn]$ Yellow	$[In^-]$ Red	Color to Average Eye	
100 x K_{HIn}	0.99C_0	0.01C_0	yellow	
10 x K_{HIn}	0.91C_0	0.09C_0	yellow	
1 x K_{HIn}	0.5C_0	0.5C_0	orange	Transition range of indicator
0.1 x K_{HIn}	0.09C_0	0.91C_0	red	
0.01 x K_{HIn}	0.01C_0	0.99C_0	red	

2. As far as the eye is concerned, the transition from one-colored form to the other has been completed when the hydrogen-ion concentration has changed from 10 K_{HIn} to 0.1 K_{HIn}.

The dependence of the ratio of the colored forms of the typical indicator base, InOH, upon the pH of the solution follows a similar pattern.

$$\text{InOH} = \text{In}^+ + \text{OH}^-.$$
Assume it to be red   Assume it to be yellow

$$\frac{[\text{In}^+][\text{OH}^-]}{[\text{InOH}]} = K_{InOH}$$

$$\frac{[\text{In}^+]}{[\text{InOH}]} = \frac{K_{InOH}}{[\text{OH}^-]}$$

In any aqueous solution,

$$[H^+][OH^-] = K_w \text{ or } [OH^-] = \frac{K_w}{[H^+]}.$$

Substituting this relation, we find:

$$\frac{[\text{yellow form}]}{[\text{red form}]} = \frac{[\text{In}^+]}{[\text{InOH}]} = \frac{K_{InOH}}{K_w} \cdot [H^+] = K \cdot [H^+]$$

The transition range of a two-color basic indicator is determined by the same reasoning as used previously in the case of the weak-acid indicator. In this case, the transition from one-colored form to the other occurs as the hydrogen-ion concentration changes from 10 K' to 0.1 K'. We thus see that for both basic and acid indicators, we can express the relative amounts of the two forms as a constant times the hydrogen-ion concentration. Expressed in pH units, the transition interval corresponding to a change in hydrogen-ion concentration from 10 K_{In} to 0.1 K_{In} is pH = pK ± 1.

In general, therefore, an indicator will provide a precise end-point in an acid-base titration if there is a change of 1-2 pH units within one or two parts per thousand of the equivalence-point, and if the pK_{In} is approximately equal to the pH at the equivalence-point. On this basis, reference to Figure 10-1 shows that it should be possible to use any acid-base indicator having a transition between pH 4 and pH 10 and obtain precise end-points in the titration of 0.1 N strong acids with 0.1 N strong bases. For 0.001 N acids and bases, the indicator must have a transition interval between pH 6 and pH 8.

Transition ranges and color changes of some of the most frequently used acid-base indicators are given in Table 10-2.

TABLE 10-2

The Transition Ranges and Color Changes of Some Acid-Base Indicators

Trade Name	"Acid" Color	"Basic" Color	Transition Range (pH units)
Methyl orange	red	orange-yellow	3.1- 4.6
Brom Phenol blue	yellow	blue-violet	3.0- 4.6
Methyl red	red	yellow	4.2- 6.3
Bromthymol blue	yellow	blue	6.0- 7.6
Thymol blue	yellow	blue	8.0- 9.6
Phenolphthalein	colorless	red	8.0- 9.8
Thymolphthalein	colorless	blue	9.4-10.6

Titration of a Weak Monobasic Acid with a Strong Base

If sodium hydroxide is added to a weak acid such as acetic acid, HAc, the following reaction occurs:

$$HAc + OH^- = Ac^- + H_2O$$

This process is called neutralization. On the other hand, if

sodium acetate is dissolved in pure water the following reaction takes place:
$$Ac^- + H_2O = HAc + OH^-$$
This reaction, called the hydrolysis of acetate ion, is the reverse of neutralization. Actually, in any solution involving the above substances, both reactions will proceed until an equilibrium is established. At the equivalence-point in the titration of acetic acid with sodium hydroxide, the number of equivalents of hydroxide ion added is exactly equal to the number of equivalents of acetic acid originally present. The resulting solution, however, is not neutral because the hydrolysis of the acetate ion is appreciable at this point.

During this titration, there are four substances that change in concentration: HAc, Ac^-, H^+ and OH^-. The concentrations of these substances, however, are related because of the equilibrium that is established. It is convenient to express these relationships in terms of the following processes:

1. Dissociation of the weak acid:

$$HAc = H^+ + Ac^- \qquad \frac{[H^+][Ac^-]}{[HAc]} = K_a = 1.8 \times 10^{-5}$$

$$[H^+] = K_a \cdot \frac{[HAc]}{[Ac^-]} \qquad pH = pK_a - \log \frac{[HAc]}{[Ac^-]}$$

2. Dissociation of water:
$$H_2O = H^+ + OH^- \qquad [H^+][OH^-] = K_w = 10^{-14}$$
$$pH + pOH = pK_w = 14$$

3. Hydrolysis of the weak-acid ion:

$$Ac^- + H_2O = HAc + OH^- \qquad \frac{[HAc][OH^-]}{[Ac^-]} = K_h$$

If we use the device of writing a H^+ on each side of the hydrolysis equation, it can be seen that the equilibrium is related very simply to the two dissociation reactions, thus:

$$\underbrace{\overbrace{\lfloor H^+ + Ac^- \rfloor + \lceil H_2O \rceil = \lfloor HAc \rfloor + \lceil OH^- + H^+ \rceil}^{K_w \longrightarrow}}_{\longleftarrow K_a}$$

ACIDIMETRY AND ALKALIMETRY

The constant, K, for this equilibrium is given by the relation:

$$K = \boxed{\frac{[HAc]\; [OH^-]\; [H^+]}{[H^+]\; [Ac^-]} \quad \frac{K_w}{K_a}}$$

which differs from the hydrolysis constant above only in the appearance of $[H^+]$ in the numerator and denominator. The two expressions therefore are identical and so we can write $K = K_h$.

The relative importance of the three processes listed above depends upon the relative concentrations of the species HAc, Ac^-, H^+ and OH^-. To illustrate this fact, consider the estimation of the pH at various points during the titration of 50 ml of 0.100 N HAc with 0.100 N NaOH.

Estimation of the Initial pH.—At the beginning of the titration, the only source of Ac^- is the dissociation of the 0.100 N HAc. This also is the principal source of H^+ since the dissociation of water is very small compared to that of HAc. Therefore, as a first approximation, the following concentration relationships may be used:

$[H^+] = [Ac^-]$ + negligible amount from $H_2O \cong [Ac^-]$
$[HAc] = 0.1$ − very small amount that forms $Ac^- \cong 0.1$

The pH may then be estimated in the following way:

$$\frac{[H^+]\,[Ac^-]}{[HAc]} = K_a = 1.80 \times 10^{-5} \cong \frac{[H^+]^2}{0.1}$$

$[H^+] \cong \sqrt{1.80 \times 10^{-6}} \cong 1.34 \times 10^{-3}\, M$ or pH $\cong 2.87$

If a more exact value is desired, the method of successive approximations described in Chapter 5 may be applied. For most practical purposes, the approximate methods used in this section are adequate.

Estimation of the pH in the Buffer Region.—When hydroxyl ion is added to the HAc solution, the reaction $HAc + OH^- = Ac^- + H_2O$ occurs and so the concentration of Ac⁻ becomes greater than that of H⁺. This increase in the concentration of acetate ion represses the ionization of the remaining acetic acid, causing a large initial decrease in the hydrogen-ion concentration. The resultant solution then contains HAc and Ac⁻ as the principal species. Solutions that contain significant concentrations of a weak acid (or a weak base) and the corresponding weak acid ion (or base ion) are called *buffer solutions* and we shall consider their properties in more detail in a subsequent section of this chapter. At this point, we are concerned only with the estimation of the pH in the buffer region. This may be roughly defined by saying that the concentration of the HAc and the concentration of the Ac⁻ are individually more than ten times the concentrations of the H⁺ and the OH⁻.

To illustrate the concentration relationships involved, consider the point at which 10 ml of 0.1 N NaOH have been added to 50 ml of the 0.1 N HAc. Since 10 ml of 0.1 N NaOH neutralizes 10 ml of 0.1 N HAc, this solution corresponds exactly to one prepared by mixing 10 ml of 0.1 N NaAc with 40 ml of 0.1 N HAc and then diluting to a total volume of 60 ml. This leads to the following relationships:

$$[\text{Ac}^-] = \frac{10}{60} \times 0.1 + \text{negligible amount from ionization of HAc}$$

$$[\text{HAc}] = \frac{40}{60} \times 0.1 - \text{negligible amount that dissociates}$$

The [H⁺] may be estimated using the equation derived in the beginning of this section.

$$[\text{H}^+] = K_a \cdot \frac{[\text{HAc}]}{[\text{Ac}^-]} \simeq 1.8 \times 10^{-5} \cdot \frac{\frac{40}{60} \times 0.1}{\frac{10}{60} \times 0.1} \simeq 7.2 \times 10^{-5}$$

The most significant thing to note in this result is that the total volume of the solution, 60 ml in this case, is unimportant in the first approximation. It is only the mole ratio of acetic acid to acetate ion that is important. The dilution of the solution has a negligible effect on this ratio until the concentrations of HAc and Ac⁻ become of the same order of magnitude as the [H⁺] or [OH⁻].

We therefore can simplify the estimation of the pH in the buffer region since it is necessary to consider only the mole ratio of HAc to Ac⁻ at each point without regard to the total volume. It also is convenient to obtain the pH directly from the previously derived equation.

$$pH = pK_a - \log \frac{[HAc]}{[Ac^-]} = 4.74 - \log \frac{[HAc]}{[Ac^-]}$$

The method of making calculations in this way is illustrated by the following examples based upon the titration of 50 ml of 0.1 N HAc with a 0.1 N strong base.

Base Added ml	0.1 N HAc Remaining ml	0.1 N Ac⁻ Formed ml	$\frac{[HAc]}{[Ac^-]}$	pH
5	45	5	45/5	3.79
25	25	25	25/25	4.74
45	5	45	5/45	5.69

Estimation of pH at the Equivalence-Point.—The buffer region extends almost from the beginning of the titration to near the equivalence-point. At the beginning of the titration, the [Ac⁻] is essentially equal to the [H⁺]. As the equivalence-point is approached, the [HAc] becomes essentially equal to the [OH⁻]. When 50 ml of 0.1 N NaOH have been added to 50 ml of 0.1 N HAc, the solution is identical with one prepared by dissolving enough sodium acetate to make a 0.05 M NaAc solution. The only source of HAc is the hydrolysis of Ac⁻ and this reaction is the principal source of OH⁻ and so from the reaction Ac⁻ + H_2O = HAc + OH⁻ the concentration relationships are:

[Ac⁻] = 0.05 − negligible amount of HAc formed ≅ 0.05
[OH⁻] = [HAc] + negligible amount from H_2O ≅ [HAc]

The [OH⁻] and pH can be estimated by substituting these relationships in the hydrolysis equation.

$$\frac{[HAc][OH^-]}{[Ac^-]} = K_h = \frac{K_w}{K_a} = 5.6 \times 10^{-10}$$

$$\frac{[OH^-]^2}{0.05} \cong 5.6 \times 10^{-10}$$

$$[OH^-] \cong \sqrt{0.28 \times 10^{-10}} \cong 0.53 \times 10^{-5} M$$

$$pOH \cong 5.28; \qquad pH = 14 - pOH \cong 8.72$$

Estimation of the pH in the Presence of Excess Base. The addition of excess strong base represses the hydrolysis of the Ac^- to such an extent that it is negligible and so the concentration of OH^- and H^+ can be calculated as in the titration of a strong acid with a strong base. For example, when 51 ml of base have been added, the solution is identical with one obtained by adding 1 ml of 0.1 N base to 100 ml of 0.05 N NaAc. The concentration relationships are then:

$$[OH^-] = \frac{1}{101} \times 0.1 + \text{negligible amount from } Ac^-$$
hydrolysis $\cong 0.001$.

$$[H^+] \cong \frac{10^{-14}}{10^{-3}} \cong 10^{-11} M \text{ or } pH \cong 11.$$

Indicator Selection.—The pH at various points in the titration of 50 ml of 0.1 N HAc with a 0.1 N strong base is given in Table 10-3. These values have been calculated by the approximate methods just outlined.

There are two main facts to notice in regard to the selection of an indicator for this titration. First, the solution is not neutral at the equivalence-point because of the hydrolysis of the weak-acid ion. Second, the fact that only a small fraction of the weak acid is dissociated keeps the pH high during the titration and makes the pH change near the equivalence-point much less than in the corresponding titration of a strong acid with a strong base. For these reasons, the indicator must be selected carefully to avoid serious errors. In general, an indicator having a transition interval within ± 1 pH unit of the pH at the equivalence-point must be used. For the titration described by the data in Table

TABLE 10-3

The pH During the Titration of 50.0 ml 0.100 N HAc with 0.100 N Strong Base

Base ml	$[H^+]$ M	pH	Method of Estimation
0	1.3×10^{-3}	2.9	Estimation of initial pH
5	1.6×10^{-4}	3.8	
10	7.2×10^{-4}	4.1	
25	1.8×10^{-5}	4.7	Estimation of pH in buffer region
45	2.0×10^{-6}	5.7	
49.90	3.6×10^{-8}	7.4	
50.00	1.9×10^{-9}	8.7	Estimation of pH at equivalence-point
50.10	1×10^{-10}	10.0	Estimation of pH in the presence of excess base
55	2.1×10^{-12}	11.6	

10-3, the indicators thymol blue and phenolphthalein listed in Table 10-2 are satisfactory.

Practical Titration Limitations.—The change in pH near the equivalence-point depends upon the concentrations of the weak acid and the strong base employed in the titration and upon the ionization constant of the weak acid. If we assume that a precision of one to two parts per thousand is desired and that the volume to be titrated is 50 ml, we can estimate the conditions under which a titration may be feasible. From the discussion of the color change interval of typical indicators, we can conclude that the addition of an excess of 0.05 − 0.1 ml of the base must change the pH by about 1 unit to give a sharp end-point. For each concentration, C_0, that is considered, the pH of a solution containing this excess of base can be calculated as described in the titration of acetic acid. The pH at the equivalence-point then has to be about one unit smaller than this calculated value to provide the required pH change. From this fact, we can calculate the minimum dissociation constant of a weak acid that will give this pH at the equivalence-point. The required calculation is based upon a consideration of the hydrolysis of the weak acid ion, A⁻, at the end-point as outlined below:

$$\underbrace{\overbrace{|H^+ + A^-|}^{K_a} + |H_2O|}_{K_w} = |HA| + |OH^- + H^+|$$

$$\frac{[HA]\,[OH^-]\,[H^+]}{[H^+]\,[A^-]} = \frac{K_w}{K_a} = K_h$$

At the equivalence-point in the titration of C_0 N HA with C_0 N base

$$[HA] = [OH^-] \qquad [A^-] = 1/2\,C_0$$

Making these substitutions and rearranging the equation we obtain

$$K_a = \frac{K_w\,[\tfrac{1}{2}C_0]}{[OH^-]^2} = \frac{10^{-14}C_0}{2[OH^-]^2}$$

The minimum K_a that can be expected to allow a precision titration at various concentrations is estimated in the following tabulation.

C_0 N	pH with 0.1 ml excess C_0 N base	pH at equivalence-point	Minimum K_a approx.
0.1	10	9	5×10^{-6}
0.01	9	8	5×10^{-5}
0.001	8	7	5×10^{-4}

The minimum K_a values listed must be regarded as establishing orders of magnitude only. The titration curve of a weak acid with an ionization constant of 10^{-10} is shown later in Figure 10-2 to illustrate the effect of the magnitude of K_a on the titration curve. This is an extreme case and clearly shows that the *p*H change near the equivalence-point is too small to permit a suitable detection of an end-point.

Titration of a Weak Monoacidic Base with a Strong Acid

The titration of a weak base with a strong acid is analogous to the titration of a weak acid with a strong base. Thus, in the titration of 0.1 N NH_4OH with 0.1 N HCl the essential equilibrium is:

$$NH_4OH + H^+ = NH_4^+ + H_2O$$

$$\xrightarrow{\text{neutralization}}$$
$$\xleftarrow{\text{hydrolysis}}$$

During the titration, the four substances that change in concentration are NH_4OH, NH_4^+, OH^- and H^+. It again is convenient to express the equilibrium relationships between the concentrations of these species in terms of the following processes:

1. Dissociation of the weak base:
$$NH_4OH = NH_4^+ + OH^-$$

$$\frac{[NH_4^+][OH^-]}{[NH_4OH]} = K_b = 1.8 \times 10^{-5}$$

$$[OH^-] = K_b \cdot \frac{[NH_4OH]}{[NH_4^+]} \text{ or } pOH = 4.74 - \log\frac{[NH_4OH]}{[NH_4^+]}$$

2. Dissociation of water:
$$H_2O = H^+ + OH^-$$

$$[H^+][OH^-] = K_w \text{ or } pH + pOH = pK_w = 14$$

3. Hydrolysis of the weak-base ion:

$$\overline{|OH^- + NH_4^+|} + \overline{|H_2O|} \xrightarrow{K_w} \overline{|NH_4OH|} + \overline{|H^+ + OH^-|}$$
$$\xleftarrow{K_b}$$

$$K_h = \frac{[NH_4OH][H^+][OH^-]}{[OH^-][NH_4^+]} = \frac{K_w}{K_b}$$

As in the weak-acid discussion, the relative concentrations of the species involved at various points in the titration determine the type of approximation that is useful. The reasoning used to determine the concentration relationships that are important has been described in detail in connection with the preceding titration of acetic acid. When applied to the titration of 50 ml of 0.1 N NH_4OH, the following results are obtained:

Estimation of the Initial pH:

$NH_4OH = NH_4^+ + OH^-$

$[NH_4OH] \cong 0.1\ M \qquad [NH_4^+] \cong [OH^-]$

$$\frac{[NH_4^+][OH^-]}{[NH_4OH]} = 1.8 \times 10^{-5} \qquad \frac{[OH^-]^2}{0.1} \cong 1.8 \times 10^{-5}$$

$[OH^-] \cong 1.34 \times 10^{-3}\ M \qquad pOH \cong 2.87$

$pH \cong 11.13$

Estimation of the pH in the Buffer Region.—As in the weak acid titration, there is a buffer region in which the concentration of the weak base and the concentration of the weak-base ion are at least ten times as large as the concentrations of OH^- and H^+. The method of making the required calculations in this region follows directly from the preceding discussion of the weak-acid titration. The calculations for three points in this region are summarized below:

Acid Added Ml	0.1 N NH_4OH Remaining Ml	0.1 N NH_4^+ Formed Ml	pOH	pH
5	45	5	3.79	10.21
25	25	25	4.74	9.26
45	5	45	5.69	8.31

Estimation of pH at the Equivalence-Point.—When 50 ml of 0.1 N HCl have been added, the resultant solution corresponds to 0.05 M NH_4Cl. The calculation of the pH can therefore be made as follows:

$[NH_4^+] \cong 0.05\,M$

$NH_4^+ + H_2O = NH_4OH + H^+$

$[NH_4OH] \cong [H^+]$

$K_h = \dfrac{[NH_4OH][H^+]}{[NH_4^+]} = \dfrac{K_w}{K_b} = \dfrac{10^{-14}}{1.8 \times 10^{-5}} = 5.5 \times 10^{-10}$

$\dfrac{[H^+]^2}{0.05} \cong 5.5 \times 10^{-10}$

$[H^+] \cong 0.53 \times 10^{-5}\,M \qquad pH \cong 5.28$

Estimation of pH in the Presence of Excess Acid.— When 50.10 ml of 0.1 N HCl have been added,

$[H^+] = \dfrac{0.1}{100.1} \times 0.1 +$ negligible amount from

NH_4^+ hydrolysis $\cong 10^{-4}M \qquad pH = 4$

Practical Conclusions.—The above calculations show the close analogy between the titration of a weak base with a strong acid and the titration of a weak acid with a strong base. It will be left as an exercise to use this analogy in order to solve the following practical problems.

1. Estimate the pH during the titration of 50 ml of 0.1 N NH$_4$OH with 0.1 N strong acid (see Table 10-3).

2. Select a suitable indicator (Table 10-2) for this titration.

3. Estimate the minimum dissociation constant, K_b, that would permit a precise titration of 50 ml of 0.1, 0.01, and 0.001 N weak base with a strong acid of the corresponding concentration.

Titration of a Weak Acid with a Weak Base

The titration of a weak acid with a weak base is of no practical analytical significance since the pH change near the equivalence-point is too small to permit the detection of a precise end-point. A qualitative understanding of this fact follows from the preceding discussion. A quantitative consideration of the limiting conditions under which such titrations might be made is of little practical value since there is rarely any reason for wanting to perform them.

Buffer Solutions

Normally, the addition of a strong acid or a strong base to a solution results in a corresponding change in the number of milliequivalents of hydrogen or hydroxyl ion present. A solution is *buffered* when the change in the number of equivalents of hydrogen or hydroxyl ion is less than the number of added equivalents of strong acid or base. It is on the basis of this definition that part of the titration curve of acetic acid with sodium hydroxide was labelled the buffer region. The data calculated for this titration in Table 10-3 are plotted in Figure 10-2. The titration curve for a strong acid (Table 10-1) and the curve for an acid HA having a dissociation constant, K_a, of 10^{-10} are included for comparison.

The buffering effect which occurs for the two weak acids in the region of Figure 10-2 can be shown very clearly by calculating the change in milliequivalents of hydrogen ion produced in each of these solutions by the addition of a given number of milliequivalents of base. In each case, we have calculated the milliequivalents of hydrogen ion present when 5 ml of base have been added and again after the addition of 45 ml of the base using the data in Tables 10-1 and 10-3. The number of milliequivalents of base added to each solution is then 40×0.1 or 4.0. The change in milliequivalents of hydrogen ion is shown below:

Solution	Meq. H^+ 5 Ml Base	Meq. H^+ 25 Ml Base	Change in H^+ (Meq.)
NaCl, HCl	4.5	0.5	4.0
NaAc, HAc	8.9×10^{-3}	1.9×10^{-4}	8.7×10^{-3}
NaA, HA	4.95×10^{-8}	1.05×10^{-9}	4.85×10^{-8}

The solution containing HCl and NaCl clearly is not buffered because the change in milliequivalents of hydrogen ion in the solution is exactly equal to the milliequivalents of strong base added. However, the addition of 4 milliequivalents of

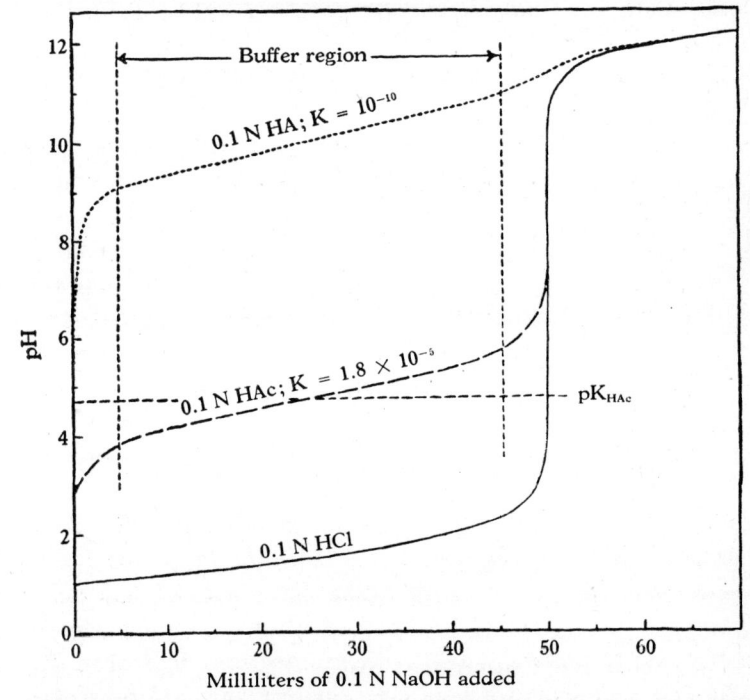

FIG. 10-2. Curves for the titration of strong and weak acids with $0.1N$ NaOH.

base to the HAC, NaAc and to the HA, NaA solutions changes the milliequivalents of hydrogen ion only by 8.7×10^{-3} and 4.85×10^{-8} respectively.

Composition of Buffer Solutions.—In order to be buffered, a solution must contain substances that tend to maintain the concentrations of hydrogen and hydroxyl ions either by removing them if they are added or by supplying them if they are removed. The type of buffer most frequently used consists of a solution of a weak acid and one of its salts. A slightly soluble acid or base in combination with a solution of a corresponding salt sometimes is used as a buffer. If an excess of the solid is present the acid or base need not be weak. The qualitative action of such buffers is indicated below in connection with a specific example of each type.

Buffer	Reaction with H^+	Reaction with OH^-
HAc Ac^-	$H^+ + Ac^-$ $\parallel$ HAc	$HAc + OH^-$ $\parallel$ $Ac^- + H_2O$
NH_4OH NH_4^+	$NH_4OH + H^+$ $\parallel$ $NH_4^+ + H_2O$	$NH_4^+ + OH^-$ $\parallel$ NH_4OH
$Zn(OH)_{2(s)}$ Zn^{++}	$Zn(OH)_{2(s)} + 2H^+$ $\parallel$ $Zn^{++} + 2H_2O$	$Zn^{++} + 2OH^-$ $\parallel$ $Zn(OH)_{2(s)}$
$C_6H_5COOH_{(s)}$ $C_6H_5COO^-$	$C_6H_5COO^- + H^+$ $\parallel$ $C_6H_5COOH_{(s)}$	$C_6H_5COOH_{(s)} + OH^-$ $\parallel$ $C_6H_5COO^- + H_2O$

In the following quantitative discussion of buffers, only those based upon the use of soluble weak acids and bases are considered.

Quantitative Considerations.—The method of calculating the pH of a buffer was described in the section on the titration of weak acids and weak bases. Thus the pH of a solution containing acetic acid and acetate ion in concentrations at least ten times greater than the concentrations of hydrogen and hydroxyl ions is obtained by direct substitution in the equation:

$$p\text{H} = \text{p}K_a - \log \frac{[\text{HAc}]}{[\text{Ac}^-]}$$

This equation applies regardless of how the solution containing acetic acid and acetate ion is prepared—whether by mixing acetic acid and an acetate, acetic acid and a strong base, or an acetate and a strong acid.

Neglecting the distinction between activity and concentration, the pH of a solution depends only upon the ratio of the concentration of non-ionized acetic acid to that of acetate ion. Thus, a solution that is 0.001 M in acetic acid and acetate ion will have the same pH as one that is 1 M

in these substances. However, the practical value of these solutions to act as buffers is not the same because they differ markedly in their capacity to maintain an essentially constant pH. This quality of a buffer is usually described by saying that the smaller the change in the concentration of hydrogen and hydroxyl ions produced by the addition of a given amount of hydrogen or hydroxyl ion the greater the *buffer capacity* of the system. The following calculations illustrate the effect of concentration on the buffer capacity of an acetic acid-acetate ion buffer. For convenience, we have made the calculations in terms of pH rather than concentration of hydrogen ion.

If we add 5 ml of 0.1 M OH$^-$ to 100 ml of a solution that is 0.1 M in HAc, and 0.1 M in Ac$^-$, the resultant change in pH can be estimated as follows:

100 ml solution	10.0 meq HAc	10.0 meq Ac$^-$
+		
5 ml 0.1 M OH$^-$	$-$ 0.5 meq HAc	$+$ 0.5 meq Ac$^-$
Final solution	9.5 meq HAc	10.5 meq Ac$^-$

Original pH = $4.74 - \log \dfrac{10.0}{10.0} = 4.74$

Final pH = $4.74 - \log \dfrac{9.5}{10.5} = 4.78$

Change in pH = $+0.04$

If in place of the OH$^-$ solution, we had used 5 ml 0.1 M H$^+$, the change could be estimated as follows:

100 ml solution	10.0 meq HAc	10.0 meq Ac$^-$
+		
5 ml 0.1 M H$^+$	$+$ 0.5 meq HAc	$-$ 0.5 meq Ac$^-$
Final solution	10.5 meq HAc	9.5 meq Ac$^-$

Final pH = $4.74 - \log \dfrac{10.5}{9.5} = 4.70$

Change in pH = -0.04

If these calculations are repeated, substituting 1 and 0.01 M solutions of the buffer, the resultant pH differences are as follows:

Concentration Used	1 M	0.1 M	0.01 M
pH change (H$^+$ added)......	0.00	−0.04	−0.48
pH change (OH$^-$ added).....	0.00	0.04	0.48

The difference in behavior of the above solutions is due to their different buffer capacities. A study of the above calculations shows that the buffer capacity depends upon the number of milliequivalents of acetic acid and acetate ions present.

The effect of decreasing the concentration of either the acetic acid or the acetate is shown in Figure 10-3. The methods of calculation described in connection with Table 10-3 have been used to estimate the pH, pOH, pHAc and PAc$^-$ during the titration of 50 ml 0.1 M HAc with a 0.1 N strong base.

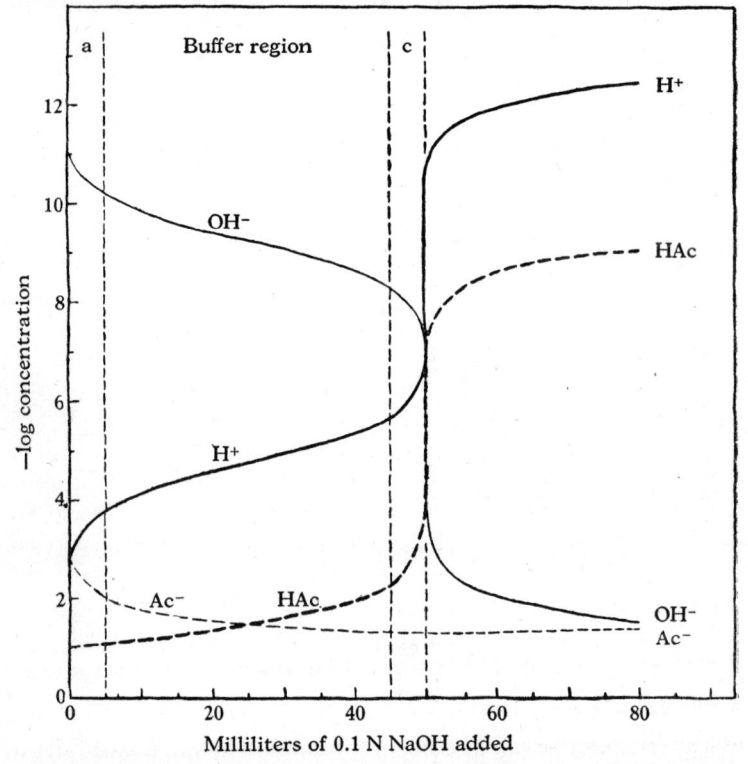

FIG. 10-3. The negative of the logarithms of the concentrations of the various reacting species during the titration of 50 ml of 0.1 N HAc with 0.1 N NaOH.

From Figure 10-3, it is evident that the minimum change in pH per ml of added base is found when the concentrations of the acetic acid and the acetate are equal. Near the beginning of the titration, in region a, the buffer capacity becomes very small due to the fact that the acetate concentration is very small. In this region, the order of magnitude of the acetate-ion concentration can be changed by the addition of a small amount of strong acid or base. Just prior to the equivalence-point in region c, the buffer capacity again becomes very small because the acetic acid concentration is very small. Here the order of magnitude of the acetic-acid concentration can be changed by the addition of a small amount of strong acid or base. Figure 10-3 illustrates the general practical principle that a given weak acid or base is of most value as a buffer in the range where pH equals pK $\pm$ 1. Attempts to buffer appreciably outside of this range lead to solutions of quite limited buffer capacity.

The applications of the above principles to a buffer solution consisting of ammonium hydroxide and ammonium ion is left as an exercise.

Buffers based upon solution of dibasic acids will be considered in connection with the following discussion of carbonate titrations.

TITRATIONS AND EQUILIBRIA IN CARBONATE SYSTEMS

As an illustration of the factors involved in the titration and the buffer properties of dibasic acids, the carbonate system will be considered. It is not the most general example that can be chosen because of the special property that carbon dioxide is a gas of limited solubility in water. It has been selected because the system is of great practical importance in biology as well as in chemistry.

The solubility of carbon dioxide in water at 20° C is 0.04 moles per liter when the pressure of the gas is one atmosphere. It is customary to use the term carbonic acid to mean all the dissolved carbon dioxide present in non-ionized form, although it is now known that only a small portion of the dissolved gas is actually present as the species H_2CO_3. This convention is useful and leads to no erroneous conclusions in the following discussion.

Since carbonic acid is a dibasic acid, there are two ionization equilibria to be considered:

$$H_2CO_3 = H^+ + HCO_3^- \qquad K_1 = \frac{[H^+][HCO_3^-]}{[H_2CO_3]}$$

$$pH = pK_1 - \log \frac{[H_2CO_3]}{[HCO_3^-]}$$

$$HCO_3^- = H^+ + CO_3^{--} \qquad K_2 = \frac{[H^+][CO_3^{--}]}{[HCO_3^-]}$$

$$pH = pK_2 - \log \frac{[HCO_3^-]}{[CO_3^{--}]}$$

In addition, of course, the equilibrium between water and its ions must be taken into account. It is tedious and of little practical value to attempt to calculate exact concentrations of the species present in carbonate solutions of various compositions. We shall, therefore, consider the use of approximate methods that are applicable within limited ranges of composition.

Estimation of pH in Carbonic Acid Solutions.—As an example, consider the concentration relationships that exist, and the approximations that can be made in a 0.04 M H_2CO_3 solution. There are three sources of H^+:

$$H_2CO_3 = H^+ + HCO_3^- \qquad K_1 = 4.3 \times 10^{-7}$$
$$HCO_3^- = H^+ + CO_3^{--} \qquad K_2 = 4.7 \times 10^{-11}$$
$$H_2O = H^+ + OH^- \qquad K_w = 1 \times 10^{-14}$$

From the relative values of the dissociation constants, it is evident that the H_2CO_3 is much more dissociated than the other two acids. Furthermore, the hydrogen ions obtained by dissociation of the H_2CO_3 act to decrease the dissociation of HCO_3^- and H_2O. We can, therefore, say that the principal source of H^+ in a carbonic acid solution is the dissociation of H_2CO_3 into H^+ and HCO_3^- and so the following approximations can be made:

$[H^+] \cong [HCO_3^-]$ and $[H_2CO_3] \cong 0.04$ (neglecting dissociation)

$$\frac{[H^+][HCO_3^-]}{[H_2CO_3]} = 4.3 \times 10^{-7} \cong \frac{[H^+]^2}{0.04}$$

$[H^+] \cong 1.3 \times 10^{-4} M$ or $pH \cong 3.9$

The validity of this approximation can be checked by substituting the value found for the $[H^+]$ and $[HCO_3^-]$ in the other equilibrium relationships, as was done in Chapter 5 when the method of successive approximations was used. In this case, the error due to the approximations prove to be negligible. It is suggested that this statement be checked by making the required calculations in order to gain a clearer insight into the nature of the approach used here and throughout the remainder of this section.

Estimation of pH in Carbonic Acid-Bicarbonate Buffers.—Solutions that have been made, or can be duplicated, by mixing carbonic acid and a soluble bicarbonate act as buffers. Such solutions are analogous in their buffering action to the acetic acid-acetate solutions discussed previously. As long as we restrict our consideration to solutions more than $0.001 M$ in H_2CO_3 and HCO_3^-, having $[H_2CO_3]/[HCO_3^-]$ ratios from 0.1 to 10, the solutions are buffered and the pH can readily be estimated from the equation:

$$pH = pK_1 - \log\frac{[H_2CO_3]}{[HCO_3^-]} = 6.4 - \log\frac{[H_2CO_3]}{[HCO_3^-]}$$

Since the mole ratio of carbonic acid to bicarbonate determines the pH in this region, the total volume of solution is not important as we showed in the acetic acid-acetate discussion. Within the limits given, the pH of buffered carbonic acid-bicarbonate mixtures is:

H_2CO_3/HCO_3^-	10	1	0.1
pH	5.4	6.4	7.4

Solutions having carbonic acid-bicarbonate ratios within these limits can be prepared in the following three ways:

1. Mix a solution of carbonic acid with a solution of a bicarbonate or carbonate.
2. Add a strong acid to a soluble carbonate or bicarbonate.
3. Add a strong base to carbonic acid.

Estimation of pH in Bicarbonate-Carbonate Buffers. Solutions that have been made, or can be duplicated, by mixing a solution of a bicarbonate with a solution of a carbonate act as buffers. These solutions are similar to the buffered carbonic acid-bicarbonate solutions described above. Within the corresponding concentration limits and concentration ratios, the pH can be estimated from the equation:

$$pH = pK_2 - \log \frac{[HCO_3^-]}{[CO_3^{--}]} = 10.3 - \log \frac{[HCO_3^-]}{[CO_3^{--}]}$$

Thus within the range of application of this equation the pH of carbonate-bicarbonate mixtures is:

HCO_3^-/CO_3^{--}	10	1	0.1
pH	9.3	10.3	11.3

Solutions having ratios of bicarbonate to carbonate in this range can be prepared in the following three ways:

1. Mix a solution of a carbonate with a solution of a bicarbonate or carbonic acid.
2. Add a strong base to carbonic acid or bicarbonate.
3. Add a strong acid to a soluble carbonate.

Estimation of pH in a Bicarbonate Solution.—If a bicarbonate is dissolved in water, several reactions occur until equilibrium is established among the various species present. The equilibrium is independent of the path by which it was attained. However, it is convenient to consider that the establishment of equilibrium proceeds from the species initially present in large amounts. A knowledge of these concentration relationships can then be used to select the equilibrium expressions that provide the most direct method of calculation. The three reactions involving bicarbonate ion that should be considered are as follows:

1. Bicarbonate ion can dissociate into carbonate and hydrogen ions.
$$HCO_3^- = H^+ + CO_3^{--} \qquad K_2 = 4.7 \times 10^{-11}.$$

2. Bicarbonate ion can acquire a hydrogen ion from another bicarbonate ion.

$$HCO_3^- + HCO_3^- \underset{K_1}{\overset{K_2}{=}} H_2CO_3 + CO_3^{--}$$

$$K = \frac{K_2}{K_1} = 1.1 \times 10^{-4}$$

3. Bicarbonate ion can acquire a hydrogen ion from water.

$$HCO_3^- + H_2O \underset{K_1}{\overset{K_w}{=}} H_2CO_3 + OH^-$$

$$K_h = \frac{K_w}{K_1} = 2.3 \times 10^{-8}$$

The solution, therefore, must contain equal amounts of carbonate ion and carbonic acid from reaction (2) plus some carbonate ion and hydrogen ion from reaction (1) or some carbonic acid and hydroxyl ion from reaction (3). Since K_h is much larger than K_2, reaction (3) must proceed to a much greater extent than reaction (1) and so the concentration relationships are obtained as follows:

$2\,HCO_3^- = H_2CO_3 + CO_3^{--}$ and so equal amounts of H_2CO_3 and CO_3^{--} are obtained from this source.

$HCO_3^- + H_2O = H_2CO_3 + OH^-$ and so an additional amount of H_2CO_3 equal to the OH^- formed is obtained.

Therefore $\qquad [H_2CO_3] = [CO_3^{--}] + [OH^-]$

The [H$_2$CO$_3$] and the [CO$_3^{--}$] can be expressed in terms of the [H$^+$] and the [HCO$_3^-$] in order to use the above relation for a calculation of the pH from a knowledge of the [HCO$_3^-$] in the solution.

$$\frac{[H^+][HCO_3^-]}{[H_2CO_3]} = K_1 \text{ and so } [H_2CO_3] = \frac{[H^+][HCO_3^-]}{K_1}$$

$$\frac{[CO_3^{--}][H^+]}{[HCO_3^-]} = K_2 \text{ and so } [CO_3^{--}] = \frac{[HCO_3^-]K_2}{[H^+]}$$

Substitution of these expressions yields the relation:

$$\frac{[H^+][HCO_3^-]}{K_1} = \frac{[HCO_3^-]K_2}{[H^+]} + [OH^-]$$

In order to convert this equation into one that gives a direct expression for the [H$^+$], we may multiply each term by K$_1$[H$^+$] and divide each term by the [HCO$_3^-$] to obtain the relation:

$$[H^+]^2 = K_1K_2 + \frac{K_1}{[HCO_3^-]}[H^+][OH^-] = K_1K_2 + \frac{K_1 K_w}{[HCO_3^-]}$$

The numerical value of K$_1$K$_2$ is 2.0×10^{-17} and that of K$_1$K$_w$ is 4.3×10^{-21}. Therefore, if the [HCO$_3^-$] is greater than $2 \times 10^{-3}M$, the term K$_1$K$_2$ is more than ten times as large as the term K$_1$K$_w$/[HCO$_3^-$] and so the following approximation may be used:

$$[H^+]^2 \simeq K_1K_2 \quad [H^+] \simeq \sqrt{K_1K_2} \simeq 4.5 \times 10^{-9} M$$
$$p\text{H} \simeq 8.3$$

To a first approximation, the [HCO$_3^-$] is equal to the initial concentration of bicarbonate since K for the reaction: 2HCO$_3^-$ = H$_2$CO$_3$ + CO$_3^{--}$ is 1.1×10^{-4}. The pH of a bicarbonate solution more than $2 \times 10^{-3}M$ will be approximately 8.3 therefore, independent of concentration.

The method of approach used above may be applied to the estimation of pH in solutions of the intermediate salts of all polybasic acids, such as solutions of H$_2$PO$_4^-$ or HPO$_4^{--}$.

Estimation of pH in Carbonate Solutions.—When we start with a solution that has been made, or that can be duplicated, by dissolving a carbonate in water, the first process that occurs is the hydrolysis of CO_3^{--} to form HCO_3^- and OH^-. Additional sources of OH^- are subsequent hydrolysis of the HCO_3^- and the dissociation of water. The most important process is the hydrolysis of the carbonate which represses the secondary sources. The hydrolysis constant can be obtained from K_2 and K_w. An estimation of the pH can be made in the following way:

$$CO_3^{--} + H_2O = HCO_3^- + OH^- \quad K_h = \frac{K_w}{K_2} = 2.1 \times 10^{-4}$$

$$[OH^-] \cong [HCO_3^-]$$

$[CO_3^{--}] \cong$ concentration of added carbonate. If we take a 0.05 M Na_2CO_3 solution as an example, the pH is estimated as follows:

$$\frac{[HCO_3^-][OH^-]}{[CO_3^{--}]} = K_h = 2.1 \times 10^{-4} \cong \frac{[OH^-]^2}{0.05}$$

$$[OH^-] \cong 3.2 \times 10^{-3} \quad pOH \cong 2.5 \quad pH \cong 11.5.$$

The Titration of Carbonic Acid or Carbonate Ion.—By using the approximations outlined, we can calculate a titration curve corresponding to the addition of a strong base to carbonic acid and a titration curve corresponding to the addition of a strong acid to a carbonate solution. For ease of comparison with the other titration curves, consider the titration of 50 ml of 0.1 N H_2CO_3 with 0.1 N NaOH and the titration of 50 ml of 0.1 N Na_2CO_3 with 0.1 N HCl. A 0.1 N H_2CO_3 solution can be prepared by increasing the presence of CO_2 above one atmosphere. During the course of these titrations, the analytical composition of the solutions can be described as follows:

ml NaOH   0 ⟶ 25 ⟶ 50 ⟶

Solution contains H_2CO_3 $\begin{cases} H_2CO_3 \\ HCO_3^- \end{cases}$ HCO_3^- $\begin{cases} HCO_3^- \\ CO_3^{--} \end{cases}$ CO_3^{--} $\begin{cases} CO_3^{--} \\ OH^- \end{cases}$

                    Buffer   Buffer

ml HCl ←———— 50 ←———————— 25 ←———————— 0
Solution H_2CO_3 ⎫   ⎧H_2CO_3⎫   ⎧HCO_3^-⎫
contains H^+ ⎭H_2CO_3⎨HCO_3^-⎬HCO_3^-⎨CO_3^{--}⎬CO_3^{--}
                         ⎩ Buffer ⎭   ⎩ Buffer ⎭

The calculation of the pH after the addition of 0, 2.5, 12.5, 22.5, 25, 27.5, 37.5, 47.5, 50 and 50.5 ml of 0.1 N HCl to 50 ml of 0.1 N Na$_2$CO$_3$, and after the addition of corresponding amounts of 0.1 N NaOH to 50 ml of 0.1 N H$_2$CO$_3$, will be left as an exercise. The calculated titration curves are shown in Figure 10-4 and the pH values found there may be used to check your calculations.

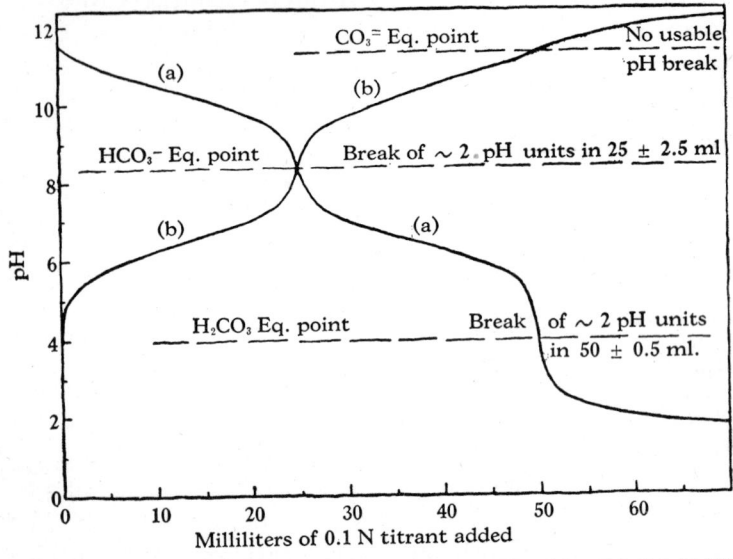

Fig. 10-4. The titration of (a) 50 ml of 0.1 N Na$_2$CO$_3$ with 0.1 N HCl, and of (b) 50 ml of 0.1 N H$_2$CO$_3$ with 0.1 N NaOH.

Factors of general importance that should be noted in Figure 10-4 are:

1. The buffer regions that exist in carbonic acid-bicarbonate solutions and in bicarbonate-carbonate solutions.

2. The negligible buffer capacity of a bicarbonate solution.

3. The high pH of a carbonate solution due to extensive hydrolysis.

4. The large initial pH increase in the carbonic acid titration curve.

Figure 10-4 should be referred to throughout the following discussion of practical methods of titration.

Use of the Bicarbonate Equivalence-Point.—The two titrations that depend upon the use of the bicarbonate equivalence-point are:

$$H_2CO_3 + OH^- = HCO_3^- + H_2O$$
$$CO_3^{--} + H^+ = HCO_3^-$$

The first may be used to determine carbonic acid alone or in the presence of bicarbonate, and the second may be used to determine carbonate alone or in the presence of bicarbonate. A difficulty with these titrations arises because there is a change of only about one pH unit per 2.5 ml of added base or acid at the bicarbonate equivalence-point (pH 8.3) when 0.1 N solutions are employed. An indicator of suitable pK, such as phenolphthalein or thymol blue, therefore, shows only a gradual change in color and the resultant end-point is uncertain to the extent of a few percent. The precision can be improved by the use of a reference bicarbonate solution. The over-all composition of the reference solution is made to correspond as nearly as possible with the expected composition of the unknown solution at the equivalence-point. Equal amounts of the indicator are added to the reference and to the unknown, and the end-point is reached when the colors of the two solutions match. A *mixed indicator* consisting of thymol blue and cresol red can also be used, to improve the precision of the end-point. The mixed indicator serves to provide a reproducible color change close to the required pH of 8.3. A precision of 1-2 parts per thousand cannot be obtained with color indicators at the bicarbonate equivalence-point.

Use of the Carbonate Equivalence-Point

The two titrations that depend upon the use of the carbonate equivalence-point are:

$$H_2CO_3 + 2\ OH^- = CO_3^{--} + 2\ H_2O$$
$$HCO_3^- + OH^- = CO_3^{--} + H_2O$$

The first can be used to determine carbonic acid alone and the second can be used to determine bicarbonate alone or in the presence of carbonate. The total acidity of a mixture of carbonic acid and bicarbonate is of course obtained by titration with base to the carbonate end-point. These titrations are impossible according to Figure 10-4 because the change in pH per ml of added base at the equivalence-point is too small to be clearly detected. The difficulty is due to the extensive hydrolysis of carbonate ion and it can be removed by precipitating the carbonate ion from solution. This is usually done by adding a solution of barium ion or by titrating with barium hydroxide instead of some other strong base. In practice, an excess of standard barium hydroxide or a standard base plus barium ion is added, and the total amount of base is measured. The excess base is then determined by titration with a standard acid using phenolphthalein as an indicator. In this way, the amount of standard base required for the reaction is determined by difference.

Use of the Carbonic Acid Equivalence-Point

The two titrations that depend upon the use of the carbonic acid equivalence-point are:

$$CO_3^{--} + 2\ H^+ = H_2CO_3$$
$$HCO_3^- + H^+ = H_2CO_3$$

The total alkalinity of a solution containing carbonate and bicarbonate can be determined from the amount of acid used to obtain this equivalence-point. The first reaction can be used to determine carbonate alone and the second reaction can be used to determine bicarbonate alone or in the presence of carbonic acid. According to Figure 10-4, there is a change of about one pH unit per ml of added acid at the carbonic acid equivalence-point (pH = 4). An indicator of suitable pK, such as methyl orange, therefore, shows a distinct color change close to the equivalence-point and a reasonably precise end-point can be obtained. In practice, an end-point precise to 1-2 parts per thousand is attained by boiling the solution close to the equivalence-point in order to remove the carbon dioxide. When this is done, the carbonic acid concentration at the equivalence-point is very small and a much more definite end-point is obtained.

A method for the standardization of an acid with sodium carbonate and a method for the determination of bicarbonate and carbonate in a mixture are presented in the last two sections of the chapter.

Titration of Weak Acid Anions with Strong Acids

The preceding titrations of carbonate and bicarbonate with a strong acid illustrate a general method of determining anions of many weak acids. Another example of this type is the titration of $Na_2B_4O_7 \cdot 10H_2O$ by strong acids. This reaction is of particular interest because of the use of $Na_2B_4O_7 \cdot 10H_2O$ as a primary standard. Tetraborate ion hydrolyzes in water according to the following reaction:

$$B_4O_7^{--} + 5H_2O = 2H_3BO_3 + 2H_2BO_3^-$$

Since the ionization constant for the first dissociation of boric acid is about 6×10^{-10}, the addition of a strong acid causes the following reaction to occur:

$$H_2BO_3^- + H^+ = H_3BO_3$$

From the following considerations, it can be seen that a satisfactory change in the pH of the solution at the equivalence-point is obtained. Assume that some solid $Na_2B_4O_7 \cdot 10H_2O$ has been weighed and dissolved in 50 ml of water and that 50 ml of 0.1 N HCl are required for its titration. One mole of boric acid is produced for each equivalent of acid added and, in addition, a similar amount of boric acid is furnished by the hydrolysis of $Na_2B_4O_7 \cdot 10H_2O$. Therefore, since the volume at the equivalence-point is twice the volume of the acid used, the final concentration of boric acid is equal to the initial concentration of the hydrochloric acid. The pH can be estimated as follows:

$$[\text{H}^+] \simeq [\text{H}_2\text{BO}_3^-] \qquad [\text{H}_3\text{BO}_3] \simeq 0.1\ M$$

$$\frac{[\text{H}^+]^2}{0.1} \simeq 6 \times 10^{-10} \qquad [\text{H}^+] \simeq 8 \times 10^{-6} \qquad p\text{H} \simeq 5.1$$

The addition of 0.1 ml of acid, an excess of two parts per thousand, yields the following hydrogen ion concentration:

$$[\text{H}^+] = \frac{0.1}{100} \times 0.1 = 10^{-4} \qquad p\text{H} = 4.0$$

Such a pH change insures a reasonably sharp end-point with an indicator such as methyl red (see Table 10-1).

The minimum concentration, C_0, of anion that can be satisfactorily titrated with a strong acid likewise having a concentration, C_0, is related to the ionization constant of the weak acid. This is shown as follows (see also p. 166):

$$\text{Reaction: } \text{H}^+ + \text{A}^- = \text{HA} \qquad K_a = \frac{[\text{H}^+][\text{A}^-]}{[\text{HA}]}$$

At equivalence-point: $[\text{H}^+] \simeq [\text{A}^-] \qquad [\text{HA}] \simeq \dfrac{C_0}{2}$

$$[\text{H}^+]^2 = K_a \frac{C_0}{2} \qquad K_a = [\text{H}^+]^2 \cdot \frac{2}{C_0}$$

If 50 ml of acid are needed in the titration, a satisfactory end-point requires that the pH change by about one unit on the further addition of 0.1 ml if a precision of two parts per thousand is necessary. At this point:

$$[\text{H}^+] = \frac{0.1}{100} \times C_0 = C_0 \times 10^{-3}\ M$$

The maximum dissociation constants that will conform to the above requirements are calculated for several concentrations of strong acid in the table below.

C_0 N	pH − 0.1 Ml Excess C_0 N Acid	pH at Equivalence-Point	Max. K_a Approx.
0.1	4	5	2×10^{-9}
0.01	5	6	2×10^{-10}
0.001	6	7	2×10^{-11}

Titrations in Phosphate Systems

The principles and methods of calculation employed in the previous sections may readily be extended to polybasic acids. Their application to the phosphate systems is outlined in this section. Phosphoric acid has three dissociation equilibria:

$$H_3PO_4 = H^+ + H_2PO_4^- \qquad K_1 = 7 \times 10^{-3}$$
$$H_2PO_4^- = H^+ + HPO_4^{--} \qquad K_2 = 7 \times 10^{-8}$$
$$HPO_4^{--} = H^+ + PO_4^{---} \qquad K_3 = 5 \times 10^{-13}$$

The essential composition of a solution during the addition of a strong base to phosphoric acid or of a strong acid to phosphate ion is shown schematically as follows:

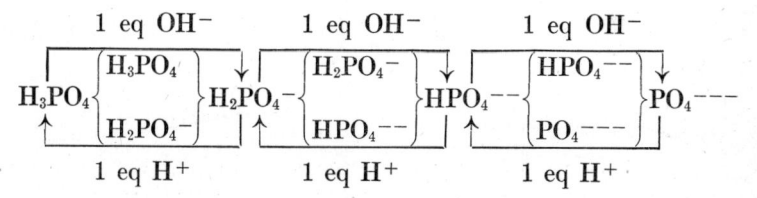

$$\underset{1 \text{ eq } H^+}{\overset{1 \text{ eq } OH^-}{H_3PO_4 \left\{ \begin{matrix} H_3PO_4 \\ H_2PO_4^- \end{matrix} \right.}} \underset{1 \text{ eq } H^+}{\overset{1 \text{ eq } OH^-}{\left\{ \begin{matrix} H_2PO_4^- \\ HPO_4^{--} \end{matrix} \right\}}} \underset{1 \text{ eq } H^+}{\overset{1 \text{ eq } OH^-}{\left\{ \begin{matrix} HPO_4^{--} \\ PO_4^{---} \end{matrix} \right\}}} PO_4^{---}$$

The corresponding curves for the various possible titrations are given in Figure 10-5.

From this figure, it can be seen that the following titrations are feasible:

$$H_3PO_4 + 2OH^- = HPO_4^{--}$$
$$H_2PO_4^- + OH^- = HPO_4^{--} \quad \text{Indicator—}$$
$$PO_4^{---} + H^+ = HPO_4^{--} \quad \text{Phenolphthalein}$$

$$H_3PO_4 + OH^- = H_2PO_4^-$$
$$PO_4^{---} + 2H^+ = H_2PO_4^- \quad \text{Indicators—Methyl Red or}$$
$$HPO_4^{--} + H^+ = H_2PO_4^- \qquad \text{Bromcresol Green}$$

On the other hand, the following titrations cannot be satisfactorily performed except under special conditions:

$$HPO_4^- + OH^- = PO_4^{---} \text{ (Also } H_3PO_4 + 3OH^- \text{ and}$$
$$H_2PO_4^- + 2OH^-)$$

$$H_2PO_4^- + H^+ = H_3PO_4 \text{ (Also } PO_4^{---} + 3H^+ \text{ and}$$
$$HPO_4^- + 2H^+)$$

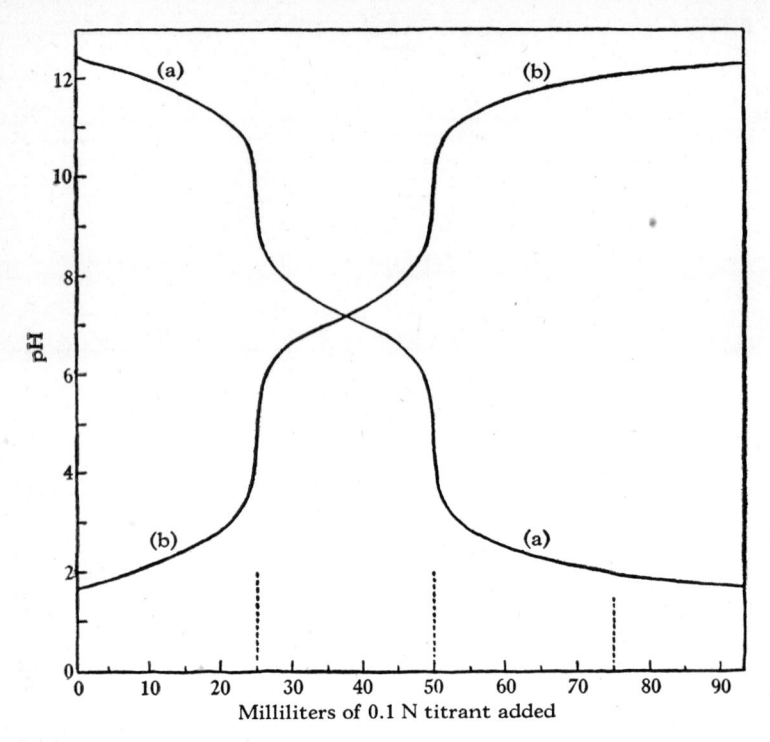

FIG. 10-5. The titration of (a) 25 ml of 0.1 M Na$_3$PO$_4$ with 0.1 N HCl, and of (b) 25 ml of 0.1 M H$_3$PO$_4$ with 0.1 N NaOH.

Some Practical Considerations in Acid-Base Titrations

Primary Standards.—In practice, it is necessary to have reliable primary standards available. Over the course of time, many such standards have been developed, each one having certain advantages and disadvantages. In the determinations that follow, we shall describe the use of potassium acid phthalate as a standard acid and sodium carbonate as a standard base. These two substances are generally available and frequently used primary standards, although they are not necessarily the most desirable under all circumstances. Discussions of the preparation and use of other primary standard acids and bases may be found in the literature.

Preparation and Storage of Strong Bases.—There are

ACIDIMETRY AND ALKALIMETRY 189

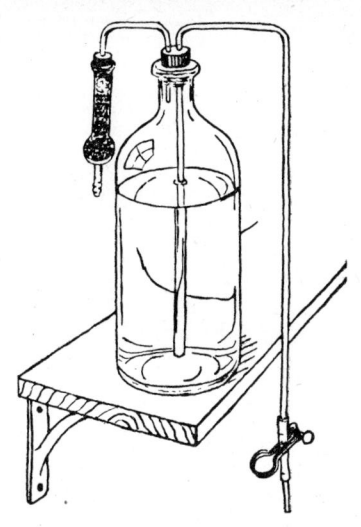

FIG. 10-6. The sodium hydroxide storage bottle is fitted with a drying tube containing soda lime to prevent entrance of CO_2. The tube has a plug of cotton or glass wool to hold the soda lime in place and to filter the air. The bottle illustrated is equipped with a simple siphon delivery system.

no important problems connected with the preparation and storage of solutions of the common strong acids having approximate concentrations ranging from 0.001 to 1 M, but there are two general problems in connection with the use of the common strong bases. One difficulty is due to the fact that bases react with glass to dissolve silica with a corresponding decrease in the hydroxyl-ion concentration. This action is reasonably slow and is of little general importance in the storage of bases for short periods of time if the concentration is 0.1 M or less. When more concentrated bases are stored or when dilute bases must be kept for long periods, glass containers must be coated with an inert material such as paraffin. Sometimes bottles made of inert plastics are used.

The major difficulty is due to the presence of carbon dioxide in the air which dissolves in basic solution and reacts with hydroxyl ions until, as a limit, essentially a bicarbonate solution is obtained. The nature of the difficulties that arise from this source is discussed in the subsequent standardization of a sodium hydroxide solution. We will restrict our consideration to the preparation and storage of sodium hydroxide which is the most frequently used strong base. Sodium hydroxide that is sufficiently free from carbonate can conveniently be obtained by preparing a saturated solution of the hydrated solid in a waxed or otherwise base-resistant vessel. Sodium carbonate is moderately insoluble in this solution and settles slowly over a period of days. A suitable, small portion of the clear, concentrated solution is decanted or pipetted and diluted with carbon dioxide free water to obtain a base solution of the desired approximate concentration. If the solution is used immediately for a few determinations, stoppering the storage bottle to minimize access of air provides sufficient protection. If longer storage is required or if many determinations are to be performed, the solution should be protected from entrance of carbon dioxide by an arrangement such as shown in Figure 10-6.

Standardization of 0.1 N NaOH with $KHC_8H_4O_4$

In this determination, approximately 0.1 N carbonate-free NaOH is standardized against pure potassium acid phthalate, $KHC_8H_4O_4$. An approximately 0.1 N HCl solution is titrated with the base before standardization to establish familiarity with the techniques and with the endpoint.

Discussion.—Acid phthalate ion is a weak acid comparable in strength to acetic acid.

$$HC_8H_4O_4^- = H^+ + C_8H_4O_4^{--} \quad K_2 = 5 \times 10^{-6}$$

In the standardization of 50 ml of 0.1 N base, the concentration of phthalate ion will be approximately 0.05 M at the equivalence-point if the final volume of the solution is 100 ml. We can therefore calculate the hydroxyl ion concentration as shown below:

$$C_8H_4O_4^{--} + H_2O = HC_8H_4O_4^- + OH^- \quad K_h = \frac{[HC_8H_4O_4^-][OH^-]}{[C_8H_4O_4^{--}]}$$

(with K_w over the forward reaction and K_2 under the reverse)

$$[OH^-] \cong [HC_8H_4O_4^-] \qquad [C_8H_4O_4^{--}] \cong 0.05\ M$$

$$\frac{[OH^-]^2}{0.05} \cong \frac{10^{-14}}{5 \times 10^{-6}} \cong 2 \times 10^{-9}$$

$$[OH^-] \cong 10^{-5}\ M \qquad pH \cong 9$$

In the presence of 0.1 ml of excess base:

$$[OH^-] = \frac{0.1}{100} \times 0.1 = 10^{-4}\ M \qquad pH = 10$$

Since the pH changes from 9 to 10, phenolphthalein is a suitable indicator for the titration.

At the end-point, carbon dioxide dissolves from the air and removes the excess hydroxyl ion to form carbonate. As more carbon dioxide dissolves, bicarbonate and finally a mixture of bicarbonate and carbonic acid is produced. As this occurs, the pH decreases and the pink phenolphthalein color disappears. The rate of fading of the color due to this cause depends primarily upon the rate of agitation of the solution. This may cause serious errors unless the effect is recognized.

Carbon dioxide in the water used to dissolve the acid and carbon dioxide that may be present in the base as carbonate also cause difficulty. The concentration of carbon dioxide in water is small, but it can dissolve in the base until the latter has been essentially converted to a bicarbonate solution. To the extent that carbon dioxide has dissolved in either solution, it will be titrated in accordance with the reaction:

$$CO_2 + OH^- = HCO_3^-$$

This follows from the discussion associated with Figure 10-4 in which it was shown that the principal carbonate species present at pH 9 (the end-point in this case) is bicarbonate. In addition to the stoichiometric error shown above, the presence of appreciable amounts of bicarbonate at the end-point decreases the rate of change of pH (see Figure 10-4) and makes the end-point less precise as well as less accurate.

Errors due to carbon dioxide are minimized in the following ways. The distilled water is boiled just before dissolving potassium acid phthalate in it. Carbonate-free base is protected from carbon dioxide of the air by (a) opening the stock bottle as seldom as possible, (b) adding the base from the buret to the acid in the flask, (c) covering the buret with a test tube, and (d) discarding any base that has been in the buret for more than one hour. In general, it is poor technique to place the bulk of a base in a flask for titration, since this favors contact with air and absorption of carbon dioxide.

General Preparations.—Thermal decomposition of potassium acid phthalate is a possible source of error. The pure phthalate and the unknown phthalate samples should not be dried above 110-120° C. It is desirable to limit the drying time to one or two hours. Store the dried standard and the unknown sample in the desiccator until needed.

Obtain or prepare one liter of carbonate-free 0.1 N NaOH in a clean screw-cap or rubber-stoppered bottle and one liter of 0.1 N HCl in another bottle which may be glass stoppered. Shake both solutions *thoroughly* before using them.

Clean two 50 ml burets and store them as described in Chapter 8. Clean three or four 250 ml Erlenmeyer flasks.

Heat 200-300 ml of distilled water to the boiling point.

Permanence of the End-Point.—Rinse a 50 ml buret with the base, fill it and bring the liquid level within the graduated portion as described in Chapter 8. Similarly, fill the other buret with the acid solution.

Add about 50 ml of the boiling water to an Erlenmeyer, cool to about room temperature, add 5-6 drops of phenolphthalein solution, and enough base (one drop or less) to obtain a faint but discernible pink in the solution. Swirl the solution and note the time required for the color to disappear. Repeat this experiment with different rates of swirling until an estimate of the time of fading can be obtained.

Titration of the HCl with the Base.—Carefully read and record the levels of the burets that contain the acid and the base. Deliver 35-40 ml of the acid into an Erlenmeyer and add 5-6 drops of the phenolphthalein indicator. Using the technique described in Chapter 8, add the base rapidly while swirling the acid solution until the pink color begins to persist where the base enters the solution. Add the base in small portions while swirling the solution and decrease these portions to drop-by-drop addition as the degree of color persistence shows that the end-point is near. Continue drop-wise addition until *one drop or less* is *observed* to change the whole solution from colorless to a faint but discernible pink. The end-point is not the intensity of pink obtained; it is the *observation* that one drop or less changes the solution from colorless to pink. The pink should remain as long as found in the previous tests of the persistence of the end-point in air. If the end-point was overstepped, or if it appears uncertain, add another ml or so of the acid and again obtain an end-point.

Record the final buret readings and calculate the ratio of the acid and base volumes to the precision that is experimentally justified. Repeat determinations of the volume ratios until a precision of 1-2 parts per thousand is obtained or until you are satisfied with your technique and ability to recognize the end-point.

Standardization of the Base.—Accurately weigh a 0.7-0.9 g portion of the pure dry phthalate into each of three Erlenmeyers. Add about 50 ml of boiling distilled water to a weighed sample, swirl the flask until the solid dissolves, and cool to about room temperature. Add 5-6 drops of phenolphthalein solution and titrate with the base as described above. Calculate the normality of the base from the volume used and the weight of the potassium acid phthalate taken. The three determinations should agree within an average deviation of 1-2 parts per thousand.

Determination of Acid Phthalate in an Unknown.— Various unknown acids may be determined with a standardized base. If an impure acid phthalate sample is used, accurately weigh 0.8-1.0 g portions of the dry unknown into Erlenmeyers and proceed exactly as in the above standardization.

Save the acid and base solution until your experimental results have been checked so that their normalities may be redetermined if circumstances require.

Standardization of 0.1 N HCl with Sodium Carbonate (Optional)

Dry pure sodium carbonate at 270-300° C for an hour and store in a desiccator until needed. Accurately weigh 0.2-0.25 g portions into each of three Erlenmeyers.

Dissolve a carbonate sample in about 25 ml of water and add 2 drops of phenolphthalein. Titrate with the acid until the solution becomes colorless, at which point the solution consists of bicarbonate and a small amount of carbonic acid. The total volume of acid required will, therefore, be slightly less than twice the amount needed to decolorize the phenolphthalein and this fact can be used in carrying out the rest of the titration efficiently. Add 4-5 drops of bromcresol green and titrate until the indicator begins to show a green color. Boil the solution gently for a few minutes until the color changes to a violet or blue violet and then cool it to about room temperature. Titrate until there is an observed color change to green. Normalities of the acid calculated from the three determinations should agree with an average precision of 2-3 parts per thousand. Compare the normality obtained in this case with that obtained in the previous comparison with the standardized base.

Determination of Carbonate and Bicarbonate in a Mixture (Optional)

Accurately weigh and transfer about 2 g of the unknown to a 250 ml volumetric flask. Dilute to volume and mix the solution thoroughly. Pour 3-4 ml of this solution into each of three clean test tubes. Add a drop of phenolphthalein to one test tube, a drop of thymolphthalein to another, and a drop of alizarine to the third. From the observed colors and the data in Table 10-2, estimate the pH of the solution. From this value of the pH, estimate the ratio of carbonate to bicarbonate (see p. 178).

Determination of Total Alkalinity.—Pipet two 25 ml portions of the sample into separate Erlenmeyers and titrate with the acid as in the preceding standardization against sodium carbonate to determine the total alkalinity. Calculate the total milliequivalents of carbonate and bicarbonate present. The results should agree within 5 parts per thousand.

Determination of the Bicarbonate Present.—Pipet 25 ml portions of the sample into each of two Erlenmeyers. Add 25 ml of 0.1 N standardized base followed by 10 ml of 10% $BaCl_2$, and 4-5 drops of phenolphthalein solution. Titrate with acid until the solution just becomes colorless. To obtain the most precise results, run a blank determination by titrating a solution made by adding 25 ml of the base and 10 ml of the barium chloride to 25 ml of water. The difference between the amount of acid used to titrate this solution to the phenolphthalein end-point and the amount used to titrate the unknown is a measure of the amount of bicarbonate in the unknown. From this result, calculate the milliequivalents of bicarbonate in the unknown solution. Duplicate results should agree within 5-10 parts per thousand unless the amount of bicarbonate is very small. Combine this result with the determination of total alkalinity and calculate the percentages of sodium carbonate and sodium bicarbonate in the sample.

Problems

1. Calculate the molarity of a hydrochloric acid solution that requires 47.35 ml of the acid to neutralize 1.2755 g of pure sodium carbonate. Methyl orange is used as the indicator. *Ans.* **0.5082** M

2. An approximately 0.1 M HCl solution is standardized by precipitating the chloride as silver chloride. An excess of silver nitrate is added to 50.00 ml of the acid; the precipitate is filtered, dried and weighed. The weight of silver chloride is 0.7675 g. Calculate the molarity of the hydrochloric acid. *Ans.* **0.1071** M

3. Calculate the molarity of a hydrochloric acid solution

that requires 45.55 ml of the acid to neutralize 1.1575 g of pure $Na_2B_4O_7 \cdot 10H_2O$. Methyl red is used as the indicator.

Ans. **0.1332** *M*

4. Mercuric oxide can be used as a primary standard base. Iodide is added in order to bring the solid into solution through the formation of a complex mercuric iodide in accordance with the following reaction:

$$HgO + 4I^- + H_2O = HgI_4^{--} + 2OH^-$$

Calculate the molarity of a hydrochloric acid solution that requires 42.75 ml of the acid to quantitatively react with the hydroxyl ion formed by 0.5000 g of mercuric oxide according to the above reaction. Methyl red is the indicator used.

Ans. **0.1080** *M*

5. Distillation of a hydrochloric acid solution yields a fraction of reproducible composition. The composition of this fraction is known as a function of the pressure employed. This fraction is commonly referred to as constant boiling hydrochloric acid and is sometimes used as a primary standard. A 1.5000 g sample of constant boiling hydrochloric acid solution that is 20.24% HCl by weight is titrated with 44.50 ml of a sodium hydroxide solution. Calculate the molarity of the base.

Ans. **0.1871** *M*

6. Calculate the molarity of a sodium hydroxide solution that requires 35.65 ml of the base to neutralize 0.9436 g of pure potassium acid phthalate. Phenolphthalein is the indicator used.

Ans. **0.1296** *M*

7. To 0.2056 g of pure calcium carbonate, 50.00 ml of a hydrochloric acid solution is added. The solution is boiled to expel carbon dioxide, cooled and titrated to a methyl red end-point with 10.53 ml of 0.05360 *M* NaOH. Calculate the molarity of the hydrochloric acid solution.

Ans. **0.07092** *M*

8. A 25.00 ml sample of a phosphoric acid solution is titrated to the phenolphthalein end-point with 36.92 ml of

0.1034 M NaOH. Calculate the molarity of the phosphoric acid. *Ans.* **0.0764 M**

9. To a 25.00 ml sample of Na_3PO_4 solution, 50.00 ml of 0.1000 M HCl are added. Since the phosphate solution may contain carbonate, the solution is boiled to expel carbon dioxide. After cooling, it is titrated to a methyl red endpoint with 15.65 ml of 0.0200 M NaOH. Calculate the molarity of the sodium phosphate solution. *Ans.* **0.0937 M**

10. An excess of barium chloride is added to 25.00 ml of a sulfuric acid solution. The precipitate is transferred and dried as described in the gravimetric sulfate determination. The weight of barium sulfate obtained is 0.4736 g. Calculate the normality of the sulfuric acid solution. *Ans.* **0.1613 N**

11. Calculate the hydrogen ion concentration and pH in each of the following solutions and state what color would be imparted to the solution by (1) a drop of methyl red, (2) a drop of bromphenol blue.
    a. 0.05 M HCl   c. 0.1 M HAc
    b. 1.2×10^{-4} M HCl   d. 0.002 M NaOH

12. Calculate the hydroxyl ion concentration and pH in each of the following solutions and state what color would be imparted to the solution by (1) a drop of phenolphthalein, (2) a drop of bromthymol blue.
    a. 1.3 M NaOH   c. 1.8×10^{-5} M NaOH
    b. Freshly boiled water   d. 2×10^{-3} M HAc

13. What indicators would you choose to produce a color change over each of the following ranges of hydrogen ion concentration?
    a. 1×10^{-3} to 5×10^{-6}
    b. 8×10^{-9} to 1×10^{-10}
    c. 7×10^{-5} to 6×10^{-7}

14. Calculate the $[H^+]$, pH, pOH and $[OH^-]$ when 50.0 ml of 0.100 M HCl are added to each of the following solutions:
    a. 100.0 ml of 0.100 M NaOH

b. 30.0 ml of 0.200 M NaOH
c. 35.0 ml of 0.108 M Ca(OH)$_2$

15. A solution of 0.25 M NaOH is used to titrate 50.0 ml of 0.25 M HX. $K_{HX} = 3.6 \times 10^{-7}$. For the addition of each of the following volumes of sodium hydroxide, estimate the pH of the resultant solution: (a) 0.0 ml, (b) 1.0 ml, (c) 25.0 ml, (d) 45.0 ml, (e) 49.9 ml, (f) 50.1 ml, (g) 55.0 ml. Construct a titration curve from the above data.
Ans. (a) 3.52, (b) 4.75

16. Calculate the pH of the following solutions:
   a. 1 M NaAc; $K_{HAc} = 1.8 \times 10^{-5}$
   b. 1 M NaHSO$_4$; $K_{HSO_4^-} = 10^{-2}$
   c. 0.1 M NH$_4$Cl; $K_{NH_4OH} = 1.8 \times 10^{-5}$
   Ans. (a) 9.37, (b) 1.02, (c) 5.13

17. What is the final pH of the following solutions?
   a. 50 ml of 0.1 M NaOH are added to 100 ml of 0.1 M HCl.
   b. 50 ml of 1 M NaOH are added to 50 ml of 2 M HAc.
   c. 50 ml of 1 M NaAc are added to 50 ml of 1 M HAc.
   d. 200 ml of 1 M NaAc are added to 50 ml of 1 M HAc.
   Ans. (a) 0.48, (b) 4.74, (c) 4.74, (d) 5.34

18. What weight of NaAc·3H$_2$O should be added to one liter of 0.1 M HAc to prepare (a) a buffer solution having a pH of 4.74? (b) a buffer solution having a pH of 5.24?
Ans. (a) 13.6 g, (b) 43.0 g

19. What weight of NH$_4$Cl should be added to 500 ml of 0.1 M NH$_4$OH to prepare (a) a buffer solution having a pH of 9.26? (b) a buffer solution having a pH of 10.00?
Ans. (a) 2.68 g, (b) 0.486 g

20. A buffer solution is prepared by adding 0.68 g of NaAc·3H$_2$O to 100 ml of 0.1 M HAc. What additional weight of NaAc·3H$_2$O must be added to the solution to increase the pH by 1 unit?
Ans. 6.1 g

21. A solution containing a mixture of acetic acid and

sodium acetate has a pH of 3.74. What is the mole ratio of these two substances?   *Ans.* $HAc/Ac^- = 10$

22. A solution containing a mixture of ammonium hydroxide and ammonium chloride has a pH of 10.50. What is the mole ratio of these two substances?
Ans. $NH_4OH/NH_4^+ = 17.4$

23. a. What weight of $NaAc \cdot 3H_2O$ must be added to 100 ml of 0.0100 M HAc to obtain a pH of 6.74?
   b. If 1.00 ml of 1 M NaOH is added to the buffer prepared in (a), what is the pH of the resultant solution?
   c. If 1.00 ml of 1 M HCl is added to the buffer prepared in (a), what is the pH of the resultant solution?
Ans. **(a) 13.6 g, (b) 9.37, (c) 6.43**

24. A buffer is prepared by making a solution 1 M in acetic acid and 1 M in sodium acetate. What must be the volume of the buffer solution so that the addition of 100 ml of 0.1 M HCl will change the pH by only 1 unit? *Ans.* **12 ml**

25. A buffer is prepared by making a solution 0.01 M in acetic acid and 0.01 M in sodium acetate. What must be the volume of the buffer solution so that the addition of 100 ml of 0.1 M HCl will change the pH by only 1 unit?
Ans. 1.2×10^3 **ml**

26. A buffer is prepared by making a solution 1 M in ammonium hydroxide and 1 M in ammonium chloride. What should be the volume of the buffer solution so that the addition of 100 ml of 0.01 M NaOH will not change the pH by more than 0.1 pH unit?   *Ans.* **9 ml**

27. The pH of 0.1 M HA is 1.70. Calculate K_{HA}.
Ans. 5×10^{-3}

28. To 100 ml of a solution that is 0.2 M in A^- and 0.1 M in HA, 100 ml of 0.1 M HCl are added. The resultant pH is 4.50. Calculate K_{HA}.   *Ans.* 1.6×10^{-5}

29. To 100 ml of a solution that is 0.1 M in BOH and 0.2 M in BCl, 100 ml of 0.05 M HCl are added. The resultant

pH is 10.60 Calculate K_{BOH}. *Ans.* 2×10^{-3}

30. a. To one liter of water x moles of NaA and $(0.1-x)$ moles of HA are added. The resultant pH = 6. $K_{HA} = 1 \times 10^{-5}$. Calculate the number of moles of NaA per liter of solution.

b. To one liter of water, y moles of NaB and $(0.1-y)$ moles of HB are added. The resultant pH = 6. $K_{HB} = 1 \times 10^{-6}$. Calculate the number of moles of NaB per liter of solution.

c. To each of the above solutions, 100 ml of 0.1 M NaOH are added. Which solution will have the greater buffer capacity? *Ans.* (a) **0.91 moles;** (b) **0.05 moles,** (c) **NaB-HB**

31. What weight of sodium bicarbonate must be added to 500 ml of 0.1 M Na_2CO_3 to obtain a buffer solution having a pH of 11.0? *Ans.* **0.600 g**

32. What weight of $NaH_2PO_4 \cdot H_2O$ must be added to one liter of 0.1 M H_3PO_4 to obtain a pH of 3.0? *Ans.* **96.6 g**

33. What weight of $NaH_2PO_4 \cdot H_2O$ must be added to 500 ml of 0.1 M Na_2HPO_4 to obtain a pH of 8.5? *Ans.* **0.308 g**

34. What weight of $Na_3PO_4 \cdot 12H_2O$ must be added to one liter of 0.5 M Na_2HPO_4 to obtain a pH of 12.0? *Ans.* **95.0 g**

35. What volume of 1 M NaOH must be added to one liter of 0.1 M H_3PO_4 to obtain a pH of 11.4? *Ans.* **211 ml**

36. What volume of 1 M HCl must be added to 500 ml of 0.1 M Na_3PO_4 to obtain a pH of 2.5? *Ans.* **135 ml**

37. Solid sodium hydroxide containing 2.0% by weight of sodium carbonate is dissolved in water. The solution is standardized with potassium acid phthalate using phenolphthalein as the indicator and found to be 0.1000 M. What will be the error if this sodium hydroxide solution is used to titrate an approximately 0.1 M HCl solution?

a. With phenolphthalein as the indicator (assume pH at end-point is 8.5)?

b. With methyl red as the indicator and a titration at

room temperature (assume pH at end-point is 5.2)?

c. With methyl red when carbon dioxide is removed by boiling the solution just before the end-point?

Ans. (a) **none;** (b) ***N* HCl low by 0.7%;**
(c) ***N* HCl low by 0.8%**

38. Assuming that the equilibrium concentration of carbonic acid in aqueous solution in the laboratory is 5×10^{-5} M explain the following:

a. At the phenolphthalein end-point in the standardization of 0.5 M NaOH with potassium acid phthalate, the pink color of the indicator slowly fades.

b. At the phenolphthalein end-point in the titration of sodium carbonate with 0.5 M HCl, the intensity of the pink color slowly increases.

Chapter 11

PRINCIPLES AND APPLICATIONS OF OXIDATION-REDUCTION REACTIONS

Oxidation-reduction reactions are characterized by an exchange of electrons between the reacting substances. Such reactions are widely applicable in inorganic analysis for determinations and for purposes of separation. The factors that need to be considered in the analytical application of these reactions are discussed in connection with a limited number of specific determinations.

Half-Reactions

In previous discussions, a net reaction frequently has been written as the sum or difference of two reactions. Thus, the net reaction for the neutralization of acetic acid with a strong base has been obtained as the sum of the two contributory reactions:

$$HAc = H^+ + Ac^-$$
$$\underline{OH^- + H^+ = H_2O}$$
$$OH^- + HAc = H_2O + Ac^-$$

In the neutralization of carbonic acid with a strong base, the net reaction also can be obtained as the sum of two reactions, provided a factor is used to make the number of hydrogen ions involved in the reactions equal. Thus:

$$H_2CO_3 = 2H^+ + CO_3^{--}$$
$$\underline{2(H^+ + OH^- = H_2O)}$$
$$H_2CO_3 + 2OH^- = H_2O + CO_3^{--}$$

The significant process in the above acid-base reactions is the exchange of protons between the reacting substances. This fact has been used by Brönsted and others to generalize the definition of acidic and basic substances. According to this concept, an acid is a substance that provides protons and a base is a substance that combines with protons in a reaction. In every acid-base reaction, there is a transfer of protons from an acid to a base to produce a new acid and a new base as shown in the following example:

$$\underset{\text{Base}_2}{\underset{\text{Acid}_1}{\text{HAc}} + \text{OH}^-} = \underset{\text{Acid}_2}{\underset{\text{Base}_1}{\text{Ac}^-} + \text{H}_2\text{O}}$$

Viewed in this way, there is a close general analogy between acid-base reactions, based upon the exchange of protons, and oxidation-reduction reactions based upon the exchange of electrons. Thus a *reducing agent* is a substance that provides electrons and an *oxidizing agent* is one that combines with electrons in a reaction. Every oxidation-reduction reaction involves the transfer of electrons from a reductant to an oxidant to form a new reductant and a new oxidant. It is particularly useful to separate oxidation-reduction reactions into two reactions in a manner similar to that shown in the preceding acid-base examples. In this case, each partial reaction describes the loss or gain of electrons by the reacting substances. One of the half-reactions describes the loss of electrons by a given *reductant* to form a related *oxidant* and the other half reaction describes a gain of electrons by a given oxidant to form a related reductant. It is customary to call these partial reactions *half-reactions*. For example, in the reaction between ferric ion and chromous ion, the relation between the net reaction and the half-reactions is as follows:

Net reaction: $\text{Fe}^{+++} + \text{Cr}^{++} = \text{Fe}^{++} + \text{Cr}^{+++}$

Half-reactions: $\text{Fe}^{+++} + e^- = \text{Fe}^{++}$

$$\underline{\text{Cr}^{++} = \text{Cr}^{+++} + e^-}$$
Sum: $\text{Fe}^{+++} + \text{Cr}^{++} = \text{Fe}^{++} + \text{Cr}^{+++}$

To the extent that this reaction proceeds from left to right, there is a reduction of ferric ion and an oxidation of chromous ion.

As a further example, consider the reaction between ferric and iodide ions:

Net reaction: $2Fe^{+++} + 2I^- = 2Fe^{++} + I_2$

Half-Reactions: $Fe^{+++} + e^- = Fe^{++}$ (multiply by two to obtain sum)

Sum: $$\frac{2I^- = I_2 + 2e-}{2Fe^{+++} + 2I^- = 2Fe^{++} + I_2}$$

This reaction is typical of all oxidation-reduction reactions in that two oxidizing agents (Fe^{+++} and I_2) and two reducing agents (Fe^{++} and I^-) are involved. The equilibrium established depends upon the relative tendency of the ferrous and iodide ions to lose electrons, and upon the relative tendency of ferric ion and iodine to gain electrons. It is easier to remove electrons from iodide ion to form iodine than it is to remove electrons from ferrous ion to form ferric ion. Therefore, this reaction does proceed until most of the iodide is oxidized to iodine with a corresponding reduction of ferric to ferrous ion.

In order to systematize oxidation-reduction reactions, it is convenient to tabulate the various possible half-reactions. Such a tabulation can be used qualitatively to write balanced net reactions for a large number of possible oxidation-reduction reactions. At this point, only a method for writing the half-reactions is of concern.

Writing Half-Reactions.—To write a half-reaction, it is necessary to know the formulas of the oxidized and the reduced species and whether the reaction occurs in acid or basic solution. The number of electrons involved is determined by the condition that the total electrical charge must be constant. In addition, the following principles apply to half-reactions in aqueous solution:

1. Water and its ions may be required to obtain a material balance.

2. Reactions in acid solutions must not contain OH^- as a reacting species.

OXIDATION-REDUCTION REACTIONS

3. Reactions in basic solutions must not contain H^+ as a reacting species.

These principles are illustrated by the following examples in which the convention of writing the electrons on the right-hand side of the equation has been adopted.

1. Write the half-reaction for the conversion of Sn^{++} to Sn^{++++} in acid solution.

$Sn^{++} = Sn^{++++} + ne^-$

A charge balance requires that n be 2

$Sn^{++} = Sn^{++++} + 2e^-$

$2 = 4 - 2 = 2$

2. Write the half-reaction for the conversion of Cr^{+++} to $Cr_2O_7^{--}$ in acid solution.

The oxygen atoms required in this conversion must be supplied by water molecules and, since the reaction occurs in acid solution, the resultant product must be H^+. Therefore, qualitatively:

$$Cr^{+++} + H_2O \rightarrow Cr_2O_7^{--} + H^+ + e^-$$

A material balance requires that:

$$2Cr^{+++} + 7H_2O = Cr_2O_7^{--} + 14H^+ + ne^-$$

A charge balance requires that n be 6.

$$2Cr^{+++} + 7H_2O = Cr_2O_7^{--} + 14H^+ + 6e^-$$
$$+6 \qquad\qquad = -2 \quad +14 \quad -6 \;=\; +6$$

3. Write the half-reaction for the conversion of I^- to IO^- in basic solution. The oxygen atoms required must be supplied either by water molecules or by hydroxide ion, and since the reaction is to occur in basic solution, H^+ must not appear in the equation. Using OH^+ as the source of oxygen atoms the qualitative relationship is:

$$I^- + OH^- \rightarrow IO^- + H_2O + e^-$$

A material balance requires:

$$I^- + 2OH^- = IO^- + H_2O + ne^-$$

A charge balance requires that $n = 2$

$$I^- + 2OH^- = IO^- + H_2O + 2e^-$$

If the equation for the reaction had been balanced using water as the source of oxygen atoms, we would have obtained the equation:

$$I^- + H_2O = IO^- + 2H^+ + 2e^-$$

This equation violates the requirement that H^+ should not appear in basic solution.

Use in Balancing Equations.—In balancing oxidation-reduction reactions, two general methods are available. One method depends upon the assignment of *oxidation numbers* to each element appearing in the reaction. This method will be discussed later. The other method depends upon the separation of the reaction into its component half-reactions. The guiding principle employed is that the number of electrons lost by the reducing agent must be equal to the number accepted by the oxidizing agent as illustrated below.

1. Complete and balance the equation for the reaction between Sn^{++} and Fe^{+++} in acid solution. To complete the equation, it is necessary to know the fact that Sn^{++} is oxidized to Sn^{++++} and that Fe^{+++} is reduced to Fe^{++}.

Half-Reactions	Electron Balance
$Sn^{++} = Sn^{++++} + 2e^-$	$Sn^{++} = Sn^{++++} + 2e^-$
$Fe^{++} = Fe^{+++} + e^-$	$2(Fe^{+++} + e^- = Fe^{++})$
	$Sn^{++} + 2Fe^{+++} = Sn^{++++} + 2Fe^{++}$

If the reaction has been balanced, the total electrical charge must be constant and this condition should be used to check the equation.

Charge on left $= 2 + (2 \times 3) = 8 =$ Charge on right $= (2 \times 2) + 4$

2. Complete and balance the equation for the reaction between Fe^{++} and $Cr_2O_7^{--}$ in acid solution. It is necessary to know that the products are Fe^{+++} and Cr^{+++}.

Half-Reactions
$$Fe^{++} = Fe^{+++} + e^-$$
$$2Cr^{+++} + 7H_2O = Cr_2O_7^{--} + 14H^+ + 6e^-$$

Electron Balance
$$6(Fe^{++} = Fe^{+++} + e^-)$$
$$\underline{6e^- + 14H^+ + Cr_2O_7^{--} = 2Cr^{+++} + 7H_2O}$$
$$6Fe^{++} + 14H^+ + Cr_2O_7^{--} = 6Fe^{+++} + 2Cr^{+++} + 7H_2O$$

Charge on left $= (6 \times 2) + 14 - 2 = 24$
Charge on right $= (6 \times 3) + (2 \times 3) = 24$

The use of water molecules and hydrogen ions to provide a material balance in this reaction follows from the discussion of the preceding section.

3. Complete and balance the equation for the reaction between I^- and MnO_4^- in acid solution.

Knowing that I_2 and Mn^{++} are products, we may proceed as follows:

Half-Reactions
$$2I^- = I_{2(s)} + 2e^-$$
$$Mn^{++} + 4H_2O = MnO_4^- + 8H^+ + 5e^-$$

Electron Balance
$$5(2I^- = I_{2(s)} + 2e^-)$$
$$\underline{2(5e^- + MnO_4^- + 8H^+ = Mn^{++} + 4H_2O)}$$
$$10I^- + 2MnO_4^- + 16H^+ = 5I_{2(s)} + 2Mn^{++} + 8H_2O$$

Charge on left $= -10 - 2 + 16 = 4$
Charge on right $= (2 \times 2) = 4$

Oxidation Numbers

Assignment of Oxidation Numbers.—By oxidation number, we mean the electrical charge formally assigned to an atom as it exists in a molecule or ion. A half-reaction states the total number of electrons that are involved in a given oxidation without implying that these electrons are lost by any particular atom in a molecule or a polyatomic ion. The concept of oxidation numbers identifies the electron

change with specific atoms. Oxidation numbers usually are assigned arbitrarily according to the following conventions:
   1. The oxidation number of a monatomic ion is equal to the charge on the ion.
   2. The oxidation number of the atoms in an elementary substance is zero.
   3. Except in peroxides, molecular oxygen, ozone, and fluorine oxides, oxygen is assigned an oxidation number of -2.
   4. Except in hydrides and molecular hydrogen, hydrogen is assigned an oxidation number of $+1$.
   5. The sum of the oxidation numbers of the constituent atoms equals the charge on the polyatomic ion or molecule.

The application of these conventions is illustrated by the following examples:

Species	Method		Oxidation Number
Fe^{++}	$---$		$+2$
Fe_2O_3	Total charge	0	
	Charge on 3 O atoms	-6	
	Charge on 2 Fe atoms	$+6$	$+3$ for Fe
$HCrO_4^-$	Total charge	-1	
	Charge on 4 O atoms	-8	
	Charge on 1 H atom	$+1$	
	Charge on 1 Cr atom	$+6$	$+6$ for Cr
Fe_3O_4	Total charge	0	
	Charge on 4 O atoms	-8	
	Charge on 3 Fe atoms	$+8$	$+8/3$ for Fe

The fractional value in the last example results from the assumption that all the Fe atoms in the molecule are equivalent.

Use in Balancing Equations.—The change in oxidation number of an atom is equal to the number of electrons lost or gained in its oxidation or reduction. The following examples illustrate the use of this fact in balancing equations:

OXIDATION-REDUCTION REACTIONS

1. Complete and balance the equation for the reaction, $Fe^{+++} + Sn^{++}$ in acid solution.

The products are known to be Fe^{++} and Sn^{++++} and so:

$$\overset{\text{Ox. No. 3}}{\underset{Fe^{+++}}{\overline{\text{Gain of } 1e^-/\text{mole of Fe}}}} + \underset{\underset{\text{Ox. No. 2}}{\overline{Sn^{++}}}}{\overset{\text{Ox. No. 2}}{Sn^{++}}} = Fe^{++} + \underset{\text{Ox. No. 4}}{Sn^{++++}}$$

Loss of $2e^-/$mole of Sn

The changes in oxidation number show that 2 moles of Fe^{+++} are required to react with 1 mole of Sn^{++} and so the balanced equation is:

$$2Fe^{+++} + Sn^{++} = 2Fe^{++} + Sn^{++++}$$

2. Complete and balance the equation for the reaction between Fe^{++} and MnO_4^- in acid solution. The products are known to be Fe^{+++} and Mn^{++}. H_2O and H^+ must be used to provide a material balance.

$$\overset{\text{Ox. No. 2}}{\underset{Fe^{++}}{\overline{\text{Loss of } 1e^-/\text{mole Fe}}}} + \underset{\underset{\text{Ox. No. 7}}{\overline{MnO_4^-}}}{MnO_4^-} + H^+ = \underset{\text{Ox. No. 3}}{Fe^{+++}} + H_2O + \underset{\text{Ox. No. 2}}{Mn^{++}}$$

Gain of $5e^-/$mole MnO_4^-

In order to obtain an electron balance, 5 moles of Fe^{++} must react with 1 mole of MnO_4^-. The imposition of a material balance leads to the final equation:

Electron Balance:
$$5Fe^{++} + MnO_4^- + ?H^+ = 5Fe^{+++} + Mn^{++} + ?H_2O$$

Material Balance:
$$5Fe^{++} + MnO_4^- + 8H^+ = 5Fe^{+++} + Mn^{++} + 4H_2O$$

Charge Balance:
$$+10 \quad -1 \quad +8 = +15 \quad +2$$

3. Complete and balance the equation for the reaction between Sn^{++} and $Cr_2O_7^{--}$ in acid solution. The products

are Sn^{++++} and Cr^{+++}. H_2O and H^+ must be used for a material balance.

Loss of $2e^-$/mole Sn

Ox. | No. 2   Ox. | No. 4
$Sn^{++} + Cr_2O_7^{--} + H^+ = Sn^{++++} + H_2O + Cr^{+++}$
2Cr | 12   2Cr | 6

Gain of $6e^-$/mole of $Cr_2O_7^{--}$

Electron Balance:
$3Sn^{++} + Cr_2O_7^{--} + ?H^+ = 3Sn^{++++} + 2Cr^{+++} + ?H_2O$

Material Balance:
$3Sn^{++} + Cr_2O_7^{--} + 14H^+ = 3Sn^{++++} + 2Cr^{+++} + 7H_2O$

Charge Balance:
   +6   −2   +14 = +12   +6 .

In the last example, the change in oxidation number of two Cr atoms was considered because the reacting species, $Cr_2O_7^{--}$, contains two Cr atoms per "mole". It is the change in oxidation number per mole of reactant that is directly involved in balancing an equation.

For the reactions encountered most frequently, oxidation numbers provide a useful method for balancing equations. In more complex reactions, whenever the assignment of an oxidation number seems uncertain, the use of half-reactions is more satisfactory and less liable to lead to error.

Equivalent Weight and Stoichiometry

Equivalent Weights.—The concept of equivalent weights is particularly useful in the stoichiometry of oxidation-reduction reactions. The equivalent weight of an oxidizing agent is the weight that accepts one mole of electrons. The equivalent weight of a reducing agent is the weight that loses one mole of electrons. From these definitions, it follows that one equivalent weight of any oxidizing agent is just sufficient to react with exactly one equivalent weight of any reducing agent. The equivalent weight of a substance can be most simply obtained by writing the half-reaction that describes the oxidation or reduction process involved. Sometimes a given substance may be converted to more than one product, depending upon the conditions employed. In such cases, there will be more than one equivalent weight for the substance, depending upon the particular reaction involved. These points are illustrated in the following examples:

1. What is the equivalent weight of tin in any reaction that involves the conversion of Sn^{++} to Sn^{++++}?

$$Sn^{++} = Sn^{++++} + 2e^-.$$

One mole of Sn^{++} loses 2 moles of electrons.
One-half mole of Sn^{++} loses one mole of electrons.
Therefore, one eq wt Sn^{++} = At wt $Sn/2$

No matter what substance is used to oxidize Sn^{++} to Sn^{++++} or to reduce Sn^{++++} to Sn^{++}, this weight of tin is just sufficient to react with one equivalent of the substance used.

2. What is the equivalent weight of $KMnO_4$ in any reaction in which there is a conversion to Mn^{++}?

$$Mn^{++} + 4H_2O = MnO_4^- + 8H^+ + 5e^-$$

One mole $KMnO_4$ produces one mole MnO_4^-.
One mole MnO_4^- accepts 5 moles of electrons.
One-fifth mole MnO_4^- can accept one mole of electrons.
Therefore $1/5$ MW $KMnO_4$ = one eq wt.

3. What is the equivalent weight of $KMnO_4$ in any reaction in which MnO_2 is the product?

$$MnO_{2(s)} + 2H_2O = MnO_4^- + 4H^+ + 3e^-.$$

One mole $KMnO_4$ produces one mole MnO_4^-.
One mole MnO_4^- accepts 3 moles of electrons.
One-third mole MnO_4^- can accept one mole electrons.
Therefore, 1 eq wt $KMnO_4$ = $1/3$ MW $KMnO_4$.

Whenever more than one reaction of a given substance is possible as in the last two examples, it is necessary to know or to determine which of the half-reactions is involved in the process under consideration before the equivalent weight can be calculated.

Stoichiometry.—The equivalence-point in any oxidation-reduction titration is reached when the same number of equivalents of oxidant and reductant have been added to the solution. Stoichiometric calculations may then be made in terms of normality as the unit of concentration in the manner previously presented in the discussion of acid-base reactions. The following examples illustrate the basic types of calculations that are encountered:

1. What is the normality of a solution made by dissolving 0.830 g of pure KI to make 100 ml of solution:
(a) In any reaction in which I_2 is the product,

$$2I^- = I_{2(s)} + 2e^-.$$

One mole KI produces one mole I^- which can lose 1 mole of electrons.
One eq of I^- is therefore 1 mole.
No. eq KI = 0.830/eq wt = 0.830/166.0

$$N \text{ KI} = \frac{\text{No. eq}}{\text{No. liters}} = \frac{0.830/166.0}{100/1000} = \frac{1000 \times 0.830}{100 \times 166.0}.$$

(b) In any reaction in which IO_3^- is the product,

$$I^- + 3H_2O = IO_3^- + 6H^+ + 6e^-.$$

One mole KI produces one mole I^- which can lose 6 moles of electrons.
One eq KI is therefore 1/6 MW KI = 27.67 g
No. eq KI = 0.830/eq wt = 0.830/27.67.

$$N \text{ KI} = \frac{\text{No. eq}}{\text{No. liters}} = \frac{0.830/27.67}{100/1000} = \frac{1000 \times 0.830}{100 \times 27.67}.$$

2. A solution containing Sn^{++} and no other reducing agent requires 50.00 ml of 0.05 N $KMnO_4$ for titration under conditions where Sn^{++++} and Mn^{++} are formed. Calculate the weight of tin in the sample.

No. eq Sn^{++} in sample = No. eq MnO_4^- used in titration.
meq MnO_4^- = meq Sn^{++} = $N \times$ ml = 0.05 $\times$ 50.00

$$Sn^{++} = Sn^{++++} + 2e^- \quad \text{meq wt} = \frac{\text{At wt Sn}}{1000 \times 2} = \frac{118.7}{2000}$$

$$\text{Wt Sn} = \text{No. meq} \times \text{meq wt} = 0.05 \times 50.00 \times \frac{118.7}{2000}$$

3. Under conditions where CO_2 and Mn^{++} are the products, 0.500 g of pure $Na_2C_2O_4$ requires 47.86 ml of $KMnO_4$ for titration. Calculate the normality of the $KMnO_4$.

One mole of $Na_2C_2O_4$ forms one mole of $H_2C_2O_4$ which can lose two moles of electrons according to the reaction:

$$H_2C_2O_4 = 2CO_2 + 2H^+ + 2e^-$$

and so eq wt $Na_2C_2O_4 = \dfrac{MW}{2} = 67.0$ g.

No. eq $Na_2C_2O_4$ in 0.500 g $= 0.500/\text{eq wt} = 0.500/67.0$
No. eq MnO_4^- in 48.86 ml $= $ eq $Na_2C_2O_4 = 0.500/67.0$

$$N \; KMnO_4 = \frac{\text{No. eq}}{\text{No. liters}} = \frac{0.500/67.0}{47.86/1000} = \frac{1000 \times 0.500}{47.86 \times 67.0}$$

Oxidation Potentials

The tendency for a given half-reaction to occur can be quantitatively expressed in terms of the *oxidation potential* of the half-reaction. These oxidation potentials can then be used to calculate the equilibrium constant of a resultant reaction. The oxidation potentials of a large number of half-reactions have been systematically tabulated. The use of these data to make the calculations required in analytical applications is considered in this section.

Electrolytic cells.—Although the methods of measuring oxidation potentials are not of direct concern, it is desirable to consider briefly cells in which such measurements can be made.

If a piece of zinc is placed in a solution that contains cupric sulfate, the following reaction occurs at the surface of the zinc:

$$Zn_{(s)} + Cu^{++} = Zn^{++} + Cu_{(s)}$$

This reaction can also occur in an electrolytic cell of the type shown schematically in Figure 11-1.

At the zinc *electrode*, zinc goes into solution leaving two electrons on the metal for each zinc ion formed. The electrons travel through the connecting wire to the copper electrode. At the copper surface, cupric ions are converted to metallic copper by the transfer of two electrons from the electrode to each cupric ion that is converted to metal. A complete electrical circuit must be available for the cell to operate. The *salt bridge* shown in Figure 11-1 serves as the needed connection. Sodium and sulfate ions move in the salt bridge to conduct the required current between the two electrodes. The accumulation of zinc ions at the anode is balanced by the sum of the zinc ions that leave, and the sulfate ions that enter, this half cell. Similarly, the depletion of cupric ions at the cathode is balanced by the sum of the sodium ions that enter, and the sulfate ions that leave, this half cell. The reactions that occur at the electrodes are called *electrode reactions;* they are identical with the half-reactions previously discussed. The electrode where reduction occurs is called the *cathode* ($Cu^{++} + 2e^- = Cu_{(s)}$) and the electrode where oxidation occurs is called the *anode* ($Zn_{(s)} = Zn^{++} + 2e^-$).

The significant fact is that the operation of the cell corresponds to the occurrence of a specified chemical reaction. The net reaction is the sum of the two electrode reactions:

Anode reaction.......	$Zn_{(s)} = Zn^{++} + 2e^-$
Cathode reaction.....	$2e^- + Cu^{++} = Cu_{(s)}$
Net reaction.........	$Zn_{(s)} + Cu^{++} = Zn^{++} + Cu_{(s)}$

During the operation of the cell, there is a difference of potential, E, between the electrodes that can be experimentally measured by a suitable volt meter. This difference in potential is a measure of the tendency of the reaction to occur. It depends upon the relative concentrations of the reacting substances and upon their nature. The tendency of the half reaction, $Zn_{(s)} = Zn^{++} + 2e^-$, to proceed depends upon the concentrations of zinc and zinc ion. If metallic zinc is dissolved in mercury or otherwise diluted, the tendency of the metal to go into solution is decreased. If the concentration of zinc ion in solution is decreased, the tendency of the reaction to occur is increased. Similarly, the tendency for reduction to occur at the cathode may be increased by increasing the concentration of cupric ion or by decreasing the concentration of copper. The following equation describes the dependence of the potential upon the concentrations of the reacting species:

$$E = E^0 - \frac{2.3RT}{nF} \log \frac{[Cu][Zn^{++}]}{[Zn][Cu^{++}]} =$$

$$E^0 - \frac{0.059}{n} \log \frac{[Cu][Zn^{++}]}{[Zn][Cu^{++}]} \quad \text{at } 25° \text{ C}$$

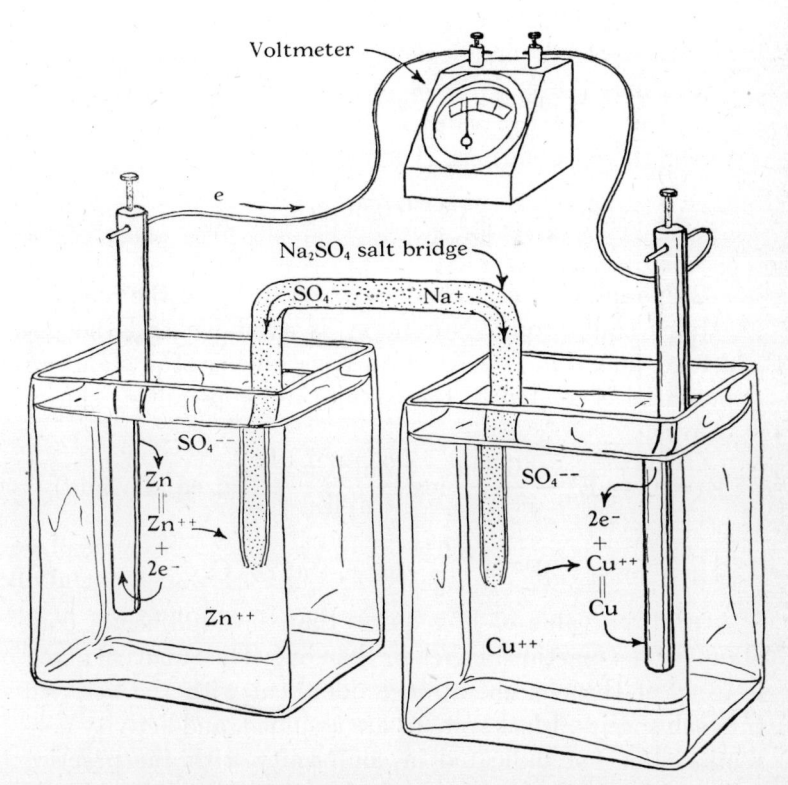

Fig. 11-1. Schematic diagram of an electrolytic cell.

In this equation:
R is the molar gas constant = 1.987 cal/deg/mole
T is the absolute temperature
F is the Faraday, 96,500 coulombs or 23,066 cal
n is the number of moles of electrons specified by either of the half-reactions that comprise the balanced net reaction. In this example n is 2.
E^0 is the *standard oxidation potential* of the reaction.

It is convenient to use the numerical value of 0.059 v for the term $\dfrac{2.3\ RT}{F}$ at 25° C in the subsequent discussion.

The quantity E^0 has the following significance.

1. E^0 is the observed potential when all of the reacting substances are at unit activity. In the example, E^0 is the observed potential when pure zinc and pure copper are used as electrodes in one molar solutions of zinc and copper ions. Since the activity of pure solids is unity by definition, the numerical value of the logarithmic term is zero under these conditions. Therefore,

$$E = E^0 - \frac{0.059}{2} \log 1 = E^0$$

2. No net chemical change can occur when the reaction attains equilibrium. No energy is available and the observed potential is zero. As a consequence, the standard potential is related to the equilibrium constant as shown below:

$$E = 0 = E^0 - \frac{0.059}{2} \log \frac{[Zn][Cu^{++}]}{[Cu][Zn^{++}]} \text{ (at equilibrium)}$$

Therefore, $\quad E^0 = \dfrac{0.059}{2} \log K \quad$ at 25° C.

A positive value of E^0 requires that the equilibrium constant for the reaction be greater than one. The equation given is exact if the concentration is identical with the activity for each species. Ideal systems are assumed, and activity corrections are not indicated in conformity with the practice followed in this text. In practical analytical problems, it is seldom either possible or necessary to make such corrections.

In the preceding example, metals that take part in the chemical reaction are used as electrodes in the cell. Cells that employ reactions of the types, $Cr^{++} = Cr^{+++} + e^-$ or $\frac{1}{2}H_{2(g)} = H^+ + e^-$ require the use of *inert electrodes* because the half-reactions do not directly involve metals. Any metal or other conductor that does not react with the oxidation-reduction couple in a half cell may serve as an inert electrode. In practice, the noble metals, particularly platinum and gold, are often used for this purpose. For example, if a platinum electrode is placed in a solution containing hydrogen ions and hydrogen gas is bubbled through the solution, a half cell is obtained in which the following reaction can occur at the surface of the platinum:

$$\frac{1}{2}H_{2(g)} = H^+ + e^-$$

When the pressure of hydrogen is maintained at one atmosphere and the activity of hydrogen ion is unity (approximately one molar), this half cell is called the *standard hydrogen electrode*.

Standard Oxidation Potentials.—The numerical values assigned to most physical quantities are of relative significance only. The actual values depend upon the arbitrary selection of a reference standard such as a standard of mass, of length, of time, etc. Similarly, in establishing a numerical scale for oxidation potentials, the standard hydrogen electrode has been selected arbitrarily as the reference. The oxidation potential of the zinc electrode with reference to the standard hydrogen electrode can be determined in a cell of the type outlined below:

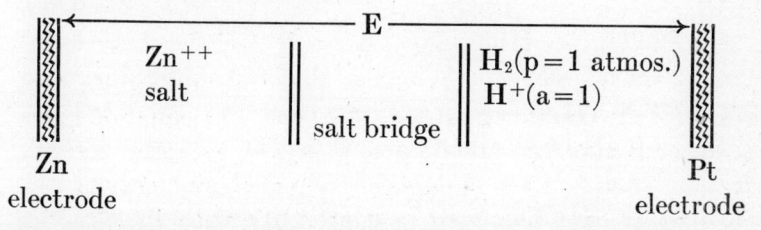

	←——————— E ———————→	
Zn^{++} salt	salt bridge	H$_2$(p=1 atmos.) H$^+$(a=1)
Zn electrode		Pt electrode

The potential observed corresponds to the reaction:

$$Zn_{(s)} + 2H^+ (a=1) = Zn^{++} + H_{2(g)} (p=1 \text{ atmos.})$$

Since the activities of the species $Zn_{(s)}$, H^+ and $H_{2(g)}$ are all unity, the potential of this cell at 25° C is given by the equation:

$$E = E^0 - \frac{0.059}{n} \log \frac{[H^+]^2 [Zn^{++}]}{P_{H2} [Zn]} = E^0 - \frac{0.059}{2} \log [Zn^{++}]$$

The quantity E^0 in this equation includes the potential of the standard hydrogen electrode. This unknown but constant contribution of the reference electrode to a cell is assigned a value of zero. The E^0 in the previous equation is

TABLE 11-1
Some Standard Oxidation Potentials

Reaction	E^0
$Na_{(s)} = Na^- + e^-$	2.712
$Zn_{(s)} = Zn^{++} + 2e^-$	0.762
$Fe_{(s)} = Fe^{++} + 2e^-$	0.440
$Cr^{++} = Cr^{+++} + e^-$	0.41
$Sn_{(s)} = Sn^{++} + 2e^-$	0.136
$Pb_{(s)} = Pb^{++} + 2e^-$	0.126
$H_{2(g)} = 2H^+ + 2e^-$	0.000
$Sn^{++} = Sn^{+4} + 2e^-$	−0.15
$Cu^+ = Cu^{++} + e^-$	−0.167
$Ag_{(s)} + Cl^- = AgCl_{(s)} + e^-$	−0.2222
$2I^- = I_{2(s)} + 2e^-$	−0.5345
$3I^- = I_3^- + 2e^-$	−0.5355
$H_3AsO_3 + H_2O = H_3AsO_4 + 2H^+ + 2e^-$	−0.559
$H_2O_2 = O_{2(g)} + 2H^+ + 2e^-$	−0.682
$Fe^{++} = Fe^{+++} + e^-$	−0.77
$Ag_{(s)} = Ag^+ + e^-$	−0.7995
$CuI_{(s)} = Cu^{++} + I^- + e^-$	−0.877
$2H_2O = O_{2(g)} + 4H^+ + 4e^-$	−1.23
$2Cl^- = Cl_{2(g)} + 2e^-$	−1.358
$2Cr^{+++} + 7H_2O = Cr_2O_7^{--} + 14H + 6e^-$	−1.36
$Mn^{++} + 4H_2O = MnO_4^- + 8H^+ + 5e^-$	−1.52
$Ce^{+3} = Ce^{+4} + e^-$	−1.61
$MnO_{2(s)} + 4H_2O = MnO^-_4 + 4H^+ + 3e^-$	−1.67
$2H_2O = H_2O_2 + 2H^+ + 2e^-$	−1.77

called the standard oxidation potential of the Zn–Zn^{++} couple even though it is really a measure of the oxidation potential corresponding to the complete reaction written above. Cells, similar in principle to the one above, can be employed to determine the standard oxidation potential of many half-reactions with reference to the standard hydrogen electrode. The oxidation potentials of many other half-reactions can be obtained indirectly. Values of the standard oxidation potentials of some half-reactions are given in Table 11-1. Much more extensive tabulations are found in the literature.

It should be noted that the relative values of the potentials listed in Table 11-1 are independent of the value assigned to the reference hydrogen electrode. Thus, if the assigned value is changed from 0 to 0.500, every value in the table is increased by 0.500 v and the relative values remain unchanged. As shown in the following section, it is only the differences in oxidation potentials that are significant.

Calculation of Equilibrium Constants.—There is a close similarity in the use of oxidation potentials to quantitatively correlate oxidation-reduction reactions and the use of dissociation constants to correlate acid-base reactions. This similarity is illustrated by the following example:

Acid-Base Reaction

$$HAc + OH^- = Ac^- + H_2O$$
$$HAc = H^+ + Ac^- \quad pK_1 = 4.74$$
$$H_2O = H^+ + OH^- \quad pK_2 = 14.0$$
$$\overline{pK_{react} = pK_1 - pK_2 = -9.26}$$
$$K_{react} = 10^{9.26}$$

Oxidation-Reduction Reaction

$$2Fe^{+++} + 2I^- = 2Fe^{++} + I_{2(s)}$$
$$2I^- = I_{2(s)} + 2e^- \quad E^0_1 = -0.54 \text{ v}$$
$$2Fe^{++} = 2Fe^{+++} + 2e^- \quad E^0_2 = -0.77 \text{ v}$$
$$\overline{E^0_{react} = \frac{0.059}{2} \log K = E^0_1 - E^0_2 = 0.23 \text{ v}}$$
$$\log K = 7.3 \text{ or } K = 10^{7.3}$$

In this example, it was necessary to multiply the $Fe^{++} = Fe^{+++} + e^-$ half-reaction by a factor of two to obtain a balanced equation. The E^0 value for the reaction $2(Fe^{++} = Fe^{+++} + e^-)$ is identical with the value for the reaction $Fe^{++} = Fe^{+++} + e^-$. In all cases, the E^0 value for a given half-reaction is unchanged when a multiple of the half-reaction is used.

In Chapter 10, the equilibrium constant for the reaction between acetic acid and hydroxyl ion was used to calculate the amounts of the two reactants present at the equivalence-point in the titration. The result, considered in connection with the hydrolysis of acetate ion, served to indicate the feasibility of performing the titration. The equilibrium constant for the reaction between ferric and iodide ions may similarly be used to investigate the feasibility of a direct titration under ordinary conditions. For example, suppose that 50 ml of $0.1\ M\ Fe^{+++}$ is titrated with 50 ml of $0.1\ M\ I^-$. Since solid iodine is formed, the concentrations established at the equivalence-point are:

$$2Fe^{+++} + 2I^- = 2Fe^{++} + I_{2(s)}$$
Conc.   x   x   0.05-x   1

Substitution of these relations in the equilibrium expression yields:

$$\frac{[Fe^{++}]^2\,[I_{2(s)}]}{[I^-]^2\,[Fe^{+++}]^2} = 10^{7.3} = 2 \times 10^7 = \frac{[0.05-x]^2}{[x]^2\,[x]^2}$$

To a first approximation, assume that x is small compared to 0.05. Then:

$$x^4 = 0.625 \times 10^{-10} \text{ or } x = [Fe^{+++}] = 3.3 \times 10^{-3}\ M$$

This is an approximate result since 3.3×10^{-3} is not negligible compared to 0.05 as assumed. Nevertheless, the result is sufficiently valid to indicate that about 10% of the original ferric ion remains at the equivalence-point. This value is obtained by considering that there are $100 \times 3.3 \times 10^{-3}$ mmoles of ferric ion remaining at the equivalence-point compared to the original amount of 50×0.05 mmoles. A direct titration that involves a reaction so far from completion at the equivalence-point is unsatisfactory. Actually, this particular titration can be performed indirectly by adding a large excess of iodide ion to obtain a quantitative reduction of ferric ion.

A detailed calculation of the concentration of the reacting species at the equivalence-point usually is unnecessary since the magnitude of the equilibrium constant is either very large or very small in most cases as shown below.

1. Consider a possible reaction between Sn^{++} and I_3^-

$$Sn^{++} + I_3^- = Sn^{++++} + 3I^-$$

with $E^0_1 = -0.15$ v and $E^0_2 = -0.54$ v

$$E^0_{react} = -0.15 - (-0.54) = +0.39 \text{ v} = \frac{0.059}{n} \log K$$

n, found from either half-reaction, is 2

$$\log K = \frac{2}{0.059} \times 0.39 = 13.2 \text{ or } K = 10^{13.2}$$

Conclusions:

a. Since E^0 is positive, K is greater than unity and the reaction favors the oxidation of Sn^{++} by I_3^-.

b. Since K is very large, the oxidation of Sn^{++} by I_3^- should be quantitatively complete under ordinary analytical conditions.

2. Consider a possible reaction between Fe^{++} and Sn^{++++}.

$$2Fe^{++} + Sn^{++++} = 2Fe^{+++} + Sn^{++}$$

with $E^0_1 = -0.77$ v and $E^0_2 = -0.15$ v

n found from either half reaction is 2

$$E^0_{react} = -0.77 - (-0.15) = -0.62 \text{ v} = \frac{0.059}{2} \log K$$

$$\log K = -21 \quad \text{or} \quad K = 10^{-21}$$

Conclusions:

   a. Since E^0 is negative, K is less than unity and the reaction actually favors the oxidation of Sn^{++} by Fe^{+++} not the oxidation of Fe^{++} by Sn^{++++}.

   b. Since $K = 10^{-21}$ is extremely small, the oxidation of Sn^{++} by Fe^{+++} should be quantitatively complete under ordinary analytical conditions.

3. Consider a possible reaction between H_3AsO_3 and I_3^- in acid solution.

$$\overset{\displaystyle E^0_1 = -0.559}{H_3AsO_3 + H_2O + I_3^- = H_3AsO_4 + 2H^+ + 3I^-}$$
$$\underset{E^0_2 = -0.535}{}$$

n from either half-reaction is 2

$$E^0_{react} = -0.559 - (-0.535) = -0.024 \text{ v} = \frac{0.059}{n} \log K$$
$$\log K = -0.81 \qquad K = 10^{-0.81} = 0.155$$

Conclusions:

   a. Since E^0 is negative, K is less than unity and the reaction favors the oxidation of I^- by H_3AsO_4 in 1 M H^+.

   b. Since K is close to unity, the extent to which the reaction is quantitative in either direction depends upon the set of concentrations that prevail in a given case. Actually, primarily by controlling the hydrogen ion concentration, this reaction can be used quantitatively in either direction.

Titration Curves and End-Point Detection

The equilibrium constant of an oxidation-reduction reaction can be used as the basis for calculation of the concentrations of the reacting species during the course of a titration. Titration curves, obtained in this way, show the largest percentage change in the concentrations of the reactants at the equivalence-point of the titrations. Specific properties of the reacting substances may be used to detect these changes and to provide end-points, as previously discussed in connection with precipitation reactions in Chapter

9. Thus, the end-point in permanganate titrations usually is based upon observation of the characteristic purple color of permanganate ion. Similarly, the formation of red ferric thiocyanate complexes can be employed to obtain an end-point when ferric ion is a titrant.

There also is a general property, the change in oxidation potential of the system, that can be used as a basis for end-point detection. The potential of the system at any point during a titration can be calculated by applying the equations of the preceding section. For example, consider the titration of 50 ml of 0.1 M Fe^{++} with 0.1 M Ce^{++++}. For convenience, we may designate the E^0 of the Fe^{++}–Fe^{+++} couple (-0.77 v.) as E^0_1 and the E^0 of the Ce^{+++}–Ce^{++++} couple (-1.61 v.) as E^0_2.

At any point between the beginning of the titration and the equivalence-point, the ratio $[Fe^{+++}]/[Fe^{++}]$ can be calculated from the amount of Ce^{++++} added. The reaction which is quantitatively complete is:

$$Fe^{++} + Ce^{++++} = Fe^{+++} + Ce^{+++}$$

If x ml of Ce^{++++} is added, the ratio, $[Fe^{+++}]/[Fe^{++}]$ is $x/(50 - x)$. The corresponding potentials can be obtained by substitution of the values of this ratio in the equation:

$$E = E^0_1 - 0.059 \log [Fe^{+++}]/[Fe^{++}]$$

After the equivalence-point has been passed, the ratio $[Ce^{++++}]/[Ce^{+++}]$ can be calculated directly from the volume of ceric solution added. Thus, after the addition of 55 ml of Ce^{++++}, the ratio $[Ce^{++++}]/[Ce^{+++}]$ is 5/50. Substitution of the $[Ce^{++++}]/[Ce^{+++}]$ ratios in the equation.

$$E = -1.61 - 0.059 \log \frac{[Ce^{++++}]}{[Ce^{+++}]}$$

leads directly to the desired potential values.

It is convenient to approach the calculation of the potential at the equivalence-point in the following manner. At the equivalence-point, the concentration relationships are:

Since $[Ce^{+++}] = [Fe^{+++}]$ and $[Ce^{++++}] = [Fe^{++}]$

$$E = E^0_1 - 0.059 \log \frac{[Fe^{+++}]}{[Fe^{++}]}$$

and

$$E = E^0_2 - 0.059 \log \frac{[Ce^{++++}]}{[Ce^{+++}]}$$

the sum $\quad 2E = E^0_1 + E^0_2 - 0.059 \log \dfrac{[Fe^{+++}][Ce^{++++}]}{[Fe^{++}][Ce^{+++}]}$

reduces to $E = \frac{1}{2}(E^0_1 + E^0_2) = -1.19$ v at the eq point, as can be seen by substituting the above concentration relationships into the sum.

The curve in Figure 11-2a has been obtained by the general procedure outlined above. It describes the change in potential during the titration of 50 ml of 0.1 M Fe^{++} with

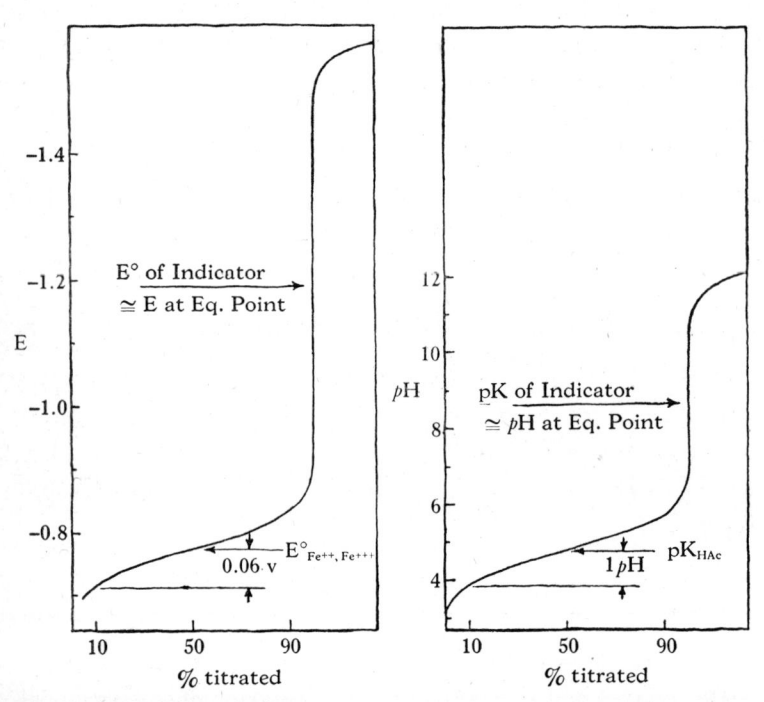

Fig. 11-2 (a). The potential during the titration of 50 ml of 0.1 M Fe^{++} with 0.1 M Ce^{+4}.

Fig. 11-2 (b). The pH during the titration of 50 ml of 0.1 M HAc with 0.1 M strong base.

0.1 M Ce^{++++}. The titration curve of acetic acid with a strong base has been plotted in Figure 11-2b to show the similarity between the change in potential during a simple oxidation-reduction titration and the change in pH during the titration of a weak acid or base. Curves of the type shown in Figure 11-2a underlie the use of *oxidation-reduction indicators*. Potentiometric titrations likewise are based upon curves of this type. In the latter case, a suitable electrode is placed in the titration vessel and a cell is constructed by connecting this electrode with a reference electrode through a salt bridge. Measurement of the potential of this cell during the course of a titration yields a curve of the type shown in Figure 11-2a. The point at which the maximum change in potential per ml of titrant occurs is taken as the end-point. Potentiometric titrations are of considerable practical value in a wide variety of determinations.

Oxidation-Reduction Indicators.—The change in potential at the equivalence-point of a titration may be detected by the addition of a suitable indicator. Such indicators exhibit a change in color corresponding to a change in oxidation state. For example, colorless diphenylbenzidine is oxidized to the colored substance, diphenylbenzidine violet as shown by the reaction:

$$\text{(colorless diphenylbenzidine)} = \text{(violet form)} + 2\,H^+ + 2\,e^-$$

If Ind_r represents the colorless form and Ind_0 represents the violet form, the equilbrium in 1 M H^+ is given by the equation:

$$E = E^0{}_{Ind} - \frac{0.059}{2} \log \frac{[Ind_0]}{[Ind_r]} = E^0{}_{Ind} - \frac{0.059}{2} \log \frac{\text{violet form}}{\text{colorless form}}$$

This equation shows that the potential determines the concentration ratio of the two forms of this indicator. This is closely analogous to the relation between the pH and the concentration ratio of the two forms of an acid-base indicator. The considerations advanced in connection with the proper choice of acid-base indicators in Chapter 10 apply equally well to the selection of oxidation-reduction indicators. The differences in behavior are those of detail and not of general principle. To a first approximation, the E^0 of an oxidation-reduction indicator should correspond to the potential at the equivalence-point as indicated in Figure 11-2a. This, of course, parallels the approximation that the pK of an acid-base indicator should correspond to the pH at the equivalence-point of a titration.

Other factors, particularly reaction rates, are involved in the practical application of oxidation-reduction indicators. Some of these factors are considered later in connection with the use of diphenylamine sulfonate as an indicator in the titration of ferrous ion with potassium dichromate.

Frequently Used Reagents

A relatively small number of reagents serve to provide methods for determining a very large number of inorganic species. There is a set of reagents directly employed as titrants, and a set of primary standards. The titrants in common use are:

For Oxidations: MnO_4^-, $Cr_2O_7^{--}$, Ce^{++++}, I_3^-, IO_3^-, BrO_3^-, and OCl^-

For Reductions: $S_2O_3^{--}$ (through I^-), Fe^{++}, Cr^{++}, and Ti^{+++}.

The usual set of primary standards consists of:

For Oxidizing Agents: As_2O_3, KI, $Na_2C_2O_4$, and
$$Fe(NH_4)_2(SO_4)_2 \cdot 6H_2O$$
For Reducing Agents: $K_2Cr_2O_7$, KIO_3 and $KBrO_3$

None of the above reagents is ideally suited to general use. Each reagent has its own advantages and disadvantages in connection with specific applications.

A set of reagents that can be used to establish required states of oxidation prior to titration also is required. It must be possible to destroy or to remove an excess of any reagent that is employed for this purpose; otherwise, the excess reagent may interfere with the subsequent titration. Thus, in the usual volumetric determination of iron, it is necessary to add a reagent that converts all of the iron to the ferrous state prior to a titration with permanganate or dichromate. Since part of the iron ordinarily is in the ferric state, a reducing agent is needed for this purpose. If an excess of the reducing reagent remains, the titration is in error due to the amount of titrant required for oxidation of the excess reagent. The reagents ordinarily employed to establish desired oxidation states are listed below and the way in which an excess can be destroyed or limited is indicated.

Oxidizing Reagents	*Removal of Excess*
$NaBiO_3(s)$	Filter or decompose by boiling
$K_2S_2O_8(s)$	At 90-100° C the excess oxidizes H_2O to O_2
H_2O_2 (basic solution)	$2H_2O_2 = H_2O + O_{2(g)}$ in hot solution
$O_{3(g)}$	Removed by boiling
$Cl_{2(g)}$	" " "
$Bi_{2(g)}$	" " "

Reducing Reagents	*Removal of Excess*
Metals and metal amalgams	Filter
$SnCl_2$	$Sn^{++} + HgCl_2 = Hg_2Cl_{2(s)} + Sn^{++++}$
$SO_{2(g)}$	Removed by boiling
$H_2S_{(g)}$	Removed by boiling

In addition to the reagents listed in this category, there are numerous examples in the literature of other reagents that have been found useful in connection with specific problems.

A survey of the applications of the reagents listed and a general comparison of their relative advantages and disadvantages are beyond the scope of an elementary text. The specific determinations presented in subsequent sections of this chapter illustrate the way in which some of the reagents in the above categories may be applied. Specific examples of the application of other of these reagents are found in the problem set at the end of the chapter. The difficulties that are discussed in connection with each of the subsequent determinations are representative of the general problems encountered.

Dichromate Determination of Iron

Potassium dichromate has several properties that make it a very useful oxidizing reagent. It can be employed as a primary standard because the salt can be obtained, and easily stored, as a pure compound. Dichromate solutions are indefinitely stable in the absence of reducing impurities—an extremely desirable quality in reagents that serve as titrants. The possibility of interfering side reactions in dichromate titrations is limited because there are no stable oxidation states in acid solution intermediate between the species $Cr_2O_7^{--}$ and Cr^{+++}. Of particular practical value is the fact that dichromate does not oxidize chloride ion at room temperature in hydrochloric acid solutions as concentrated as one to two molar. A serious limitation to the use of of dichromate as a titrant was the difficulty of detecting an end-point in the resultant green colored chromic ion solutions. This limitation has been almost eliminated by the application of the potentiometric method and by the development of suitable oxidation-reduction indicators.

In the procedure that follows, potassium dichromate is used for the determination of iron in the presence of hydrochloric acid—an application that is very frequently made. The samples considered are ores of high iron content. The sample is dissolved in concentrated hydrochloric acid. All of the iron present is reduced to the ferrous state by the addition of a slight excess of stannous chloride. The excess stannous ion is removed by oxidation with mercuric chloride prior to titration of the ferrous ion with a standard solution of potassium dichromate. Barium diphenylamine sulfonate is used as the indicator. Some of the important aspects of the chemistry of the method are discussed in connection with the procedure.

General Preparations.—Transfer the ground ore sample

and about 3 g of ground, analytical reagent potassium dichromate to individual weighing bottles. Dry these materials in the oven for an hour or longer.

Place a *short stemmed* funnel in the mouth of a 500 ml volumetric flask. Accurately weigh a 2.3 − 2.7 g portion of the dichromate into the funnel and carefully wash this material into the flask with successive small portions of water. After the solid has been transferred, raise the funnel slightly, thoroughly rinse all solution from the funnel and from the outside of the stem into the flask. Add about 200 ml of water and swirl the flask to dissolve the solid. Dilute exactly to the mark, after determining that the contents of the flask are within 5° C of normal room temperature. Mix the solution *thoroughly*. This solution is stable almost indefinitely. From the half-reaction, determine the number of equivalents per mole of dichromate and calculate the normality of this solution.

Accurately weigh a 0.4 − 0.45 g portion of the sample into each of three 500 ml Erlenmeyer flasks. Add about 10 ml of concentrated HCl and 3 ml of 5% $SnCl_2$ to each sample. To decrease deposition of unwetted sample on the flask walls, do not swirl the solution until most of the sample has dissolved. Cover the flasks with small watch glasses and heat them on the water bath or *very cautiously* over a burner. The solutions should not be boiled or materially reduced in volume because there is a possibility of volatilizing some ferric chloride under such conditions. The sample will usually dissolve in 15 minutes, but may require a longer time. A small residue of silica frequently remains. If the residue has the usual clear, glassy appearance of silica, it may be ignored. If any appreciable amount of the residue is dark colored, consult your instructor. The solutions may be stored at this point.

Reduction and Titration Procedure.—Reduction and titration of a sample will take 10 to 30 minutes, depending upon the individual. These steps must be done in unbroken sequence, since ferrous ion can be oxidized by air.

Each sample requires about 10 ml of a 5% $SnCl_2$ solution, 10 ml of a saturated mercuric chloride solution, and 300 ml of a 4-5 M H_2SO_4, 1-1.5 M H_3PO_4 mixture. It is desirable to have these reagents immediately at hand for the reduction and titration steps.

Rinse any material on the cover and walls of the flask into the solution and heat almost to the boiling point. Using a 10 or 25 ml pipet, add stannous chloride dropwise to the hot solution until one drop is seen to discharge the yellow ferric ion color, leaving a colorless or very pale green solution. Add three drops of stannous chloride in excess and cool the solution with tap water. Add 10 ml of the mercuric chloride from a graduate, while swirling the flask. *Do not* use a pipet to measure or to add the mercuric chloride under any circumstances, for it is very poisonous. Furthermore, the solution must be added rapidly. A precipitate of mercurous chloride, which usually is silky and light gray in appearance, is obtained if the reduction has been satisfactorily performed. If the precipitate appears dark gray, or if no precipitate is obtained, the sample must be discarded for reasons that are explained later.

Allow the reduced solution to stand for 5 minutes to insure complete formation of a stable mercurous chloride precipitate. Add about 300 ml of the sulfuric-phosphoric acid mixture, 6 to 8 drops of barium diphenylamine sulfonate and titrate immediately with dichromate while swirling the solution. The indicator change from colorless to a reddish-violet is obscured by the green color of chromic ion formed during the titration. As the end-point is approached, the solution shows a change from clear green to a blue-green which may be used to indicate the beginning of dropwise addition of the dichromate. At the end-point, however, there is a very sharp change from a blue or blue-green to a purple or violet-blue color. The purple also may fade upon standing. This further oxidation usually is slow. The true end-point is distinguished as the point where one drop of titrant produces a sharp change from a blue-green to a distinctly purple or violet-blue color that persists for one minute or longer. Once the violet color has been obtained, no immediate change in color is observed when ½ to 1 drop of dichromate is added in excess.

Use the result of the first titration to estimate the amounts of dichromate required for the other samples so as to facilitate their rapid titration. Calculate the percent iron present. A precision of 2 to 3 parts per thousand should be expected.

Chemistry of the Reduction Step.—The most frequent source of error in this determination is in the reduction step. The errors may be caused by incomplete reduction of the iron, the formation of finely divided mercury in the oxidation of stannous chloride by mercuric chloride, or air oxidation of ferrous ion.

The formation of a precipitate of mercurous chloride when mercuric chloride is added to the reduced solution shows the presence of some stannous ion beyond that required to reduce ferric ion. This is proof of complete reduction, since ferric and stannous ions react rapidly in hot hydrochloric acid solution. On the other hand, if no precipitate forms, the solution must be discarded because the absence of any excess stannous ion must be taken to mean that complete reduction of the iron is improbable. Once mercuric chloride has been added, it is impossible to add stannous ion to complete the reduction. The mercuric chloride will react to form mercury as well as mercurous chloride and mercury interferes in the titration as discussed below.

If the concentration of mercuric chloride is more than twice as great as that of stannous ion, mercurous chloride will be formed according to the reaction:

$$2HgCl_2 + Sn^{++} = Sn^{++++} + Hg_2Cl_{2(s)} + 2Cl^- \quad (1)$$

If the concentration of stannous ion is more than half as large as that of mercuric chloride, even if this is only in a localized part of the solution, mercury may be formed.

$$HgCl_2 + Sn^{++} = Sn^{++++} + Hg_{(l)} + 2Cl^- \quad (2)$$

The possible reduction of dichromate by solid mercurous chloride is slow compared to the rate of reaction of dichromate with ferrous ion. For this reason, the presence of a moderate amount of mercurous chloride during the titration is not a source of error. However, the oxidation of mercury by dichromate or ferric ions is fast. This direct, or indirect, reduction of dichromate by the mercury produced in reaction (2) can cause serious errors. If mercuric chloride is added slowly, or if the solution is inadequately stirred during this addition, local ratios of stannous ion to mercuric chloride larger than one half may arise. A similar situation results if a large excess of stannous chloride has been added in the reduction step. Finely divided mercury appears black. When it is intimately mixed with mercurous chloride, the resultant precipitate has a marked gray color. Any sample that yields such a precipitate should be discarded. The possibility of obtaining mercury can be minimized by limiting the excess stannous chloride to 4 to 5 drops and by adding the mercuric chloride rapidly to a cold, well-stirred solution. In this connection, it is important to have the solution hot during the addition of stannous chloride, for otherwise the rate of reduction of ferric ion is slow and a large excess of stannous chloride may be added before the disappearance of the ferric ion color.

After the iron has been completely reduced to the ferrous state, and the excess of stannous ion has been removed, air oxidation of ferrous ion becomes a possible source of error. The rate of oxidation of ferrous ion by oxygen is greatly dependent upon the acidity, the temperature, and the general composition of the solution. In the solution used for the titration, the rate is rather slow at room temperature and no serious error is made if the sample is titrated within a few minutes after the precipitation of mercurous chloride.

Chemistry of the Indicator. In considering the reactions of the indicator, the usual situation is encountered where the rates of several possible reactions, as well as equilibrium considerations, are involved in the behavior of the system. Diphenylamine* is first oxidized irreversibly to colorless diphenylbenzidine and the latter is then reversibly oxidized to diphenylbenzidine violet. If equilibrium is at-

---

*For convenience, the name of the parent compound has been used in this discussion. The value of the standard potential, however, refers to the actual indicator, diphenylamine sulfonate.

tained, this reversible oxidation, to yield the observed color change, occurs at a potential close to −0.83 v. In the absence of complex-forming species, the standard potential of the ferrous–ferric system is −0.77 v. From the equation,

$$E = -0.77 - 0.059 \log \frac{[\text{Fe}^{+++}]}{[\text{Fe}^{++}]}$$

it is found that only 90 to 95 % of the iron is oxidized at −0.83 v., where the indicator changes color. The addition of phosphoric acid reduces the concentration of ferric ions in the solution through the formation of ferric phosphate complex ions. As a result of this decrease in the concentration of ferric ion, there is a quantitative oxidation of ferrous ion at the diphenylamine sulfonate end-point.

The rate of oxidation of diphenylamine, diphenylbenzidine and the further oxidation of diphenylbenzidine violet to various colorless products by dichromate is slow. Fortunately, the first two reactions are catalyzed by the oxidation of ferrous ion, presumably by the action of reactive intermediates. As a result, the indicator reacts sufficiently fast in the titration to provide an end-point. Beyond the equivalence-point, there is no ferrous ion to catalyze a bleaching of the violet color. The end-point usually fades slowly, making a distinct end-point possible.

Standardization of a Permanganate Solution

There are no available compounds of permanganate that are pure enough to be used as primary standards. Solutions prepared from potassium permanganate, the reagent ordinarily employed, must be standardized. Sodium oxalate, arsenious oxide, and potassium iodide are the primary standards usually selected although several others can be so used.

In water solutions, permanganate is unstable with respect to the reaction*:

$$\text{MnO}_4^- = \text{MnO}_{2(s)} + \text{O}_{2(g)}$$

---

*The equilibrium constant for this reaction can be calculated from the potentials of the $\text{MnO}_{2(s)}$, MnO_4^- and the H_2O, $\text{O}_{2(g)}$ couples in Table 11-1.

The rate of this reaction is negligibly slow at room temperature in pure solutions. It can become important in acid solution, at higher temperatures, in strong light, or in the presence of manganese dioxide. Since manganese dioxide catalyzes the decomposition, the reaction is auto-catalytic. Once the decomposition is initiated, it may continue at an increasing rate and render the solution useless. Freshly prepared permanganate solutions usually are heated to oxidize any reducing agents that may be in the materials used. This solution is then filtered through a non-oxidizable material to remove any manganese dioxide that may have formed, and is stored at room temperature in a dark bottle. Solutions of permanganate, properly prepared and stored, are stable for long periods. It is desirable, however, to standardize the permanganate within one laboratory period of the time of its use, since the solution may not be free of manganese dioxide or traces of slowly acting reducing agents.

General Preparations.—Dry pure sodium oxalate contained in a weighing bottle in the oven for at least one hour —longer if convenient.

Obtain or prepare 500 ml of approximately 0.2 N $KMnO_4$. Store the reagent in a very clean, but not necessarily dry, brown bottle. Shake the bottle thoroughly to establish uniform composition.

Accurately weigh 0.3 − 0.4 g portions of the sodium oxalate into each of three 400 − 600 ml beakers. If it is inconvenient to proceed with the standardization until a later time, cover the beakers and keep them out of the light to minimize possible decomposition of the oxalate.

Procedure—In permanganate titrations, the top of the colored solution is more easily located than the bottom of the meniscus and it should be used for the buret readings.

Add approximately 150 ml of distilled water to one of the weighed sodium oxalate samples; acidify with 50 ml of 6 N H_2SO_4 and heat the solution to 80-90° C. Add 2 to 3 drops of permanganate and stir until the color disappears. If the color does not disappear within five minutes, consult your instructor. Stir the clear solution constantly and add permanganate at a moderate rate, but do not allow any appreciable amount of unreacted titrant to accumulate as shown by a persistent pink color in the solution. As the color disappears more and more slowly, make certain that the temperature still is in the 60-90° C range. Add the permanganate in smaller and smaller portions until one drop is observed to impart a pale but definite pink tinge to the previously colorless solution. The pink color will not remain indefinitely because of possible decomposition of the permanganate or reaction with manganous ions. The rate of these reactions is quite slow, however, and the color usually persists for several minutes even at 90° C. Use the result of the first titration to estimate the amount of titrant needed for the other two samples and then titrate them in the same manner.

Calculate the normality of the permanganate. The three titrations should agree within two parts per thousand. If the first titration is mishandled, satisfactory agreement between the remaining two may be regarded as an acceptable basis for calculating the normality.

Discussion.—The reaction between oxalate and permanganate is extremely complex and rates of reaction are of determining importance. Permanganate can decompose to form manganese dioxide and oxygen. It likewise can form manganese dioxide through reaction with manganous ion. It, therefore, is essential that the rate of reaction of permanganate with oxalate be greater than the rate of decomposition or the rate of reaction with manganous ions. To this end, it is important that no appreciable excess of permanganate be present during the titration. The direct reaction of permanganate with oxalate is slow, as shown by the time required to decolorize the first few drops of titrant. Fortunately, manganous ions, produced in the reduction, act as a catalyst. They react with permanganate to form intermediate oxidation states of manganese, which in turn react rapidly with oxalate. The titration also is complicated by the transient existence of partially oxidized species derived from oxalate. This makes side reactions possible, in addition to those involved in the formation of oxygen and manganese dioxide. Errors from this source are not important unless the rates of these reactions are comparable to those of the various steps in the desired stoichiometric reaction. The extent to which variations in the titration conditions are critical is not clearly understood because a detailed knowledge of the reaction mechanism and the rate determining factors is lacking. The particular conditions of acidity, temperature, and rate of permanganate addition given previously are known empirically to yield results of the required precision.

Permanganate Determination of Calcium

This determination is based upon the precipitation of calcium as calcium oxalate. The precipitate is dissolved in sulfuric acid and the oxalic acid obtained is titrated with standardized permanganate. The general principle of this determination has many other applications. For example, lead and barium may be determined by precipitation as chromates. The amount of chromate precipitated is directly or indirectly titrated to determine the amount of lead or barium present. The use of this principle markedly extends the range of application of titration methods.

The procedure given below applies to the determination of calcium in limestone. The chemistry involved is considered in connection with pertinent steps in the analysis.

Preparation of the Sample—Dry the finely ground limestone sample in a weighing bottle in the oven for one hour, or longer if convenient.

Accurately weigh 0.4 − 0.6 g portions of the dried limestone into each of three 600 ml beakers and cover the beakers with watch glasses. Use a pipet inserted under the cover glass to add 10 ml of 6 N HCl slowly to each sample. Take care to avoid loss by spattering, as carbon dioxide is evolved by the acid. When effervescence stops, heat the covered solution to incipient boiling to remove dissolved carbon dioxide. Use a stream of wash water to rinse any material on the cover glass and on the beaker walls into the solution and dilute to about 200 ml. A small portion of the sample may remain undissolved. This is primarily silica and unless the particles appear opaque or gray rather than clear and glassy, it may be ignored. The silica interferes only to the extent that it may entrap some of the soluble portion of the limestone. These solutions may be stored until it is convenient to proceed with the calcium precipitation.

Precipitation of Calcium Oxalate.—This step should not be started unless there is enough time available to precipitate, filter and wash in unbroken sequence. The time required depends upon the individual and the conditions existing in the laboratory. It may vary from one to three hours.

Heat the properly diluted limestone samples to 60-80° C and add 4 to 5 drops of methyl red to each solution. While these are heating, dissolve 15 g of ammonium oxalate in 150 ml of hot water. Filter this solution if it is not clear. Add 50 ml of this solution to each sample and, if a precipitate forms, allow the sample to stand for 5 minutes or more before proceeding. Use a pipet to add 6 N NH_4OH dropwise until the pink methyl red color is just discharged and the solution appears faintly yellow or essentially colorless. This addition can be done conveniently by partially filling a 10 ml graduate with ammonia and then lowering a graduated 10 ml pipet into the cylinder. Allow the pipet to fill without drawing upon it and then manipulate it in the usual way to add reagent to the sample. Avoid an appreciable excess of ammonia. If such an excess has been added, use 6 N HCl to re-establish the pink color and again neutralize with ammonia. Allow each solution to stand at least one-half hour but not longer than one hour before filtration.

Decant the supernatant through a filter crucible. Use *cold water* to wash the beaker and the precipitate and then transfer the bulk of the precipitate to the crucible with the first wash water. Try to keep the total wash volume under 100 ml by using 10 − 20 ml portions per wash. Calcium oxalate is only moderately insoluble in water. After the fourth wash, test each individual washing by adding silver nitrate to test for chloride after acidifying with nitric acid. Washing must be continued until no chloride test is obtained, since it is essential that no significant amount of mother liquor remain. With this accomplished, washing should be stopped to minimize the loss of calcium oxalate through solution. It is not necessary to police the beaker so as to remove all traces of precipitate, but only to wash it thoroughly, since the same beaker is used for solution of the calcium oxalate in sulfuric acid.

Rinse the outside and bottom of the crucible with a stream of wash water to remove any extraneous solution, and place each crucible in the beaker used for the precipitation. The beakers may be covered and stored until it is convenient to proceed with the titration.

Discussion of the Precipitation Step.—The major sources of error in the precipitation and washing are: solubility loss of calcium oxalate; inadequate washing of the precipitate; precipitation of calcium carbonate; coprecipitation of magnesium oxalate. These will be considered briefly.

The solubility of calcium oxalate in water is approximately 0.7 mg per 100 ml at 25° C and 1.4 mg per 100 ml at 95° C. Since oxalic acid has the dissociation constants, $K_1 = 6 \times 10^{-2}$ and $K_2 = 6 \times 10^{-5}$, the solubility increases with increasing hydrogen ion concentration in accordance with the reactions:

$$CaC_2O_4 + H^+ = Ca^{++} + HC_2O_4^- \quad pH\ 2\ to\ 5$$
$$CaC_2O_4 + 2\ H^+ = Ca^{++} + H_2C_2O_4 \quad pH\ 2\ or\ less$$

In order to obtain crystals large enough for easy filtration and washing, it is necessary to use the effect of hydrogen ions and increased temperature to form the initial precipitate under conditions of high solubility. To obtain complete precipitation, it is then essential that the pH be increased to approximately 4. This is done by the addition of ammonia until the pink, acid color of methyl red disappears. Since the effect of temperature is not large, and the solubility of calcium oxalate is decreased by the excess of oxalate present, no excessive loss of precipitate is encountered by filtering the hot solution *unless* the pH has not been brought above 3. Solubility equilibrium is not instantaneous in this case and so it is necessary to delay filtering for ½ to 1 hour, after establishing the required pH. Longer delay is to be avoided, for the solution must be filtered before magnesium oxalate precipitates. The delayed precipitation of the magnesium oxalate after the bulk of the calcium oxalate has precipitated is an example of post-precipitation.

In the washing step, there is no excess oxalate and so the solubility loss approaches the 0.7 mg per 100 ml value given above. It is necessary, therefore, to use cold water and to keep the total volume to a minimum to prevent serious losses in this step. On the other hand, all excess oxalate must be quantitatively removed from the precipitate. The washing step is rather critical and must be done carefully in the light of these two factors.

While the pH must be greater than 3, as discussed previously, there are reasons why it should not be increased beyond 4–5. Unless the ammonia has been freshly distilled, there will be carbonate present and, at high pH's, some of the calcium may be precipitated as calcium carbonate. In addition, at the higher pH values, the composition of the precipitate may deviate slightly from $CaC_2O_4 \cdot H_2O$ due to the coprecipitation of a small amount of $Ca(OH)_2$ or a small amount of basic oxalate. The higher pH also will favor precipitation of heavy metal impurities, some of which may be partially coprecipitated as oxalates, although this is of minor importance.

The amounts of iron, aluminum and other common, minor constituents in these samples do not give rise to serious errors due to their coprecipitation as oxalates. The major separation involved is that of calcium from magnesium. The solubility of $MgC_2O_4 \cdot 2H_2O$ in water at 25° C is approximately 36 mg per 100 ml. Due to the formation of magnesium oxalate complexes, this is increased to 187 mg per 100 ml when the solution contains 40 g per liter of ammonium oxalate. Fortunately, calcium does not form stable complexes so that a large excess of oxalate may be used to aid in the calcium, magnesium separation. Magnesium oxalate shows a great tendency to supersaturate, despite the presence of calcium oxalate. The rate of precipitation of magnesium under these conditions is accelerated, however, by higher temperatures. For this reason, the solution should be kept below 80° C. When larger amounts of magnesium than are contained in these samples are encountered, it may be necessary to dissolve the calcium oxalate precipitate in acid and reprecipitate it to achieve a satisfactory separation.

Solution and Titration of the Calcium Oxalate.— Add approximately 150 ml of water and 50 ml of 6 N H_2SO_4 to each precipitate in the beakers. While heating to 80–90° C, agitate the crucible with a stirring rod to facilitate solution of the precipitate. Titrate each solution with permanganate exactly as in the oxalate standardization. Use the first result to estimate the volume of titrant needed for the remaining samples.

Calculate the percent calcium oxide in the sample. The three results should agree within 2 to 3 parts per thousand. If one result shows marked deviation, two results giving the above precision may be used as a basis for reporting.

Thiosulfate, Iodide and Tri-iodide as Analytical Reagents

The Thiosulfate Reaction with Tri-iodide.—Thiosulfate, in conjunction with iodide, is the most generally useful reducing titrant available. The applications of thiosulfate are based upon the reaction:

$$I_3^- + 2\,S_2O_3^{--} = S_4O_6^{--} + 3\,I^-$$

This reaction is rapid, quantitative, and free of side reactions if properly carried out in acid solution. In even slightly basic solutions, there is a partial oxidation of thiosulfate to sulfate in accordance with the reaction:

$$4\,I_3^- + S_2O_3^{--} + 10\,OH^- = 2\,SO_4^{--} + 12\,I^- + 5\,H_2O$$

The occurrence of this reaction presumably is due to the presence of hypoiodite ion in basic solution:

$$I_3^- + 2\,OH^- = IO^- + 2\,I^- + H_2O$$

The pH at which a partial oxidation to sulfate becomes significant depends upon the concentrations of the reactants, the general composition of the solution, and the temperature. Ordinarily, the tri-iodide–thiosulfate reaction cannot be used quantitatively if the pH is greater than 7.

In acid solution, there is a possibility of error from the decomposition of thiosulfate:

$$S_2O_3^{--} + 2\,H^+ = H_2SO_3 + S_{(s)}$$

This reaction is slow compared to the reaction of thiosulfate with tri-iodide ion. During a titration, tri-iodide ion oxidizes thiosulfate before decomposition occurs unless local excesses of thiosulfate exist. Local excesses of the reagent may arise if the titrant is added rapidly to an inadequately mixed solution. Tri-iodide can be satisfactorily titrated, however, even in $5\,M\,H^+$ if the thiosulfate is added slowly to a well-stirred solution.

Use of Iodide in Connection with Thiosulfate.—The quantitative oxidation of thiosulfate to tetrathionate by tri-iodide or iodine is almost unique. Most oxidizing agents react to yield varying proportions of tetrathionate and sulfate. For this reason, thiosulfate cannot be used for direct titrations of most oxidizing species. The general method adopted is to add an excess of iodide to the oxidizing agent involved. The tri-iodide formed in such reactions is then titrated with standardized thiosulfate. Air oxidation of iodide and possible loss of iodine prior to the thiosulfate titration are the principal difficulties in such methods. Loss of iodine is minimized by working at room temperature, and by keeping agitation to a minimum. In addition, a large excess of iodide is used to keep the iodine concentration low in accordance with the reaction:

$$I_{2(s)} + I^- = I_3^-$$

Air oxidation of iodide is due to the following reaction:

$$6\,I^- + O_{2(g)} + 4\,H^+ = 2\,I_3^- + 2\,H_2O$$

At room temperature, in dilute acid solution, the rate of this reaction is relatively slow. The reaction is induced by light and is catalyzed by various ions such as those of copper. The rate also is markedly dependent upon the acidity and, in solutions where the hydrogen ion concentration is greater than $0.4 - 0.5\ M$, it usually is necessary to remove dissolved oxygen from the solutions before adding potassium iodide. In addition, the air oxidation often is *induced* by the reaction of iodide with certain oxidizing agents. This is true, for example, in the oxidation with dichromate under certain conditions. To minimize errors arising from air oxidation, either solid potassium iodide or a freshly prepared solution is added to the oxidizing agent in question. The tri-iodide obtained is titrated as soon as the reaction is complete. Special precautions in the way of removing dissolved oxygen from the solutions are taken when conditions such as high acidity or induced air oxidations require them.

Titrations with Tri-iodide.—Tri-iodide solutions can conveniently be prepared by dissolving solid iodine in potassium iodide solution. Such solutions are fairly stable if simple precautions are taken against air oxidation of iodide and volatilization of iodine. Arsenious oxide generally is used as a primary standard for these solutions, the reaction being:

$$H_3AsO_3 + I_3^- + H_2O = H_3AsO_4 + 3\ I^- + 2\ H^+$$

A quantitative reduction of tri-iodide is obtained in buffered solutions in the pH range 5 to 9, a pH of 8 being commonly employed.

Tri-iodide has a limited application. Only the stronger reducing agents, such as stannous ion, can be titrated quantitatively. It frequently is used for the determination of arsenic, antimony, tin, sulfur dioxide or sulfite, and sulfide.

End-Point Detection.—In many applications, the straw yellow color of tri-iodide itself provides a satisfactory basis for detection of an end-point. In the presence of starch, and a small amount of iodide, a distinct blue color is imparted to the solution by tri-iodide as dilute as $10^{-5}\ M$. It is this intense blue color in the presence of starch that ordinarily is employed in the titration of tri-iodide with thiosulfate and in titrations of reducing agents with tri-iodide. Starch solutions are unstable. They undergo hydrolysis and other chemical action. A starch solution should be tested before use by adding a small amount of tri-iodide or iodine. If a violet or reddish color, rather than blue, is obtained, the starch solution should not be used.

In very strong acid, starch is hydrolyzed so rapidly that it cannot be used in connection with tri-iodide end-points. Frequently, a few drops of chloroform or carbon tetrachloride are added to such solutions to concentrate the iodine in a small volume of the solvent. The appearance or disappearance of the pronounced violet color of iodine in these solvents can then be used as the basis for sharp end-points.

Preparation and Standardization of Thiosulfate Solutions

Stability of Thiosulfate Solutions.—The reagent ordinarily employed for thiosulfate titrations is sodium thiosulfate. It cannot be readily obtained as a compound of precisely known composition, hence the solutions usually must be standardized. Solutions properly prepared and stored are stable for very long periods. Precautions must be taken in regard to the following possibilities for decomposition.

1. *Acid decomposition in the presence of carbon dioxide from the air*:

$$S_2O_3^{--} + H_2CO_3 = HSO_3^- + HCO_3^- + S_{(s)}$$

Tri-iodide oxidizes bisulfite to sulfate—a reaction that requires two electrons for each bisulfite ion oxidized. To the extent that the above decomposition occurs, the apparent strength of the solution actually increases.

2. *Oxidation of thiosulfate in the presence of air*: The mechanism of the oxidation probably involves the steps:

$$2 S_2O_3^{--} + 2 H^+ = 2 HSO_3^- + 2 S_{(s)}$$
$$2 HSO_3^- + O_{2(g)} = SO_4^{--} + 2 H^+$$

net reaction $2 S_2O_3^{--} + O_{2(g)} = SO_4^{--} + 2 S_{(s)}$

To the extent that air oxidation occurs, the titer of the solution decreases.

3. *Bacterial action*: Thiobacteria from the air frequently grow in thiosulfate solutions, converting some of it into sulfite and sulfur. The sulfite may then be oxidized to sulfate by oxygen from the air.

To protect against bacteria, sterile, freshly boiled distilled water is used for the preparation, and about 0.1 g of sodium carbonate is added per liter of solution to establish a pH of 8 to 9. Serious decomposition of a thiosulfate solution can be detected by the appearance of sulfur. Any solution that is cloudy should be discarded.

Methods of Standardization.—Various primary standards may be employed in the standardization of thiosulfate for general use. Those frequently selected, and the reactions involved, are listed below.

Primary Standard   *Reaction*

$KIO_{3(s)}$ $IO_3^- + 6H^+ + 8I^- = 3I_3^- + 3H_2O$

$K_2Cr_2O_{7(s)}$ $Cr_2O_7^{--} + 14H^+ + 9I^- = 3I_3^- + 2Cr^{+++} + 7H_2O$

$KBrO_{3(s)}$ $BrO_3^- + 6H^+ + 9I^- = 3I_3^- + Br^- + 3H_2O$

Secondary Standards   *Reaction*

MnO_4^- solution

                          $2MnO_4^- + 16H^+ + 15I^- = 5I_3^- + 2Mn^{++} + 8H_2O$

I_3^- solution

In the following procedure, thiosulfate is used for the determination of copper in a brass sample. Any of the primary standards listed above could be used for the required standardization. In this particular application, however, it is convenient to employ pure copper as the standard substance. The standardization against copper minimizes systematic errors in the method when the solution subsequently is used for the determination of copper.

Standardization of Thiosulfate and Determination of Copper

The method employed in this determination, and in the standardization, involves the addition of excess iodide ion to a solution of cupric ion under conditions where the following reaction is quantitatively complete:

$$2\ Cu^{++} + 5\ I^- = 2\ CuI_{(s)} + I_3^-$$

The amount of tri-iodide ion obtained by this reaction is then determined by titration with a standardized sodium thiosulfate solution.

$$2\ S_2O_3^{--} + I_3^- = 3\ I^- + S_4O_6^{--}$$

The procedure that follows applies to the standardization of the thiosulfate solution and to the determination of copper in the unknown. It is desirable to perform the standardization first, in order to become familiar with the general procedure.

General Preparations.—Obtain pieces of copper wire, each weighing about 0.20 — 0.25 g. Clean, by means of sandpaper, and brush all loose material from the surface. Use a weighing bottle to contain the copper and accurately weigh three 0.2 — 0.25 g samples. Place each weighed sample in a 250 ml Erlenmeyer flask. Three samples of the unknown are similarly weighed. Neither the unknown nor the copper should be heated in the oven. These samples have very little surface moisture and heating them may serve only to increase the amount of surface oxide.

Obtain or prepare about 600 ml of approximately 0.1 N $Na_2S_2O_3$.

Preparation of the Cupric Solution.—Place the flasks containing the samples in a hood. Add 2-3 ml of concentrated HNO_3 to each sample and cover the flasks with small watch glasses. Heat the samples gently on a sand bath until they dissolve. Do not appreciably reduce the volume of the solution by extended heating. When the samples have dissolved, rinse any material on the cover into the flask, add 20 ml of water and 5 ml of a 4% solution of urea to each flask. Replace the cover and heat the solution to a gentle boil for one minute.

Rinse all material from the cover into the solution. Cool the flask and its contents in tap water and carefully add 6 N NH_4OH to neutralize the excess acid. This can conveniently be done by partially filling a 10 ml graduate with ammonia into which a graduated 10 ml pipet is lowered. Allow the pipet to fill and then manipulate it in the usual way to add reagent to the sample. As each solution approaches neutrality, add the base 1 to 2 drops at a time and swirl the flask between each addition. Continue the careful addition of base until a precipitate of cupric hydroxide forms or until the deep blue color of cupric tetrammine ion becomes discernible. If you have reason to believe that more than 1 ml of 6 N NH_4OH has been added in excess, acidify by dropwise addition of 3-6 N HNO_3 and neutralize with ammonium hydroxide as before. This neutralization is somewhat critical. It is important that the solution be neutral or slightly basic rather than acid. Add 5 ml of 6 N HAc to the neutral solution and cool. If necessary, the above procedure may be stopped at any point.

Chemistry of the Preparation Step.—The major constituents of these samples are copper and zinc. The most common minor constituents are tin, lead, iron, nickel, arsenic, and phosphorus.

Tin dissolves to form hydrated stannic oxide, $SnO_2 \cdot xH_2O$, which separates from the nitric acid solution as a white, flocculent precipitate. Stannic oxide does not interfere in the determination unless it occludes some of the copper. This is not a significant source of error in these samples.

Of the other substances mentioned, only iron interferes with the direct determination of copper. Solution of the sample in nitric acid yields ferric ion which oxidizes iodide to tri-iodide and is titrated as an equivalent amount of copper. There are several ways to prevent the interference of iron. Among the methods used, is the formation of very stable ferric complex ions, such as the fluoride or the phosphate, which do not oxidize iodide to tri-iodide. For simplicity, no attempt has been made to eliminate the interference of any small amounts of iron that may be present in these samples. The standard values used in evaluating the results also include the copper equivalent of any iron present.

The reduction of nitric acid by the sample does not proceed according to a simple stoichiometric reaction, although nitric oxide is the principal product formed. Reduction products, such as NO, NO_2, and HNO_2 that are obtained, must be removed before iodide is added because any one of them can initiate the following reaction chain:

$$2\ NO_2^- + 3\ I^- + 4\ H^+ = 2\ NO + I_3^- + 2\ H_2O \quad (1)$$
$$NO + 1/2\ O_{2(g)} = NO_2 \quad (2)$$
$$2\ NO_2 + 3\ I^- = I_3^- + 2\ NO_2^- \quad (3)$$

The net result of the reaction chain shown in equations (1), (2), and (3) is a catalyzed air oxidation of iodide to tri-iodide ion which can lead to serious errors in the determination. In the procedure used, NO, NO_2, and HNO_2 are reduced to nitrogen by reaction with urea in hot acid solution. The urea is oxidized to nitrogen and carbon dioxide as shown in the following reaction with nitric oxide:

$$6\ NO + 2\ (NH_2)_2CO = 5\ N_{2(g)} + 2\ CO_{2(g)} + 4\ H_2O \quad (4)$$

The appearance of cupric hydroxide is a convenient indication of approximate neutrality of the solution. Sometimes the precipitate is not observed, however. The addition of 6 N NH_4OH to a neutral solution raises the concentration of hydroxyl ion to the point where cupric hydroxide precipitates before there is a sufficient concentration of ammonia to form cupric tetrammine ions. In fact, there is a fairly wide concentration range of ammonium hydroxide in the solution in which this is true. The addition of 6 N NH_4OH to these acid solutions first produces ammonium ion until the acid is neutralized. The effect of the ammonium ion is to repress the ionization of the base and to greatly lower the hydroxyl ion concentration. The rate of precipitation of cupric hydroxide may then become so slow that no precipitate is obtained or the hydroxyl ion concentration actually may be too small to form the precipitate.

Titration Procedure.—Dissolve 5 g of potassium iodide in 10 ml of water and pour this freshly prepared solution into the cold acetic acid solution. Cover the flask and allow it to stand for 1 to 2 minutes. This solution should not be allowed to stand for an extended period of time because iodide is slowly air oxidized to tri-iodide and because some iodine may be lost due to its volatility. Gently swirl the flask and titrate rapidly with thiosulfate solution until the original reddish brown color becomes very light. As long as an appreciable amount of tri-iodide remains, the solution will become noticeably lighter in color where the added thiosulfate enters. Continue to add thiosulfate in small portions until this lightening of the color becomes barely detectable. Without swirling the flask, add one drop of starch and note the behavior. If the amount of tri-iodide remaining is large, the drop of starch forms a deep blue spot where it hits the solution. As the amount of tri-iodide decreases, a fresh drop of starch produces a larger and less intensely blue spot. Approach the end-point by the addition of one drop of starch after each small addition of titrant until a drop of starch gives a barely detectable blue-gray color. Dissolve 2 g of potassium thiocyanate in 10 ml of water. Add this solution to the flask and swirl it for about 15 seconds. Add 3-5 ml of starch and make dropwise additions of the titrant with vigorous swirling of the solution until one drop causes the complete disappearance of the blue color.

From the data obtained with pure copper, calculate the normality of the thiosulfate solution. From the data obtained with the unknown samples, calculate the percent copper in the unknown. An average precision of 2 to 3 parts per thousand should be expected.

Chemistry of the Titration.—The pH of the solution during the titration is important. If it is too low, due to incomplete neutralization of the excess nitric acid, air oxidation of iodide catalyzed by copper ions may cause serious errors. If the pH is too large, due to the addition of excess ammonium hydroxide, the reaction between iodide and cupric ions may be incomplete when the titration is started. Although tri-iodide is removed during the titration, the resulting reaction of cupric and iodide ions to maintain equilibrium is too slow to give a sharp end-point and poor results are obtained. This effect of the pH on the equilibrium between iodide and cupric ions is not evident from the reaction. It results from a decrease in the concentration of cupric ions due to the formation of complex cupric ions. The effect is dependent not only upon the pH but also upon the nature and concentration of the anions present.

A common error in this determination is due to the addition of the major portion of the starch while the tri-iodide concentration is high. A large amount of tri-iodide is adsorbed by the starch in this case and it is only slowly returned to the solution as the titration proceeds. In the extreme case, a precipitation of the starch-iodide compound may be observed. The removal of tri-iodide from the starch is so slow that the blue color may remain even at the equivalence-point. The color fades slowly, producing an unsatisfactory end-point.

When cuprous iodide precipitates, an appreciable amount of iodine or tri-iodide is adsorbed on its surface. This iodine is only slowly desorbed and, as it is gradually returned to the solution near the end-point, the color fades and the end-point becomes indefinite. When thiocyanate ions are added to the solution, the adsorbed iodine rapidly is removed from the surface of the solid. Thiocyanate ion cannot be added until the tri-iodide concentration is very small because tri-iodide may react slowly with thiocyanate.

Some of the samples contain appreciable amounts of lead. Golden yellow lead iodide separates from solutions of these samples when potassium iodide is added. Unless the amount of lead is very large, the end-point is satisfactory, since the disappearance of the blue color is clearly visible against a yellow background. Some samples may contain a small amount of nickel which colors the resulting solution green. The disappearance of the blue color against the green background is sharp, although it is easy to overstep the end-point of the first sample.

Problems

1. Write the half-reaction that occurs in acid solution for each of the following:
   a. $Cl^- = Cl_{2(g)}$
   b. $Sn_{(s)} = Sn^{++}$
   c. $Br^- = BrO_3^-$
   d. $Cl_{2(g)} = ClO_3^-$
   e. $Mn^{++} = MnO_{2(s)}$
   f. $Sn_{(s)} = SnO_{2(s)}$

2. Write the half-reaction that occurs in basic solution for each of the following:
   a. $Fe(OH)_{2(s)} = Fe(OH)_{3(s)}$
   b. $Br^- = BrO^-$
   c. $MnO_{2(s)} = MnO_4^-$
   d. $Cr(OH)_{3(s)} = CrO_4^{--}$
   e. $Zn_{(s)} = HZnO_2^-$
   f. $Al_{(s)} = AlO_2^-$

OXIDATION-REDUCTION REACTIONS

3. Complete and balance the following equations assuming that the reactions occur in acid solution:
   a. $Sn^{++} + HgCl_2 =$
   b. $I_3^- + S_2O_3^{--} =$
   c. $MnO_4^- + H_2C_2O_4 =$
   d. $MnO_4^- + H_2SO_3 =$
   e. $Cu_{(s)} + NO_3^- = NO_{(g)} +$
   f. $CuS_{(s)} + NO_3^- = S_{(s)} + NO_{(g)} +$
   g. $MnO_4^- + Mn^{++} =$

4. Complete and balance the following equations, assuming that the reactions occur in alkaline solution:
   a. $MnO_4^- + Fe(OH)_{2(s)} = MnO_{2(s)} + Fe(OH)_{3(s)}$
   b. $MnO_4^- + Mn(OH)_{2(s)} = MnO_{2(s)}$
   c. $Fe(OH)_{2(s)} + O_{2(g)} = Fe(OH)_{3(s)}$
   d. $Pt_{(s)} + O_{2(g)} = Pt(OH)_{2(s)}$
   e. $O_{3(g)} + Br^- = BrO_3^- + O_{2(g)}$

5. Calculate the equivalent weight of the underlined substance in each of the following examples. The reactants and products are given in each case:
   a. $\underline{Fe(NH_4)_2(SO_4)_2 \cdot 6H_2O}$
      $(Fe^{++}\ Cr_2O_7^{--} + H^+ = Fe^{+++} + Cr^{+++} + H_2O)$
   b. $\underline{K_2Cr_2O_7}$
      $(Sn^{++} + Cr_2O_7^{--} + H^+ = Sn^{++++} + Cr^{+++} + H_2O)$
   c. $\underline{Na_2C_2O_4}$
      $(H_2C_2O_4 + H^+ + MnO_4^- = CO_{2(g)} + Mn^{++} + H_2O)$
   d. $\underline{CuSO_4 \cdot 5H_2O}$
      $(Cu^{++} + I^- = CuI_{(s)} + I_3^-)$
   e. $\underline{Na_2S_2O_3 \cdot 5H_2O}$
      $(S_2O_3^{--} + I_3^- = I^- + S_4O_6^{--})$
   f. $\underline{As_2O_3}$
      $(H_3AsO_3 + I_3^- + H_2O = H_3AsO_4 + I^- + H^+)$

   Ans. (a) **392.15**, (b) **49.04**, (c) **67.00**, (d) **249.71**, (e) **248.19**, (f) **49.47**

6. Calculate the normality of a permanganate solution if

44.65 ml of it are required to react quantitatively with 0.4065g of $Na_2C_2O_4$. *Ans.* **0.1359 N**

7. Potassium ferrocyanide is sometimes used as a primary standard for the standardization of potassium permanganate. The half-reaction is $Fe(CN)_6^{-4} = Fe(CN)_6^{-3} + e^-$ Calculate the molarity of a permanganate solution if 30.26 ml of it are required to react quantitatively with 1.003 g of $K_4Fe(CN)_6 \cdot 3H_2O$. *Ans.* **0.01570 M**

8. Calculate the normality of a ferrous ammonium sulfate solution if 36.85 ml are required to react quantitatively with 0.2000 g of potassium dichromate. *Ans.* **0.1107 N**

9. Ferrous ammonium sulfate frequently is used as a primary standard for the standardization of ceric sulfate. The reaction is:

$$Ce^{++++} + Fe^{++} = Ce^{+++} + Fe^{+++}$$

If 48.60 ml of ceric sulfate are required to react quantitatively with 0.3895 g of ferrous ammonium sulfate, what is the molarity of the ceric sulfate solution? *Ans.* **0.02044 M**

10. Pure copper wire is used in the laboratory for the standardization of a thiosulfate solution. The copper is dissolved to form cupric ion which in turn reacts with iodide ion as follows:

$$2\ Cu^{++} + 5\ I^- = 2\ CuI_{(s)} + I_3^-$$

The tri-iodide formed is titrated with a thiosulfate solution. A 0.2500 g sample of pure copper is treated as described above and 30.67 ml of thiosulfate solution are required to react quantitatively with the tri-iodide. Calculate the normality of the thiosulfate solution. *Ans.* **0.1282 N**

11. Potassium iodate often is used as a primary standard for the standardization of a thiosulfate solution. Iodate and iodide react quantitatively in the presence of excess hydrogen ion according to the reaction:

$$IO_3^- + 8\ I^- + 6\ H^+ = 3\ I_3^- + 3\ H_2O$$

Calculate the normality of a thiosulfate solution if 46.66 ml are required to react quantitatively with the tri-iodide produced by 0.1700 g of potassium iodate. *Ans.* **0.1021 N**

12. Potassium iodate can be used as a primary standard for the standardization of an acid utilizing the reaction shown in Problem 11. The weighed potassium iodate sample is dissolved in water and excess sodium thiosulfate and potassium iodide are added. This solution is then titrated with the acid to a methyl red or methyl orange end-point. Calculate the normality of an acid solution that requires 29.65 ml to react quantitatively with 0.1365 g of potassium iodate.
Ans. **0.1291 N**

13. An iron ore sample weighing 0.4750 g is dissolved in hydrochloric acid. Sulfuric acid is added and the solution is heated in order to remove the hydrochloric acid. The ferric ion is reduced to ferrous ion by passing the solution over amalgamated zinc in a Jones reductor. The resultant ferrous solution is titrated with 24.65 ml of .1072 N $KMnO_4$. Calculate the percent Fe_2O_3 in the ore. *Ans.* **44.39%**

14. A 1.000 g sample containing both copper and iron is dissolved in nitric acid and fumed to remove oxides of nitrogen. The excess nitric acid is neutralized with ammonia. Ammonium bifluoride is added. Under these conditions, ferric fluoride complexes are formed which do not react with iodide ion to form tri-iodide. One gram of potassium acid phthalate is dissolved in the solution to buffer it, and then excess potassium iodide is added. The tri-iodide formed is titrated with 23.84 ml of 0.1000 N $S_2O_3^{--}$. Calculate the percent copper in the ore. *Ans.* **15.16%**

15. The procedure described in Problem 14 is followed, omitting the addition of ammonium bifluoride. Under these conditions, 30.0 ml of 0.1000 N $S_2O_3^{--}$ is required. Estimate the minimum percent iron in the sample. *Ans.* **3.45%**

16. Manganese in steel may be determined by adding sodium bismuthate to the dissolved sample to oxidize man-

ganous ion to permanganate. The excess bismuthate is removed by reacting to oxidize water to oxygen at 90-100° C. The amount of permanganate can then be determined by titration.

A 1.000-g sample of steel is dissolved in hydrochloric acid. Sulfuric acid is added and the solution is heated to fuming to remove the hydrochloric acid. The resultant solution is diluted with water, heated to 90-100° C and sodium bismuthate added. After the bismuthate has been decomposed, 25.00 ml of 0.100 N Fe^{++} is added and the excess ferrous ion is back-titrated with 10.36 ml of 0.0100 N $KMnO_4$. Calculate the percent manganese in the steel sample. *Ans.* **0.16%**

17. From the following two half-reactions, calculate the solubility product of AgCl:

$$Ag_{(s)} = Ag^+ + e^- \qquad E^0 = -0.7995$$
$$Cl^- + Ag_{(s)} = AgCl_{(s)} + e^- \qquad E^0 = -0.2222$$
$$\text{\textit{Ans.} } K = 1.6 \times 10^{-10}$$

18. Calculate the solubility product of CuI from the following data:

$$Cu^+ = Cu^{++} + e^- \qquad E^0 = -0.167$$
$$CuI_{(s)} = Cu^{++} + I^- + e^- \qquad E^0 = -0.877$$
$$\text{\textit{Ans.} } K = 10^{-12}$$

19. Calculate the equilibrium constant for each of the following reactions:

a. $Pb_{(s)} + Sn^{++++} = Pb^{++} + Sn^{++}$
b. $Sn_{(s)} + Sn^{++++} = Sn^{++}$
c. $Cu^{++} + I^- = CuI_{(s)} + I_3^-$
d. $Fe^{++} + MnO_4^- + = Fe^{+++} + Mn^{++} +$

Ans. (a) 2.5×10^9, (b) 5×10^9, (c) 4×10^{11}, (d) 4×10^{63}

20. a. Calculate the equilibrium constant for the reaction:

$$Sn_{(s)} + Pb^{++} = Sn^{++} + Pb_{(s)}$$

b. If 100 ml of 0.1 M Pb^{++} are added to 0.01 mole of

metallic tin, what is the concentration of Pb^{++} when equilibrium has been attained?

c. Is the reaction quantitative?

(a) 2.2, (b) 0.031M, (c) no

21. a. Calculate the equilibrium constant for the reaction:

$$Fe^{++} + Cu^{++} = Fe^{+++} + Cu^{+}$$

b. If 50 ml of 0.1 M Cu^{++} are added to 50 ml of 0.1 M Fe^{++}, what is the concentration of Fe^{+++} when equilibrium is attained?

Ans. (a) 6.2×10^{-10}, (b) 4×10^{-7} M

22. Calculate the E^0 for the half reaction:

$$Ag_{(s)} + 2\,NH_{3(aq)} = Ag(NH_3)_2^{+} + e^{-}$$

given

$$Ag_{(s)} = Ag^{+} + e^{-} \quad E^0 = -0.7995$$
$$Ag(NH_3)_2^{+} = Ag^{+} + 2\,NH_{3(aq)} \quad K = 6 \times 10^{-8}$$

Ans. -0.373

23. A solution of H$_3$AsO$_3$ can be prepared by dissolving As$_2$O$_3$ in sodium hydroxide and adding hydrochloric acid to neutralize the sodium hydroxide. A 0.2 M H$_3$AsO$_3$ solution prepared in this manner is buffered with sodium bicarbonate to yield a hydrogen ion concentration of 10^{-7} M.

a. What is the concentration of H$_3$AsO$_3$ when 100 ml of 0.2 M I$_3^{-}$ have been added to 100 ml of 0.2 M H$_3$AsO$_3$?

b. Is the reaction quantitative? *Ans.* (a) 1.6×10^{-7} M

24. A solution of H$_3$AsO$_4$ is prepared by dissolving 0.02 mole of H$_3$AsO$_4 \cdot \tfrac{1}{2}$H$_2$O in 100 ml of 1 M sulfuric acid.

a. What is the concentration of H$_3$AsO$_4$ when 100 ml of 0.4 M I^{-} have been added to the arsenic acid solution?

b. Is the reaction quantitative? *Ans.* (a) 0.047 M

25. Show that the E^0 value remains unchanged if a half-reaction is multiplied by a factor to balance an equation.

Chapter 12

RELATION OF THIS INTRODUCTION TO THE FIELD OF QUANTITATIVE ANALYSIS

The field of quantitative analysis is not limited to a fixed set of standard methods and procedures. It draws upon all of the facts and techniques of measurement in the physical sciences to provide procedures for the extremely varied and frequently complex analyses that are required. As new techniques are developed, and as new facts and principles are discovered, new methods of analysis result and older methods are improved and extended. Thus, the application of gravimetric methods has been greatly extended in recent years by the use of a large number of organic reagents that have been introduced for the more or less specific precipitation of inorganic ions. Similarly, the use of physico-chemical methods of end-point detection has expanded the application of volumetric methods very markedly. In addition, the direct use of physico-chemical properties for the quantitative determination of a wide variety of constituents has lately become routine, partly through an increased knowledge of these properties and partly through the concomitant development of reliable, commercially available instruments. The control of industrial processes in specific industries frequently involves the development and application of special methods peculiar to their own needs. For example, in many of the methods employed in the iron and steel industry, extreme speed is one of the prime factors in the selection of methods. The measurement of growth is used for the assay of such complex substances as vitamins, hormones, and bacteria in the fields of biology, medicine, and agriculture.

The material presented in the foregoing chapters may appear to be extremely limited in scope when viewed in connection with the wide variety of practical methods to which reference has been made. Actually, most of the techniques and principles discussed in the text are fundamental to and are constantly applied in these procedures. To illustrate this point, several types of methods are considered briefly in the following sections.

Colorimetric and Related Methods

Measurement of the amount of light absorbed or emitted by various elements, ions, or molecules often is a satisfactory method of quantitative analysis. These methods frequently are quite specific since the wave length of the absorbed or emitted light may be very characteristic of the species involved. This group includes the following methods.

Colorimetric methods refer to the measurement of the absorption of visible light. The absorption by the sample solution is measured by visual comparison with standards or by the use of a simple photoelectric *colorimeter*.

Spectrophotometric methods require the use of an instrument that provides essentially monochromatic light of a desired wave length. The amount of monochromatic light absorbed by a sample solution is then measured by the instrument as the basis of the quantitative determination. The use of a *spectrophotometer* for such measurements leads to a much greater degree of specificity than can be attained by the simpler colorimetric procedures.

Spectrographic methods depend upon measurement of the intensity and the precise wave lengths of the light emitted by a sample that is excited to emission in a flame, an arc, or a spark. This method is very specific because the wave lengths of the emitted light are characteristic of the elements in the sample.

Fluorescence methods involve the irradiation of a sample by light, most often in the ultra-violet region of the spectrum, and the measurement of the intensity of the fluorescent light emitted by the sample. The fluorescent light usually is in the visible region of the spectrum.

We may use the specific example of a method for the colorimetric determination of copper to indicate the extent to which the techniques and principles previously discussed apply generally to methods of this type. The procedure under consideration is based upon the addition of dithizone (diphenylthiocarbazone) to a cupric solution of controlled pH. Cupric dithizonate forms and is extracted into a known volume of carbon tetrachloride or chloroform. The amount of light absorbed by the resultant green solution is measured. The amount of copper is calculated by comparing the absorption of light by the unknown solution to the amount of light absorbed by solutions similarly prepared that contain known concentrations of copper. This comparison, visually or by means of a suitable colorimeter, actually is only a very small part of the procedure. The bulk of the operations involve the basic techniques of gravimetric and volumetric analysis. Both the sample and a standard copper compound must be accurately weighed and dissolved to obtain solutions of precise concentrations. The standard solution, and frequently the unknown, must be diluted exactly through the use of pipets and volumetric flasks. The solution must be buffered in accordance with the principles stressed in Chapter 10. Dithizone behaves as a weak acid, and the effect of hydrogen ion on the desired reaction parallels the effect of hydrogen ion on solubility considered in Chapter 5. In short, the principles and techniques considered in this introduction are fundamental to procedures of this type. In addition, however, it is necessary to understand the principles that underlie the absorption of light and the operation of the instruments used to measure it quantitatively.

Nephelometric methods are included in the group that depend upon the measurement of light intensities. The substance to be determined usually is precipitated under conditions that lead to the formation of relatively stable colloidal or very fine suspensions of the solid. A measurement of the amount of light scattered by the particles in the suspension can then be used to estimate the amount of material present.

As in the previous colorimetric example, a large portion of the procedure involves the quantitative preparation of a solution of the unknown as well as a set of standard solutions. This preparation requires the application of the basic techniques of gravimetric and volumetric procedures. In addition, control of the particle size and stability of the suspension, a critical factor in the method, is based upon the principles discussed in Chapter 6 in connection with the physical character and purity of precipitates.

Physico-Chemical Methods of End-Point Detection

Potentiometric methods of end-point detection in the titration of oxidation-reduction systems were described briefly in Chapter 11. The methods can be extended to titrations based upon acid-base, precipitation, or complex formation reactions whenever one of the reacting species is a component of an oxidation-reduction couple. An understanding of the concept of oxidation potentials presented in Chapter 11 and the nature of the titration curves involved in the various reactions is fundamental to the general application of potentiometric methods. These titrations are simply extensions of the volumetric methods discussed in the text.

Another frequently used physico-chemical method of end-point detection is based upon measurement of the electrical conductivity of a solution during a titration. The methods are known as *conductiometric titrations*. More recently *amperometric titrations* have been introduced. These involve the measurement of the current due to the oxidation or reduction of one of the reacting substances, using a small platinum or a dropping mercury electrode. The change in current during the titration provides a method for locating an end-point. As in the potentiometric methods, these are extensions of the usual volumetric titrations; an understanding of the principles in the simple applications is fundamental to the procedures that employ the physico-chemical methods of end-point detection.

Methods of Separation

Frequently, the major problem in the analysis of a complex material is the separation of the various constituents into less inclusive groups prior to their determinations.

Gravimetric methods have been discussed rather fully in the text because the principles and techniques presented are of great practical importance in such operations. The discussion of the control of solubility in Chapter 5 outlines the principles that apply to the choice of organic as well as inorganic precipitants and the selection of optimum conditions for required separations. The treatment of the factors that affect the physical character and purity of precipitates in Chapter 6 can be used as a practical guide in considering the empirical modifications in precipitation methods that may improve the quality of a separation. The specific examples of barium sulfate, ferric hydroxide, and calcium oxalate in the text illustrate many of the practical difficulties that are encountered in obtaining satisfactory precipitates.

A relatively recent development is the use of selective adsorption of inorganic ions, as well as organic compounds, on various inorganic and organic solids, followed by the selective elution of the adsorbed substances. Very recently, for example, acidic organic resins have been successfully used in this way for very difficult separations of some of the rare earths. The principles involved in the adsorption of these ions on the solid, and the elution through control of pH and the formation of complex ions are closely related to the effect of these factors on the control of solubility considered in Chapter 5.

Electrolytic methods of separation represent applications of the general principles discussed in Chapter 11. For example, in the analysis of coin silver, the difference in oxidation potential between copper and silver is employed in the separation. Advantage also is taken of the formation of insoluble lead dioxide by electrolytic oxidation. When a solution of the sample is electrolyzed under proper conditions, the lead deposits as $PbO_{2(s)}$ on the anode, and pure metallic silver deposits on the cathode since the oxidation potential of silver is much greater than that of copper. After the silver has been removed, the potential is increased and copper is then obtained on the cathode. Although special techniques are required in the proper operation of the electrolytic cell, again a large portion of the procedure depends upon precise weighing of the electrodeposited substances and the preparation of solutions of the required composition by the usual volumetric techniques.

Further Study of Analytical Methods

In the previous examples, we have shown that analytical procedures are functional combinations of simple steps that almost always involve the basic principles and techniques that have been presented in the foregoing chapters. The application of physico-chemical methods requires a command of this fundamental material as well as a knowledge of the principles and techniques that comprise the body of physical chemistry. Further experience in analysis that emphasizes the general problems of separations in connection with materials of ordinary complexity, plus familiarity with the most frequently employed physico-chemical methods, is needed by students in chemistry.

Appendices

APPENDIX 1.—LABORATORY REAGENTS

Solids

Ammonium oxalate
Barium chloride dihydrate
Copper wire—primary standard
Dextrin
Potassium acid phthalate—primary standard
Potassium dichromate—primary standard
Potassium iodide
Potassium thiocyanate
Sodium acetate
Sodium bicarbonate
Sodium chloride—primary standard
Sodium oxalate—primary standard

Solutions

6 N acetic acid
6 N ammonium hydroxide
5% barium chloride
6 N hydrochloric acid
12 N hydrochloric acid
Saturated mercuric chloride
6 N nitric acid
16 N nitric acid
0.1 N silver nitrate
4 N sodium acetate (in 6 N acetic acid)
0.25 M stannous chloride (in 1.2 N hydrochloric acid)
6 N sodium hydroxide
6 N sulfuric acid
36 N sulfuric acid
4% urea

Solutions to be Standardized

0.1 N hydrochloric acid
0.2 N potassium permanganate
0.1 N potassium thiocyanate
0.1 N silver nitrate
0.1 N sodium hydroxide
0.1 N sodium thiosulfate

Indicators

0.2% barium diphenylamine sulfonate (aqueous)
0.1% dichlorofluorescein (in 95% ethyl alcohol)
0.5 M ferric alum or ferric nitrate (in 1 N HNO_3)
0.1% methyl red (in 95% ethyl alcohol)
0.1% phenolphthalein (in 95% ethyl alcohol)
0.4% starch solution (aqueous)

APPENDIX 2. – LABORATORY EQUIPMENT

3 50 ml beakers
1 100 ml beaker
1 250 ml beaker
3 400 ml beakers
3 600 ml beakers
3 1 liter bottles
1 250 ml glass-stoppered bottle
3 20 ml weighing bottles
2 50 ml burets
1 buret holder
2 Bunsen burners
1 burner guard
3 crucibles (sintered glass or Gooch)
3 10 ml porcelain crucibles
1 iron crucible
1 10 ml graduated cylinder
1 50 ml graduated cylinder
1 desiccator
4 250 ml Erlenmeyer flasks
3 500 ml Erlenmeyer flasks

1 500 ml filter flask
2 250 ml volumetric flasks
1 500 ml volumetric flask
2 65 mm long stem glass funnels
1 65 mm short stem glass funnel
1 Gooch funnel
2 10 cm squares of wire gauze
1 Gooch rubber
2 boxes of matches
1 envelope of quantitative filter paper
1 glazed paper
1 25 ml pipet
1 50 ml pipet
1 1 ml graduated pipet
1 10 ml graduated pipet
1 porcelain plate
2 4-in. iron rings
2 7-in. glass rods
2 10-in. glass rods
1 3-in. steel spatula
1 No. 7 rubber stopper
2 iron supports
4 6-in. test tubes
1 360° thermometer
2 3-ft. lengths burner tubing
1 2-ft. length suction tubing
1 1-ft. length suction tubing
1 crucible tongs
2 towels
1 trap
2 chromel triangles
1 50 ml wash bottle
1 1000 ml wash bottle
2 50 mm watch glasses
4 100 mm watch glasses

APPENDIX 3. – SOLUBILITY PRODUCTS AND DISSOCIATION CONSTANTS

Reaction	K
$Al(OH)_3(s) = Al^{+++} + 3OH^-$	1.9×10^{-33}
$BaCO_3(s) = Ba^{++} + CO_3^{--}$	4.9×10^{-9}
$BaSO_4(s) = Ba^{++} + SO_4^{--}$	1×10^{-10}
$BaCrO_4(s) = Ba^{++} + CrO_4^{--}$	2×10^{-10}
$Ca(OH)_2(s) = Ca^{++} + 2OH^-$	7.9×10^{-6}
$CaCO_3(s) = Ca^{++} + CO_3^{--}$	4.8×10^{-9}
$CaC_2O_4(s) = Ca^{++} + C_2O_4^{--}$	2.3×10^{-9}
$CaF_2(s) = Ca^{++} + 2F^-$	3.9×10^{-11}
$Cu(NH_3)_4^{++} = Cu^{++} + 4NH_3(aq)$	4.6×10^{-14}
$Cu(OH)_2(s) = Cu^{++} + 2OH^-$	5.6×10^{-20}
$Fe(OH)_3(s) = Fe^{+++} + 3OH^-$	4×10^{-38}
$PbCl_2(s) = Pb^{++} + 2Cl^-$	1.7×10^{-5}
$PbSO_4(s) = Pb^{++} + SO_4^{--}$	1.8×10^{-8}
$Mg(OH)_2(s) = Mg^{++} + 2OH^-$	5.5×10^{-12}
$MgC_2O_4(s) = Mg^{++} + C_2O_4^{--}$	8.6×10^{-5}
$HgCl^+ = Hg^{++} + Cl^-$	1.8×10^{-7}
$HgCl_2 = Hg^{++} + 2Cl^-$	6.1×10^{-14}
$HgCl_4^{--} = HgCl_2 + 2Cl^-$	1.4×10^{-2}
$HgCl_4^{--} = Hg^{++} + 4Cl^-$	8.6×10^{-16}
$2HgCl^+ = Hg^{++} + HgCl_2$	0.55
$2HgBr^+ = Hg^{++} + HgBr_2$	0.17
$AgCl(s) = Ag^+ + Cl^-$	1.7×10^{-10}
$Ag_2CrO_4(s) = 2Ag^+ + CrO_4^{--}$	1.1×10^{-12}
$AgBr(s) = Ag^+ + Br^-$	3.3×10^{-13}
$AgI(s) = Ag^+ + I^-$	8.5×10^{-17}
$AgCN(s) = Ag^+ + CN^-$	7.0×10^{-15}
$Ag(CN)_2^- = Ag^+ + 2CN^-$	3.8×10^{-19}
$AgCNS(s) = Ag^+ + CNS^-$	1.0×10^{-12}
$Ag(NH_3)_2^+ = Ag^+ + 2NH_3(aq)$	6.0×10^{-8}
$AgIO_3(s) = Ag^+ + IO_3^-$	5.3×10^{-8}
$AgAc(s) = Ag^+ + Ac^-$	1.9×10^{-3}

Reaction	K
$Ag_2S(s) = 2Ag^+ + S^{--}$	1.0×10^{-51}
$Zn(OH)_2(s) = Zn^{++} + 2OH^-$	4.5×10^{-17}
$ZnS(s) = Zn^{++} + S^{--}$	4.5×10^{-24}
$Zn(NH_3)_4^{++} = Zn^{++} + 4NH_3(aq)$	9.8×10^{-10}

APPENDIX 4. — DISSOCIATION CONSTANTS OF ACIDS AND BASES

Reaction	K
$CH_3COOH = CH_3COO^- + H^+$	1.8×10^{-5}
$NH_4OH = NH_4^+ + OH^-$	1.8×10^{-5}
$H_2CO_3 = H^+ + HCO_3^-$	4.3×10^{-7}
$HCO_3^- = H^+ + CO_3^{--}$	4.7×10^{-11}
$HCN = H^+ + CN^-$	4×10^{-10}
$H_2S = H^+ + HS^-$	9.1×10^{-8}
$HS^- = H^+ + S^{--}$	1.2×10^{-15}
$H_2C_2O_4 = H^+ + HC_2O_4^-$	5.9×10^{-2}
$HC_2O_4^- = H^+ + C_2O_4^{--}$	6.4×10^{-5}
$H_3PO_4 = H^+ + H_2PO_4^-$	7×10^{-3}
$H_2PO_4^- = H^+ + HPO_4^{--}$	7×10^{-8}
$HPO_4^{--} = H^+ + PO_4^{---}$	5×10^{-13}
$HC_8H_4O_4^- = H^+ + C_8H_4O_4^{--}$	5×10^{-6}
$HSO_4^- = H^+ + SO_4^{--}$	2×10^{-2}
$H_2O = H^+ + OH^-$	1×10^{-14}

APPENDIX 5. — TABLE OF INDICATORS

Indicator	pH Range
Methyl Violet	0 - 2
Meta Cresol Purple	1.2 - 2.8
Thymol Blue	1.2 - 2.8
Brom Phenol Blue	3.0 - 4.6
Methyl Orange	3.1 - 4.6
Brom Cresol Green	3.8 - 5.4
Methyl Red	4.2 - 6.3

Indicator	pH Range
Propyl Red	4.8 - 6.4
Brom Phenol Red	5.2 - 6.8
Brom Cresol Purple	5.2 - 6.8
Brom Thymol Blue	6.0 - 7.6
Phenol Red	6.8 - 8.4
Cresol Red	7.2 - 8.8
Thymol Blue	8.0 - 9.6
Phenolphthalein	8.0 - 9.8
Thymolphthalein	9.3 - 10.5
Alizarin	10.1 - 12.1

APPENDIX 6.—USE OF THE LOGARITHM TABLES

The logarithm of a number is the power to which 10 must be raised to give the number itself. Thus, 1 is written as 10^0; the logarithm of 1 is 0. Likewise, 100 is written as 10^2; the logarithm of 100 is 2. The logarithm of 0.1, which can be written as 10^{-1}, is -1. Any number between 1 and 10 can be expressed as 10^x where x has a value between 0 and 1. A number between 10 and 100 can be expressed as 10^{1+x} where x again is some number between 0 and 1. The logarithm therefore, can be divided into two parts; one part is 10 to some integral power, and the other part is 10 raised to some fractional power. The integer is known as the characteristic; it may be either positive or negative. It serves merely to locate the decimal point. The fractional part is called the mantissa. It always is positive; its magnitude depends upon the numerals themselves. Tables have been prepared listing the mantissas of numbers. Using the five-place logarithms in this appendix, the logarithm of 5, for example, is 0.69897. The characteristic is 0 and the mantissa is .69897. The logarithm of 50 is 1.69897. The characteristic is 1 and the mantissa still is .69897. The logarithm of 0.05 is $\bar{2}$.69897 where the bar over the 2 indicates that the integral part is negative. Another way to express the logarithm of this number is 8.69897-10.

An antilog is defined as the number that corresponds to a given logarithm. In the preceding paragraph, 5 is the antilog of 0.69897; 0.05 is the antilog of 2.69897.

From the table, a five-place logarithm can be found directly for a four-figure number. The logarithm for a five-figure number can be found by interpolating from the column of differences on the right-hand side of the table. For example, the logarithm of 3.3349 is determined as follows:

The logarithm of 3.334 is 0.52297.

The logarithm of 3.335 is 0.52310.

The difference between these two numbers is 0.00013.

0.9 × 0.00013 = 0.00012. This can be obtained directly from the column of differences.

Therefore, 0.00012 should be added to the logarithm of 3.334.

0.52297 + 0.00012 = 0.52309

and so the logarithm of 3.3349 is 0.52309.

To multiply two numbers, add their logarithms. The product of 0.002775 × 244.3 is obtained as follows:

$$\begin{array}{ll} \log 0.002775 & = 7.44326\text{-}10 \\ \log 244.3 & = 2.38792 \\ \hline & 9.83118\text{-}10 \end{array}$$

Antilog 9.83118-10 = 0.6779

To divide two numbers, subtract their logarithms. The quotient, 0.1000/18.02 is obtained in the following way:

$$\begin{array}{ll} \log 0.1000 & = 9.00000\text{-}10 \\ \log 18.02 & = 1.25575 \\ \hline & 7.74425\text{-}10 \end{array}$$

antilog 7.74425-10 = 0.005549

To calculate the percent water in barium chloride dihydrate using the data:

Wt sample = 1.500 g

Loss in wt on heating = 0.2211 g

$$\% \text{ H}_2\text{O in BaCl}_2 \cdot 2\text{H}_2\text{O} = (0.2211)(100)/(1.500)$$

$$\begin{array}{rl} \log 0.2211 = & 9.34459\text{-}10 \\ \log 100 = & \underline{2.00000} \\ & 1.34459 \\ \log 1.5000 = & \underline{0.17609} \\ & 1.16850 \end{array}$$

antilog $1.16850 = 14.74 =$ percent H_2O

To obtain the square root of a number, find its logarithm and divide it by two. The antilog of this number is the square root of the original number.

Example:

$\log\ 0.05 = \overline{2}.69897$ or $18.69897\text{-}20$
Dividing this by two yields $9.34949\text{-}10$
Antilog $9.34949\text{-}10 = 0.2236$

$$\sqrt{0.05} = 0.2236$$

To obtain the cube root of a number by this method, the logarithm of the number must be divided by 3. It therefore is convenient to have the characteristic that is to be subtracted exactly divisible by 3. Writing the logarithm of 0.05 as 28.69897-30 and then dividing by 3 we obtain 9.56632-10. The antilog of 9.56632-10 is 0.3684, and so $\sqrt[3]{0.05}$ is 0.3684.

The logarithm of the square of a number is obtained by multiplying the logarithm of the number by 2. Multiplying the logarithm of 0.05 by 2 yields 7.39794-10. The antilog of 7.39794-10 is 0.0025 and so $(0.05)^2$ is 0.0025.

FIVE-PLACE MANTISSAS

OF THE

COMMON LOGARITHMS*

OF THE

ENTIRE NUMBERS

From 1 to 11000

1 - 100

N	M	N	M	N	M	N	M	N	M
1	.00 000	21	.32 222	41	.61 278	61	.78 533	81	.90 849
2	30 103	22	34 242	42	62 325	62	79 239	82	91 381
3	47 712	23	36 173	43	63 347	63	79 934	83	91 908
4	60 206	24	38 021	44	64 345	64	80 618	84	92 428
5	69 897	25	39 794	45	65 321	65	81 291	85	92 942
6	.77 815	26	.41 497	46	.66 276	66	.81 954	86	.93 450
7	84 510	27	43 136	47	67 210	67	82 607	87	93 952
8	90 309	28	44 716	48	68 124	68	83 251	88	94 448
9	95 424	29	46 240	49	69 020	69	83 885	89	94 939
10	00 000	30	47 712	50	69 897	70	84 510	90	95 424
11	.04 139	31	.49 136	51	.70 757	71	.85 126	91	.95 904
12	07 918	32	50 515	52	71 600	72	85 733	92	96 379
13	11 394	33	51 851	53	72 428	73	86 332	93	96 848
14	14 613	34	53 148	54	73 239	74	86 923	94	97 313
15	17 609	35	54 407	55	74 036	75	87 506	95	97 772
16	.20 412	36	.55 630	56	.74 819	76	.88 081	96	.98 227
17	23 045	37	56 820	57	75 587	77	88 649	97	98 677
18	25 527	38	57 978	58	76 343	78	89 209	98	99 123
19	27 875	39	59 106	59	77 085	79	89 763	99	99 564
20	30 103	40	60 206	60	77 815	80	90 309	100	00 000

*Reproduced by permission from "Five-Place Logarithmic and Trigonometric Tables" edited by James M. Taylor, published by Ginn & Company.

1000 - 1500

N	0	1	2	3	4	5	6	7	8	9	Dif.	
100	.00 000	.00 043	.00 087	.00 130	.00 173	.00 217	.00 260	.00 303	.00 346	.00 389	40	39
101	432	475	518	561	604	647	689	732	775	817	4	4
102	860	903	945	988	01 030	01 072	01 115	01 157	01 199	01 242	8	8
103	01 284	01 326	01 368	01 410	452	494	536	578	620	662	12	12
104	703	745	787	828	870	912	953	995	02 036	02 078	16	16
105	.02 119	.02 160	.02 202	.02 243	.02 284	.02 325	.02 366	.02 407	.02 449	.02 490	20	20
106	531	572	612	653	694	735	776	816	857	898	24	23
107	938	979	03 019	03 060	03 100	03 141	03 181	03 222	03 262	03 302	28	27
108	03 342	03 383	423	463	503	543	583	623	663	703	32	31
109	743	782	822	862	902	941	981	04 021	04 060	04 100	36	35
110	.04 139	.04 179	.04 218	.04 258	.04 297	.04 336	.04 376	.04 415	.04 454	.04 493	38	36
111	532	571	610	650	689	727	766	805	844	883	4	4
112	922	961	999	05 038	05 077	05 115	05 154	05 192	05 231	05 269	8	7
113	05 308	05 346	05 385	423	461	500	538	576	614	652	11	11
114	690	729	767	805	843	881	918	956	994	06 032	15	14
115	.06 070	.06 108	.06 145	.06 183	.06 221	.06 258	.06 296	.06 333	.06 371	.06 408	19	18
116	446	483	521	558	595	633	670	707	744	781	23	22
117	819	856	893	930	967	07 004	07 041	07 078	07 115	07 151	27	25
118	07 188	07 225	07 262	07 298	07 335	372	408	445	482	518	30	29
119	555	591	628	664	700	737	773	809	846	882	34	32
120	.07 918	.07 954	.07 990	.08 027	.08 063	.08 099	.08 135	.08 171	.08 207	.08 243	34	33
121	08 279	08 314	08 350	386	422	458	493	529	565	600	3	3
122	636	672	707	743	778	814	849	884	920	955	7	7
123	991	09 026	09 061	09 096	09 132	09 167	09 202	09 237	09 272	09 307	10	10
124	09 342	377	412	447	482	517	552	587	621	656	14	13
125	.09 691	.09 726	.09 760	.09 795	.09 830	.09 864	.09 899	.09 934	.09 968	.10 003	17	17
126	10 037	10 072	10 106	10 140	10 175	10 209	10 243	10 278	10 312	346	20	20
127	380	415	449	483	517	551	585	619	653	687	24	23
128	721	755	789	823	857	890	924	958	992	11 025	27	26
129	11 059	11 093	11 126	11 160	11 193	11 227	11 261	11 294	11 327	361	31	30
130	.11 394	.11 428	.11 461	.11 494	.11 528	.11 561	.11 594	.11 628	.11 661	.11 694	32	31
131	727	760	793	826	860	893	926	959	992	12 024	3	3
132	12 057	12 090	12 123	12 156	12 189	12 222	12 254	12 287	12 320	352	6	6
133	385	418	450	483	516	548	581	613	646	678	10	9
134	710	743	775	808	840	872	905	937	969	13 001	13	12
135	.13 033	.13 066	.13 098	.13 130	.13 162	.13 194	.13 226	.13 258	.13 290	.13 322	16	16
136	354	386	418	450	481	513	545	577	609	640	19	19
137	672	704	735	767	799	830	862	893	925	956	22	22
138	988	14 019	14 051	14 082	14 114	14 145	14 176	14 208	14 239	14 270	26	25
139	14 301	333	364	395	426	457	489	520	551	582	29	28
140	.14 613	.14 644	.14 675	.14 706	.14 737	.14 768	.14 799	.14 829	.14 860	.14 891	30	29
141	922	953	983	15 014	15 045	15 076	15 106	15 137	15 168	15 198	3	3
142	15 229	15 259	15 290	320	351	381	412	442	473	503	6	6
143	534	564	594	625	655	685	715	746	776	806	9	9
144	836	866	897	927	957	987	16 017	16 047	16 077	16 107	12	12
145	.16 137	.16 167	.16 197	.16 227	.16 256	.16 286	.16 316	.16 346	.16 376	.16 406	15	15
146	435	465	495	524	554	584	613	643	673	702	18	17
147	732	761	791	820	850	879	909	938	967	997	21	20
148	17 026	17 056	17 085	17 114	17 143	17 173	17 202	17 231	17 260	17 289	24	23
149	319	348	377	406	435	464	493	522	551	580	27	26
150	.17 609	.17 638	.17 667	.17 696	.17 725	.17 754	.17 782	.17 811	.17 840	.17 869		
N	0	1	2	3	4	5	6	7	8	9		

.00 000 - .17 869

1500 - 2000

N	0	1	2	3	4	5	6	7	8	9	Dif.	
150	.17 609	.17 638	.17 667	.17 696	.17 725	.17 754	.17 782	.17 811	.17 840	.17 869	29	27
151	898	926	955	984	18 013	18 041	18 070	18 099	18 127	18 156	3	3
152	18 184	18 213	18 241	18 270	298	327	355	384	412	441	6	5
153	469	498	526	554	583	611	639	667	696	724	9	8
154	752	780	808	837	865	893	921	949	977	19 005	12	11
155	.19 033	.19 061	.19 089	.19 117	.19 145	.19 173	.19 201	.19 229	.19 257	.19 285	15	14
156	312	340	368	396	424	451	479	507	535	562	17	16
157	590	618	645	673	700	728	756	783	811	838	20	19
158	866	893	921	948	976	20 003	20 030	20 058	20 085	20 112	23	22
159	20 140	20 167	20 194	20 222	20 249	276	303	330	358	385	26	24
160	.20 412	.20 439	.20 466	.20 493	.20 520	.20 548	.20 575	.20 602	.20 629	.20 656	26	25
161	683	710	737	763	790	817	844	871	898	925	3	3
162	952	978	21 005	21 032	21 059	21 085	21 112	21 139	21 165	21 192	5	5
163	21 219	21 245	272	299	325	352	378	405	431	458	8	8
164	484	511	537	564	590	617	643	669	696	722	10	10
165	.21 748	.21 775	.21 801	.21 827	.21 854	.21 880	.21 906	.21 932	.21 958	.21 985	13	13
166	22 011	22 037	22 063	22 089	22 115	22 141	22 167	22 194	22 220	22 246	16	15
167	272	298	324	350	376	401	427	453	479	505	18	18
168	531	557	583	608	634	660	686	712	737	763	21	20
169	789	814	840	866	891	917	943	968	994	23 019	23	23
170	.23 045	.23 070	.23 096	.23 121	.23 147	.23 172	.23 198	.23 223	.23 249	.23 274	25	24
171	300	325	350	376	401	426	452	477	502	528	3	2
172	553	578	603	629	654	679	704	729	754	779	5	5
173	805	830	855	880	905	930	955	980	24 005	24 030	8	7
174	24 055	24 080	24 105	24 130	24 155	24 180	24 204	24 229	254	279	10	10
175	.24 304	.24 329	.24 353	.24 378	.24 403	.24 428	.24 452	.24 477	.24 502	.24 527	13	12
176	551	576	601	625	650	674	699	724	748	773	15	14
177	797	822	846	871	895	920	944	969	993	25 018	18	17
178	25 042	25 066	25 091	25 115	25 139	25 164	25 188	25 212	25 237	261	20	19
179	285	310	334	358	382	406	431	455	479	503	23	22
180	.25 527	.25 551	.25 575	.25 600	.25 624	.25 648	.25 672	.25 696	.25 720	.25 744	24	23
181	768	792	816	840	864	888	912	935	959	983	2	2
182	26 007	26 031	26 055	26 079	26 102	26 126	26 150	26 174	26 198	26 221	5	5
183	245	269	293	316	340	364	387	411	435	458	7	7
184	482	505	529	553	576	600	623	647	670	694	10	9
185	.26 717	.26 741	.26 764	.26 788	.26 811	.26 834	.26 858	.26 881	.26 905	.26 928	12	12
186	951	975	998	27 021	27 045	27 068	27 091	27 114	27 138	27 161	14	14
187	27 184	27 207	27 231	254	277	300	323	346	370	393	17	16
188	416	439	462	485	508	531	554	577	600	623	19	18
189	646	669	692	715	738	761	784	807	830	852	22	21
190	.27 875	.27 898	.27 921	.27 944	.27 967	.27 989	.28 012	.28 035	.28 058	.28 081	22	21
191	28 103	28 126	28 149	28 171	28 194	28 217	240	262	285	307	2	2
192	330	353	375	398	421	443	466	488	511	533	4	4
193	556	578	601	623	646	668	691	713	735	758	7	6
194	780	803	825	847	870	892	914	937	959	981	9	8
195	.29 003	.29 026	.29 048	.29 070	.29 092	.29 115	.29 137	.29 159	.29 181	.29 203	11	11
196	226	248	270	292	314	336	358	380	403	425	13	13
197	447	469	491	513	535	557	579	601	623	645	15	15
198	667	688	710	732	754	776	798	820	842	863	18	17
199	885	907	929	951	973	994	30 016	30 038	30 060	30 081	20	19
200	.30 103	.30 125	.30 146	.30 168	.30 190	.30 211	.30 233	.30 255	.30 276	.30 298		
N	0	1	2	3	4	5	6	7	8	9		

.17 609 - .30 298

N	0	1	2	3	4	5	6	7	8	9	Dif.
200	.30 103	.30 125	.30 146	.30 168	.30 190	.30 211	.30 233	.30 255	.30 276	.30 298	21
201	320	341	363	384	406	428	449	471	492	514	2
202	535	557	578	600	621	643	664	685	707	728	4
203	750	771	792	814	835	856	878	899	920	942	6
204	963	984	31 006	31 027	31 048	31 069	31 091	31 112	31 133	31 154	8
205	.31 175	.31 197	.31 218	.31 239	.31 260	31. 281	.31 302	.31 323	.31 345	.31 366	11
206	387	408	429	450	471	492	513	534	555	576	13
207	597	618	639	660	681	702	723	744	765	785	15
208	806	827	848	869	890	911	931	952	973	994	17
209	32 015	32 035	32 056	32 077	32 098	32 118	32 139	32 160	32 181	32 201	19
210	.32 222	.32 243	.32 263	.32 284	.32 305	.32 325	.32 346	.32 366	.32 387	.32 408	20
211	428	449	469	490	510	531	552	572	593	613	2
212	634	654	675	695	715	736	756	777	797	818	4
213	838	858	879	899	919	940	960	980	33 001	33 021	6
214	33 041	33 062	33 082	33 102	33 122	33 143	33 163	33 183	203	224	8
215	.33 244	.33 264	.33 284	.33 304	.33 325	.33 345	.33 365	.33 385	.33 405	.33 425	10
216	445	465	486	506	526	546	566	586	606	626	12
217	646	666	686	706	726	746	766	786	806	826	14
218	846	866	885	905	925	945	965	985	34 005	34 025	16
219	34 044	34 064	34 084	34 104	34 124	34 143	34 163	34 183	203	223	18
220	.34 242	.34 262	.34 282	.34 301	.34 321	.34 341	.34 361	.34 380	.34 400	.34 420	19
221	439	459	479	498	518	537	557	577	596	616	2
222	635	655	674	694	713	733	753	772	792	811	4
223	830	850	869	889	908	928	947	967	986	35 005	6
224	35 025	35 044	35 064	35 083	35 102	35 122	35 141	35 160	35 180	199	8
225	.35 218	.35 238	.35 257	.35 276	.35 295	.35 315	.35 334	.35 353	.35 372	.35 392	10
226	411	430	449	468	488	507	526	545	564	583	11
227	603	622	641	660	679	698	717	736	755	774	13
228	793	813	832	851	870	889	908	927	946	965	15
229	984	36 003	36 021	36 040	36 059	36 078	36 097	36 116	36 135	36 154	17
230	.36 173	.36 192	.36 211	.36 229	.36 248	.36 267	.36 286	.36 305	.36 324	.36 342	18
231	361	380	399	418	436	455	474	493	511	530	2
232	549	568	586	605	624	642	661	680	698	717	4
233	736	754	773	791	810	829	847	866	884	903	5
234	922	940	959	977	996	37 014	37 033	37 051	37 070	37 088	7
235	.37 107	.37 125	.37 144	.37 162	.37 181	.37 199	.37 218	.37 236	.37 254	.37 273	9
236	291	310	328	346	365	383	401	420	438	457	11
237	475	493	511	530	548	566	585	603	621	639	13
238	658	676	694	712	731	749	767	785	803	822	14
239	840	858	876	894	912	931	949	967	985	38 003	16
240	.38 021	.38 039	.38 057	.38 075	.38 093	.38 112	.38 130	.38 148	.38 166	.38 184	17
241	202	220	238	256	274	292	310	328	346	364	2
242	382	399	417	435	453	471	489	507	525	543	3
243	561	578	596	614	632	650	668	686	703	721	5
244	739	757	775	792	810	828	846	863	881	899	7
245	.38 917	.38 934	.38 952	.38 970	.38 987	.39 005	.39 023	.39 041	.39 058	.39 076	9
246	39 094	39 111	39 129	39 146	39 164	182	199	217	235	252	10
247	270	287	305	322	340	358	375	393	410	428	12
248	445	463	480	498	515	533	550	568	585	602	14
249	620	637	655	672	690	707	724	742	759	777	15
250	.39 794	.39 811	.39 829	.39 846	.39 863	.39 881	.39 898	.39 915	.39 933	.39 950	
N	0	1	2	3	4	5	6	7	8	9	

.30 103 - .39 950

2500 - 3000

N	0	1	2	3	4	5	6	7	8	9	Dif.
250	.39 794	.39 811	.39 829	.39 846	.39 863	.39 881	.39 898	.39 915	.39 933	.39 950	18
251	967	985	40 002	40 019	40 037	40 054	40 071	40 088	40 106	40 123	2
252	40 140	40 157	175	192	209	226	243	261	278	295	4
253	312	329	346	364	381	398	415	432	449	466	5
254	483	500	518	535	552	569	586	603	620	637	7
255	.40 654	.40 671	.40 688	.40 705	.40 722	.40 739	.40 756	.40 773	.40 790	.40 807	9
256	824	841	858	875	892	909	926	943	960	976	11
257	993	41 010	41 027	41 044	41 061	41 078	41 095	41 111	41 128	41 145	13
258	41 162	179	196	212	229	246	263	280	296	313	14
259	330	347	363	380	397	414	430	447	464	481	16
260	.41 497	.41 514	.41 531	.41 547	.41 564	.41 581	.41 597	.41 614	.41 631	.41 647	17
261	664	681	697	714	731	747	764	780	797	814	2
262	830	847	863	880	896	913	929	946	963	979	3
263	996	42 012	42 029	42 045	42 062	42 078	42 095	42 111	42 127	42 144	5
264	42 160	177	193	210	226	243	259	275	292	308	7
265	.42 325	.42 341	.42 357	.42 374	.42 390	.42 406	.42 423	.42 439	.42 455	.42 472	9
266	488	504	521	537	553	570	586	602	619	635	10
267	651	667	684	700	716	732	749	765	781	797	12
268	813	830	846	862	878	894	911	927	943	959	14
269	975	991	43 008	43 024	43 040	43 056	43 072	43 088	43 104	43 120	15
270	.43 136	.43 152	.43 169	.43 185	.43 201	.43 217	.43 233	.43 249	.43 265	.43 281	16
271	297	313	329	345	361	377	393	409	425	441	2
272	457	473	489	505	521	537	553	569	584	600	3
273	616	632	648	664	680	696	712	727	743	759	5
274	775	791	807	823	838	854	870	886	902	917	6
275	.43 933	.43 949	.43 965	.43 981	.43 996	.44 012	.44 028	.44 044	.44 059	.44 075	8
276	44 091	44 107	44 122	44 138	44 154	170	185	201	217	232	10
277	248	264	279	295	311	326	342	358	373	389	11
278	404	420	436	451	467	483	498	514	529	545	13
279	560	576	592	607	623	638	654	669	685	700	14
280	.44 716	.44 731	.44 747	.44 762	.44 778	.44 793	.44 809	.44 824	.44 840	.44 855	15
281	871	886	902	917	932	948	963	979	994	45 010	2
282	45 025	45 040	45 056	45 071	45 086	45 102	45 117	45 133	45 148	163	3
283	179	194	209	225	240	255	271	286	301	317	5
284	332	347	362	378	393	408	423	439	454	469	6
285	.45 484	.45 500	.45 515	.45 530	.45 545	.45 561	.45 576	.45 591	.45 606	.45 621	8
286	637	652	667	682	697	712	728	743	758	773	9
287	788	803	818	834	849	864	879	894	909	924	11
288	939	954	969	984	46 000	46 015	46 030	46 045	46 060	46 075	12
289	46 090	46 105	46 120	46 135	150	165	180	195	210	225	14
290	.46 240	.46 255	.46 270	.46 285	.46 300	.46 315	.46 330	.46 345	.46 359	.46 374	14
291	389	404	419	434	449	464	479	494	509	523	1
292	538	553	568	583	598	613	627	642	657	672	3
293	687	702	716	731	746	761	776	790	805	820	4
294	835	850	864	879	894	909	923	938	953	967	6
295	.46 982	.46 997	.47 012	.47 026	.47 041	.47 056	.47 070	.47 085	.47 100	.47 114	7
296	47 129	47 144	159	173	188	202	217	232	246	261	8
297	276	290	305	319	334	349	363	378	392	407	10
298	422	436	451	465	480	494	509	524	538	553	11
299	567	582	596	611	625	640	654	669	683	698	13
300	.47 712	.47 727	.47 741	.47 756	.47 770	.47 784	.47 799	.47 813	.47 828	.47 842	
N	0	1	2	3	4	5	6	7	8	9	

.39 794 − .47 842

3000 - 3500

N	0	1	2	3	4	5	6	7	8	9	Dif.
300	.47 712	.47 727	.47 741	.47 756	.47 770	.47 784	.47 799	.47 813	.47 828	.47 842	15
301	857	871	885	900	914	929	943	958	972	986	2
302	48 001	48 015	48 029	48 044	48 058	48 073	48 087	48 101	48 116	48 130	3
303	144	159	173	187	202	216	230	244	259	273	5
304	287	302	316	330	344	359	373	387	401	416	6
305	.48 430	.48 444	.48 458	.48 473	.48 487	.48 501	.48 515	.48 530	.48 544	.48 558	8
306	572	586	601	615	629	643	657	671	686	700	9
307	714	728	742	756	770	785	799	813	827	841	11
308	855	869	883	897	911	926	940	954	968	982	12
309	996	49 010	49 024	49 038	49 052	49 066	49 080	49 094	49 108	49 122	14
310	.49 136	.49 150	.49 164	.49 178	.49 192	.49 206	.49 220	.49 234	.49 248	.49 262	14
311	276	290	304	318	332	346	360	374	388	402	1
312	415	429	443	457	471	485	499	513	527	541	3
313	554	568	582	596	610	624	638	651	665	679	4
314	693	707	721	734	748	762	776	790	803	817	6
315	.49 831	.49 845	.49 859	.49 872	.49 886	.49 900	.49 914	.49 927	.49 941	.49 955	7
316	969	982	996	50 010	50 024	50 037	50 051	50 065	50 079	50 092	8
317	50 106	50 120	50 133	147	161	174	188	202	215	229	10
318	243	256	270	284	297	311	325	338	352	365	11
319	379	393	406	420	433	447	461	474	488	501	13
320	.50 515	.50 529	.50 542	.50 556	.50 569	.50 583	.50 596	.50 610	.50 623	.50 637	13
321	651	664	678	691	705	718	732	745	759	772	1
322	786	799	813	826	840	853	866	880	893	907	3
323	920	934	947	961	974	987	51 001	51 014	51 028	51 041	4
324	51 055	51 068	51 081	51 095	51 108	51 121	135	148	162	175	5
325	.51 188	.51 202	.51 215	.51 228	.51 242	.51 255	.51 268	.51 282	.51 295	.51 308	7
326	322	335	348	362	375	388	402	415	428	441	8
327	455	468	481	495	508	521	534	548	561	574	9
328	587	601	614	627	640	654	667	680	693	706	10
329	720	733	746	759	772	786	799	812	825	838	12
330	.51 851	.51 865	.51 878	.51 891	.51 904	.51 917	.51 930	.51 943	.51 957	.51 970	13
331	983	996	52 009	52 022	52 035	52 048	52 061	52 075	52 088	52 101	1
332	52 114	52 127	140	153	166	179	192	205	218	231	3
333	244	257	270	284	297	310	323	336	349	362	4
334	375	388	401	414	427	440	453	466	479	492	5
335	.52 504	.52 517	.52 530	.52 543	.52 556	.52 569	.52 582	.52 595	.52 608	.52 621	7
336	634	647	660	673	686	699	711	724	737	750	8
337	763	776	789	802	815	827	840	853	866	879	9
338	892	905	917	930	943	956	969	982	994	53 007	10
339	53 020	53 033	53 046	53 058	53 071	53 084	53 097	53 110	53 122	135	12
340	.53 148	.53 161	.53 173	.53 186	.53 199	.53 212	.53 224	.53 237	.53 250	.53 263	12
341	275	288	301	314	326	339	352	364	377	390	1
342	403	415	428	441	453	466	479	491	504	517	2
343	529	542	555	567	580	593	605	618	631	643	4
344	656	668	681	694	706	719	732	744	757	769	5
345	.53 782	.53 794	.53 807	.53 820	.53 832	.53 845	.53 857	.53 870	.53 882	.53 895	6
346	908	920	933	945	958	970	983	995	54 008	54 020	7
347	54 033	54 045	54 058	54 070	54 083	54 095	54 108	54 120	133	145	8
348	158	170	183	195	208	220	233	245	258	270	10
349	283	295	307	320	332	345	357	370	382	394	11
350	.54 407	.54 419	.54 432	.54 444	.54 456	.54 469	.54 481	.54 494	.54 506	.54 518	
N	0	1	2	3	4	5	6	7	8	9	

.47 712 - .54 518

3500 - 4000

N	0	1	2	3	4	5	6	7	8	9	Dif.
350	.54 407	.54 419	.54 432	.54 444	.54 456	.54 469	.54 481	.54 494	.54 506	.54 518	13
351	531	543	555	568	580	593	605	617	630	642	1
352	654	667	679	691	704	716	728	741	753	765	3
353	777	790	802	814	827	839	851	864	876	888	4
354	900	913	925	937	949	962	974	986	998	55 011	5
355	.55 023	.55 035	.55 047	.55 060	.55 072	.55 084	.55 096	.55 108	.55 121	.55 133	7
356	145	157	169	182	194	206	218	230	242	255	8
357	267	279	291	303	315	328	340	352	364	376	9
358	388	400	413	425	437	449	461	473	485	497	10
359	509	522	534	546	558	570	582	594	606	618	12
360	.55 630	.55 642	.55 654	.55 666	.55 678	.55 691	.55 703	.55 715	.55 727	.55 739	12
361	751	763	775	787	799	811	823	835	847	859	1
362	871	883	895	907	919	931	943	955	967	979	2
363	991	56 003	56 015	56 027	56 038	56 050	56 062	56 074	56 086	56 098	4
364	56 110	122	134	146	158	170	182	194	205	217	5
365	.56 229	.56 241	.56 253	.56 265	.56 277	.56 289	.56 301	.56 312	.56 324	.56 336	6
366	348	360	372	384	396	407	419	431	443	455	7
367	467	478	490	502	514	526	538	549	561	573	8
368	585	597	608	620	632	644	656	667	679	691	10
369	703	714	726	738	750	761	773	785	797	808	11
370	.56 820	.56 832	.56 844	.56 855	.56 867	.56 879	.56 891	.56 902	.56 914	.56 926	12
371	937	949	961	972	984	996	57 008	57 019	57 031	57 043	1
372	57 054	57 066	57 078	57 089	57 101	57 113	124	136	148	159	2
373	171	183	194	206	217	229	241	252	264	276	4
374	287	299	310	322	334	345	357	368	380	392	5
375	.57 403	.57 415	.57 426	.57 438	.57 449	.57 461	.57 473	.57 484	.57 496	.57 507	6
376	519	530	542	553	565	576	588	600	611	623	7
377	634	646	657	669	680	692	703	715	726	738	8
378	749	761	772	784	795	807	818	830	841	852	10
379	864	875	887	898	910	921	933	944	955	967	11
380	.57 978	.57 990	.58 001	.58 013	.58 024	.58 035	.58 047	.58 058	.58 070	.58 081	11
381	58 092	58 104	115	127	138	149	161	172	184	195	1
382	206	218	229	240	252	263	274	286	297	309	2
383	320	331	343	354	365	377	388	399	410	422	3
384	433	444	456	467	478	490	501	512	524	535	4
385	.58 546	.58 557	.58 569	.58 580	.58 591	.58 602	.58 614	.58 625	.58 636	.58 647	6
386	659	670	681	692	704	715	726	737	749	760	7
387	771	782	794	805	816	827	838	850	861	872	8
388	883	894	906	917	928	939	950	961	973	984	9
389	995	59 006	59 017	59 028	59 040	59 051	59 062	59 073	59 084	59 095	10
390	.59 106	.59 118	.59 129	.59 140	.59 151	.59 162	.59 173	.59 184	.59 195	.59 207	11
391	218	229	240	251	262	273	284	295	306	318	1
392	329	340	351	362	373	384	395	406	417	428	2
393	439	450	461	472	483	494	506	517	528	539	3
394	550	561	572	583	594	605	616	627	638	649	4
395	.59 660	.59 671	.59 682	.59 693	.59 704	.59 715	.59 726	.59 737	.59 748	.59 759	6
396	770	780	791	802	813	824	835	846	857	868	7
397	879	890	901	912	923	934	945	956	966	977	8
398	988	999	60 010	60 021	60 032	60 043	60 054	60 065	60 076	60 086	9
399	60 097	60 108	119	130	141	152	163	173	184	195	10
400	.60 206	.60 217	.60 228	.60 239	.60 249	.60 260	.60 271	.60 282	.60 293	.60 304	
N	0	1	2	3	4	5	6	7	8	9	

.54 407 - .60 304

4000 - 4500

N	0	1	2	3	4	5	6	7	8	9	Dif.
400	.60 206	.60 217	.60 228	.60 239	.60 249	.60 260	.60 271	.60 282	.60 293	.60 304	11
401	314	325	336	347	358	369	379	390	401	412	1
402	423	433	444	455	466	477	487	498	509	520	2
403	531	541	552	563	574	584	595	606	617	627	3
404	638	649	660	670	681	692	703	713	724	735	4
405	.60 746	.60 756	.60 767	.60 778	.60 788	.60 799	.60 810	.60 821	.60 831	.60 842	6
406	853	863	874	885	895	906	917	927	938	949	7
407	959	970	981	991	61 002	61 013	61 023	61 034	61 045	61 055	8
408	61 066	61 077	61 087	61 098	109	119	130	140	151	162	9
409	172	183	194	204	215	225	236	247	257	268	10
410	.61 278	.61 289	.61 300	.61 310	.61 321	.61 331	.61 342	.61 352	.61 363	.61 374	11
411	384	395	405	416	426	437	448	458	469	479	1
412	490	500	511	521	532	542	553	563	574	584	2
413	595	606	616	627	637	648	658	669	679	690	3
414	700	711	721	731	742	752	763	773	784	794	4
415	.61 805	.61 815	.61 826	.61 836	.61 847	.61 857	.61 868	.61 878	.61 888	.61 899	6
416	909	920	930	941	951	962	972	982	993	62 003	7
417	62 014	62 024	62 034	62 045	62 055	62 066	62 076	62 086	62 097	107	8
418	118	128	138	149	159	170	180	190	201	211	9
419	221	232	242	252	263	273	284	294	304	315	10
420	.62 325	.62 335	.62 346	.62 356	.62 366	.62 377	.62 387	.62 397	.62 408	.62 418	10
421	428	439	449	459	469	480	490	500	511	521	1
422	531	542	552	562	572	583	593	603	613	624	2
423	634	644	655	665	675	685	696	706	716	726	3
424	737	747	757	767	778	788	798	808	818	829	4
425	.62 839	.62 849	.62 859	.62 870	.62 880	.62 890	.62 900	.62 910	.62 921	.62 931	5
426	941	951	961	972	982	992	63 002	63 012	63 022	63 033	6
427	63 043	63 053	63 063	63 073	63 083	63 094	104	114	124	134	7
428	144	155	165	175	185	195	205	215	225	236	8
429	246	256	266	276	286	296	306	317	327	337	9
430	.63 347	.63 357	.63 367	.63 377	.63 387	.63 397	.63 407	.63 417	.63 428	.63 438	10
431	448	458	468	478	488	498	508	518	528	538	1
432	548	558	568	579	589	599	609	619	629	639	2
433	649	659	669	679	689	699	709	719	729	739	3
434	749	759	769	779	789	799	809	819	829	839	4
435	.63 849	.63 859	.63 869	.63 879	.63 889	.63 899	.63 909	.63 919	.63 929	.63 939	5
436	949	959	969	979	988	998	64 008	64 018	64 028	64 038	6
437	64 048	64 058	64 068	64 078	64 088	64 098	108	118	128	137	7
438	147	157	167	177	187	197	207	217	227	237	8
439	246	256	266	276	286	296	306	316	326	335	9
440	.64 345	.64 355	.64 365	.64 375	.64 385	.64 395	.64 404	.64 414	.64 424	.64 434	9
441	444	454	464	473	483	493	503	513	523	532	1
442	542	552	562	572	582	591	601	611	621	631	2
443	640	650	660	670	680	689	699	709	719	729	3
444	738	748	758	768	777	787	797	807	816	826	4
445	.64 836	.64 846	.64 856	.64 865	.64 875	.64 885	.64 895	.64 904	.64 914	.64 924	5
446	933	943	953	963	972	982	992	65 002	65 011	65 021	5
447	65 031	65 040	65 050	65 060	65 070	65 079	65 089	099	108	118	6
448	128	137	147	157	167	176	186	196	205	215	7
449	225	234	244	254	263	273	283	292	302	312	8
450	.65 321	.65 331	.65 341	.65 350	.65 360	.65 369	.65 379	.65 389	.65 398	.65 408	
N	0	1	2	3	4	5	6	7	8	9	

.60 206 - .65 408

4500 - 5000

N	0	1	2	3	4	5	6	7	8	9	Dif.
450	.65 321	.65 331	.65 341	.65 350	.65 360	.65 369	.65 379	.65 389	.65 398	.65 408	10
451	418	427	437	447	456	466	475	485	495	504	1
452	514	523	533	543	552	562	571	581	591	600	2
453	610	619	629	639	648	658	667	677	686	696	3
454	706	715	725	734	744	753	763	772	782	792	4
455	.65 801	.65 811	.65 820	.65 830	.65 839	.65 849	.65 858	.65 868	.65 877	.65 887	5
456	896	906	916	925	935	944	954	963	973	982	6
457	992	66 001	66 011	66 020	66 030	66 039	66 049	66 058	66 068	66 077	7
458	66 087	096	106	115	124	134	143	153	162	172	8
459	181	191	200	210	219	229	238	247	257	266	9
460	.66 276	.66 285	.66 295	.66 304	.66 314	.66 323	.66 332	.66 342	.66 351	.66 361	9
461	370	380	389	398	408	417	427	436	445	455	1
462	464	474	483	492	502	511	521	530	539	549	2
463	558	567	577	586	596	605	614	624	633	642	3
464	652	661	671	680	689	699	708	717	727	736	4
465	.66 745	.66 755	.66 764	.66 773	.66 783	.66 792	.66 801	.66 811	.66 820	.66 829	5
466	839	848	857	867	876	885	894	904	913	922	5
467	932	941	950	960	969	978	987	997	67 006	67 015	6
468	67 025	67 034	67 043	67 052	67 062	67 071	67 080	.67 089	099	108	7
469	117	127	136	145	154	164	173	182	191	201	8
470	.67 210	.67 219	.67 228	.67 237	.67 247	.67 256	.67 265	.67 274	.67 284	.67 293	9
471	302	311	321	330	339	348	357	367	376	385	1
472	394	403	413	422	431	440	449	459	468	477	2
473	486	495	504	514	523	532	541	550	560	569	3
474	578	587	596	605	614	624	633	642	651	660	4
475	.67 669	.67 679	.67 688	.67 697	.67 706	.67 715	.67 724	.67 733	.67 742	.67 752	5
476	761	770	779	788	797	806	815	825	834	843	5
477	852	861	870	879	888	897	906	916	925	934	6
478	943	952	961	970	979	988	997	68 006	68 015	68 024	7
479	68 034	68 043	68 052	68 061	68 070	68 079	68 088	097	106	115	8
480	.68 124	.68 133	.68 142	.68 151	.68 160	.68 169	.68 178	.68 187	.68 196	.68 205	9
481	215	224	233	242	251	260	269	278	287	296	1
482	305	314	323	332	341	350	359	368	377	386	2
483	395	404	413	422	431	440	449	458	467	476	3
484	485	494	502	511	520	529	538	547	556	565	4
485	.68 574	.68 583	.68 592	.68 601	.68 610	.68 619	.68 628	.68 637	.68 646	.68 655	5
486	664	673	681	690	699	708	717	726	735	744	5
487	753	762	771	780	789	797	806	815	824	833	6
488	842	851	860	869	878	886	895	904	913	922	7
489	931	940	949	958	966	975	984	993	69 002	69 011	8
490	.69 020	.69 028	.69 037	.69 046	.69 055	.69 064	.69 073	.69 082	.69 090	.69 099	8
491	108	117	126	135	144	152	161	170	179	188	1
492	197	205	214	223	232	241	249	258	267	276	2
493	285	294	302	311	320	329	338	346	355	364	2
494	373	381	390	399	408	417	425	434	443	452	3
495	.69 461	.69 469	.69 478	.69 487	.69 496	.69 504	.69 513	.69 522	.69 531	.69 539	4
496	548	557	566	574	583	592	601	609	618	627	5
497	636	644	653	662	671	679	688	697	705	714	6
498	723	732	740	749	758	767	775	784	793	801	6
499	810	819	827	836	845	854	862	871	880	888	7
500	.69 897	.69 906	.60 914	.69 923	.69 932	.69 940	.69 949	.69 958	.69 966	.69 975	
N	0	1	2	3	4	5	6	7	8	9	

.65 321 - .69 975

N	0	1	2	3	4	5	6	7	8	9	Dif.
500	.69 897	.69 906	.69 914	.69 923	.69 932	.69 940	.69 949	.69 958	.69 966	.69 975	9
501	984	992	70 001	70 010	70 018	70 027	70 036	70 044	70 053	70 062	1
502	70 070	70 079	088	096	105	114	122	131	140	148	2
503	157	165	174	183	191	200	209	217	226	234	3
504	243	252	260	269	278	286	295	303	312	321	4
505	.70 329	.70 338	.70 346	.70 355	.70 364	.70 372	.70 381	.70 389	.70 398	.70 406	5
506	415	424	432	441	449	458	467	475	484	492	5
507	501	509	518	526	535	544	552	561	569	578	6
508	586	595	603	612	621	629	638	646	655	663	7
509	672	680	689	697	706	714	723	731	740	749	8
510	.70 757	.70 766	.70 774	.70 783	.70 791	.70 800	.70 808	.70 817	.70 825	.70 834	8
511	842	851	859	868	876	885	893	902	910	919	1
512	927	935	944	952	961	969	978	986	995	71 003	2
513	71 012	71 020	71 029	71 037	71 046	71 054	71 063	71 071	71 079	088	2
514	096	105	113	122	130	139	147	155	164	172	3
515	.71 181	.71 189	.71 198	.71 206	.71 214	.71 223	.71 231	.71 240	.71 248	.71 257	4
516	265	273	282	290	299	307	315	324	332	341	5
517	349	357	366	374	383	391	399	408	416	425	6
518	433	441	450	458	466	475	483	492	500	508	6
519	517	525	533	542	550	559	567	575	584	592	7
520	.71 600	.71 609	.71 617	.71 625	.71 634	.71 642	.71 650	.71 659	.71 667	.71 675	8
521	684	692	700	709	717	725	734	742	750	759	1
522	767	775	784	792	800	809	817	825	834	842	2
523	850	858	867	875	883	892	900	908	917	925	2
524	933	941	950	958	966	975	983	991	999	72 008	3
525	.72 016	.72 024	.72 032	.72 041	.72 049	.72 057	.72 066	.72 074	.72 082	.72 090	4
526	099	107	115	123	132	140	148	156	165	173	5
527	181	189	198	206	214	222	230	239	247	255	6
528	263	272	280	288	296	304	313	321	329	337	6
529	346	354	362	370	378	387	395	403	411	419	7
530	.72 428	.72 436	.72 444	.72 452	.72 460	.72 469	.72 477	.72 485	.72 493	.72 501	8
531	509	518	526	534	542	550	558	567	575	583	1
532	591	599	607	616	624	632	640	648	656	665	2
533	673	681	689	697	705	713	722	730	738	746	2
534	754	762	770	779	787	795	803	811	819	827	3
535	.72 835	.72 843	.72 852	.72 860	.72 868	.72 876	.72 884	.72 892	.72 900	.72 908	4
536	916	925	933	941	949	957	965	973	981	989	5
537	997	73 006	73 014	73 022	73 030	73 038	73 046	73 054	73 062	73 070	6
538	73 078	086	094	102	111	119	127	135	143	151	6
539	159	167	175	183	191	199	207	215	223	231	7
540	.73 239	.73 247	.73 255	.73 263	.73 272	.73 280	.73 288	.73 296	.73 304	.73 312	7
541	320	328	336	344	352	360	368	376	384	392	1
542	400	408	416	424	432	440	448	456	464	472	1
543	480	488	496	504	512	520	528	536	544	552	2
544	560	568	576	584	592	600	608	616	624	632	3
545	.73 640	.73 648	.73 656	.73 664	.73 672	.73 679	.73 687	.73 695	.73 703	.73 711	4
546	719	727	735	743	751	759	767	775	783	791	4
547	799	807	815	823	830	838	846	854	862	870	5
548	878	886	894	902	910	918	926	933	941	949	6
549	957	965	973	981	989	997	74 005	74 013	74 020	74 028	6
550	.74 036	.74 044	.74 052	.74 060	.74 068	.74 076	.74 084	.74 092	.74 099	.74 107	
N	0	1	2	3	4	5	6	7	8	9	

.69 897 − .74 107

5500 - 6000

N	0	1	2	3	4	5	6	7	8	9	Dif.
550	.74 036	.74 044	.74 052	.74 060	.74 068	.74 076	.74 084	.74 092	.74 099	.74 107	8
551	115	123	131	139	147	155	162	170	178	186	1
552	194	202	210	218	225	233	241	249	257	265	2
553	273	280	288	296	304	312	320	327	335	343	2
554	351	359	367	374	382	390	398	406	414	421	3
555	.74 429	.74 437	.74 445	.74 453	.74 461	.74 468	.74 476	.74 484	.74 492	.74 500	4
556	507	515	523	531	539	547	554	562	570	578	5
557	586	593	601	609	617	624	632	640	648	656	6
558	663	671	679	687	695	702	710	718	726	733	6
559	741	749	757	764	772	780	788	796	803	811	7
560	.74 819	.74 827	.74 834	.74 842	.74 850	.74 858	.74 865	.74 873	.74 881	.74 889	7
561	896	904	912	920	927	935	943	950	958	966	1
562	974	981	989	997	75 005	75 012	75 020	75 028	75 035	75 043	1
563	75 051	75 059	75 066	75 074	082	089	097	105	113	120	2
564	128	136	143	151	159	166	174	182	189	197	3
565	.75 205	.75 213	.75 220	.75 228	.75 236	.75 243	.75 251	.75 259	.75 266	.75 274	4
566	282	289	297	305	312	320	328	335	343	351	4
567	358	366	374	381	389	397	404	412	420	427	5
568	435	442	450	458	465	473	481	488	496	504	6
569	511	519	526	534	542	549	557	565	572	580	6
570	.75 587	.75 595	.75 603	.75 610	.75 618	.75 626	.75 633	.75 641	.75 648	.75 656	8
571	664	671	679	686	694	702	709	717	724	732	1
572	740	747	755	762	770	778	785	793	800	808	2
573	815	823	831	838	846	853	861	868	876	884	2
574	891	899	906	914	921	929	937	944	952	959	3
575	.75 967	.75 974	.75 982	.75 989	.75 997	.76 005	.76 012	.76 020	.76 027	.76 035	4
576	76 042	76 050	76 057	76 065	76 072	080	087	095	103	110	5
577	118	125	133	140	148	155	163	170	178	185	6
578	193	200	208	215	223	230	238	245	253	260	6
579	268	275	283	290	298	305	313	320	328	335	7
580	.76 343	.76 350	.76 358	.76 365	.76 373	.76 380	.76 388	.76 395	.76 403	.76 410	7
581	418	425	433	440	448	455	462	470	477	485	1
582	492	500	507	515	522	530	537	545	552	559	1
583	567	574	582	589	597	604	612	619	626	634	2
584	641	649	656	664	671	678	686	693	701	708	3
585	.76 716	.76 723	.76 730	.76 738	.76 745	.76 753	.76 760	.76 768	.76 775	.76 782	4
586	790	797	805	812	819	827	834	842	849	856	4
587	864	871	879	886	893	901	908	916	923	930	5
588	938	945	953	960	967	975	982	989	997	77 004	6
589	77 012	77 019	77 026	77 034	77 041	77 048	77 056	77 063	77 070	078	6
590	.77 085	.77 093	.77 100	.77 107	.77 115	.77 122	.77 129	.77 137	.77 144	.77 151	7
591	159	166	173	181	188	195	203	210	217	225	1
592	232	240	247	254	262	269	276	283	291	298	1
593	305	313	320	327	335	342	349	357	364	371	2
594	379	386	393	401	408	415	422	430	437	444	3
595	.77 452	.77 459	.77 466	.77 474	.77 481	.77 488	.77 495	.77 503	.77 510	.77 517	4
596	525	532	539	546	554	561	568	576	583	590	4
597	597	605	612	619	627	634	641	648	656	663	5
598	670	677	685	692	699	706	714	721	728	735	6
599	743	750	757	764	772	779	786	793	801	808	6
600	.77 815	.77 822	.77 830	.77 837	.77 844	.77 851	.77 859	.77 866	.77 873	.77 880	
N	0	1	2	3	4	5	6	7	8	9	

.74 036 - .77 880

6000 - 6500

N	0	1	2	3	4	5	6	7	8	9	Dif.
600	.77 815	.77 822	.77 830	.77 837	.77 844	.77 851	.77 859	.77 866	.77 873	.77 880	8
601	887	895	902	909	916	924	931	938	945	952	1
602	960	967	974	981	988	996	78 003	78 010	78 017	78 025	2
603	78 032	78 039	78 046	78 053	78 061	78 068	075	082	089	097	2
604	104	111	118	125	132	140	147	154	161	168	3
605	.78 176	.78 183	.78 190	.78 197	.78 204	.78 211	.78 219	.78 226	.78 233	.78 240	4
606	247	254	262	269	276	283	290	297	305	312	5
607	319	326	333	340	347	355	362	369	376	383	6
608	390	398	405	412	419	426	433	440	447	455	6
609	462	469	476	483	490	497	504	512	519	526	7
610	.78 533	.78 540	.78 547	.78 554	.78 561	.78 569	.78 576	.78 583	.78 590	.78 597	7
611	604	611	618	625	633	640	647	654	661	668	1
612	675	682	689	696	704	711	718	725	732	739	1
613	746	753	760	767	774	781	789	796	803	810	2
614	817	824	831	838	845	852	859	866	873	880	3
615	.78 888	.78 895	.78 902	.78 909	.78 916	.78 923	.78 930	.78 937	.78 944	.78 951	4
616	958	965	972	979	986	993	79 000	79 007	79 014	79 021	4
617	79 029	79 036	79 043	79 050	79 057	79 064	071	078	085	092	5
618	099	106	113	120	127	134	141	148	155	162	6
619	169	176	183	190	197	204	211	218	225	232	6
620	.79 239	.79 246	.79 253	.79 260	.79 267	.79 274	.79 281	.79 288	.79 295	.79 302	7
621	309	316	323	330	337	344	351	358	365	372	1
622	379	386	393	400	407	414	421	428	435	442	1
623	449	456	463	470	477	484	491	498	505	511	2
624	518	525	532	539	546	553	560	567	574	581	3
625	.79 588	.79 595	.79 602	.79 609	.79 616	.79 623	.79 630	.79 637	.79 644	.79 650	4
626	657	664	671	678	685	692	699	706	713	720	4
627	727	734	741	748	754	761	768	775	782	789	5
628	796	803	810	817	824	831	837	844	851	858	6
629	865	872	879	886	893	900	906	913	920	927	6
630	.79 934	.79 941	.79 948	.79 955	.79 962	.79 969	.79 975	.79 982	.79 989	.79 996	7
631	80 003	80 010	80 017	80 024	80 030	80 037	80 044	80 051	80 058	80 065	1
632	072	079	085	092	099	106	113	120	127	134	1
633	140	147	154	161	168	175	182	188	195	202	2
634	209	216	223	229	236	243	250	257	264	271	3
635	.80 277	.80 284	.80 291	.80 298	.80 305	.80 312	.80 318	.80 325	.80 332	.80 339	4
636	346	353	359	366	373	380	387	393	400	407	4
637	414	421	428	434	441	448	455	462	468	475	5
638	482	489	496	502	509	516	523	530	536	543	6
639	550	557	564	570	577	584	591	598	604	611	6
640	.80 618	.80 625	.80 632	.80 638	.80 645	.80 652	.80 659	.80 665	.80 672	.80 679	6
641	686	693	699	706	713	720	726	733	740	747	1
642	754	760	767	774	781	787	794	801	808	814	1
643	821	828	835	841	848	855	862	868	875	882	2
644	889	895	902	909	916	922	929	936	943	949	2
645	.80 956	.80 963	.80 969	.80 976	.80 983	.80 990	.80 996	.81 003	.81 010	.81 017	3
646	81 023	81 030	81 037	81 043	81 050	81 057	81 064	070	077	084	4
647	090	097	104	111	117	124	131	137	144	151	4
648	158	164	171	178	184	191	198	204	211	218	5
649	224	231	238	245	251	258	265	271	278	285	5
650	.81 291	.81 298	.81 305	.81 311	.81 318	.81 325	.81 331	.81 338	.81 345	.81 351	
N	0	1	2	3	4	5	6	7	8	9	

.77 815 - .81 351

6500 - 7000

N	0	1	2	3	4	5	6	7	8	9	Dif.
650	.81 291	.81 298	.81 305	.81 311	.81 318	.81 325	.81 331	.81 338	.81 345	.81 351	6
651	358	365	371	378	385	391	398	405	411	418	1
652	425	431	438	445	451	458	465	471	478	485	1
653	491	498	505	511	518	525	531	538	544	551	2
654	558	564	571	578	584	591	598	604	611	617	2
655	.81 624	.81 631	.81 637	.81 644	.81 651	.81 657	.81 664	.81 671	.81 677	.81 684	3
656	690	697	704	710	717	723	730	737	743	750	4
657	757	763	770	776	783	790	796	803	809	816	4
658	823	829	836	842	849	856	862	869	875	882	5
659	889	895	902	908	915	921	928	935	941	948	5
660	.81 954	.81 961	.81 968	.81 974	.81 981	.81 987	.81 994	.82 000	.82 007	.82 014	7
661	82 020	82 027	82 033	82 040	82 046	82 053	82 060	066	073	079	1
662	086	092	099	105	112	119	125	132	138	145	1
663	151	158	164	171	178	184	191	197	204	210	2
664	217	223	230	236	243	249	256	263	269	276	3
665	.82 282	.82 289	.82 295	.82 302	.82 308	.82 315	.82 321	.82 328	.82 334	.82 341	4
666	347	354	360	367	373	380	387	393	400	406	4
667	413	419	426	432	439	445	452	458	465	471	5
668	478	484	491	497	504	510	517	523	530	536	6
669	543	549	556	562	569	575	582	588	595	601	6
670	.82 607	.82 614	.82 620	.82 627	.82 633	.82 640	.82 646	.82 653	.82 659	.82 666	6
671	672	679	685	692	698	705	711	718	724	730	1
672	737	743	750	756	763	769	776	782	789	795	1
673	802	808	814	821	827	834	840	847	853	860	2
674	866	872	879	885	892	898	905	911	918	924	2
675	.82 930	.82 937	.82 943	.82 950	.82 956	.82 963	.82 969	.82 975	.82 982	.82 988	3
676	995	83 001	83 008	83 014	83 020	83 027	83 033	83 040	83 046	83 052	4
677	83 059	065	072	078	085	091	097	104	110	117	4
678	123	129	136	142	149	155	161	168	174	181	5
679	187	193	200	206	213	219	225	232	238	245	5
680	.83 251	.83 257	.83 264	.83 270	.83 276	.83 283	.83 289	.83 296	.83 302	.83 308	7
681	315	321	327	334	340	347	353	359	366	372	1
682	378	385	391	398	404	410	417	423	429	436	1
683	442	448	455	461	467	474	480	487	493	499	2
684	506	512	518	525	531	537	544	550	556	563	3
685	.83 569	.83 575	.83 582	.83 588	.83 594	.83 601	.83 607	.83 613	.83 620	.83 626	4
686	632	639	645	651	658	664	670	677	683	689	4
687	696	702	708	715	721	727	734	740	746	753	5
688	759	765	771	778	784	790	797	803	809	816	6
689	822	828	835	841	847	853	860	866	872	879	6
690	.83 885	.83 891	.83 897	.83 904	.83 910	.83 916	.83 923	.83 929	.83 935	.83 942	6
691	948	954	960	967	973	979	985	992	998	84 004	1
692	84 011	84 017	84 023	84 029	84 036	84 042	84 048	84 055	84 061	067	1
693	073	080	086	092	098	105	111	117	123	130	2
694	136	142	148	155	161	167	173	180	186	192	2
695	.84 198	.84 205	.84 211	.84 217	.84 223	.84 230	.84 236	.84 242	.84 248	.84 255	3
696	261	267	273	280	286	292	298	305	311	317	4
697	323	330	336	342	348	354	361	367	373	379	4
698	386	392	398	404	410	417	423	429	435	442	5
699	448	454	460	466	473	479	485	491	497	504	5
700	.84 510	.84 516	.84 522	.84 528	.84 535	.84 541	.84 547	.84 553	.84 559	.84 566	
N	0	1	2	3	4	5	6	7	8	9	

.81 291 - .84 566

7000 - 7500

N	0	1	2	3	4	5	6	7	8	9	Dif.
700	.84 510	.84 516	.84 522	.84 528	.84 535	.84 541	.84 547	.84 553	.84 559	.84 566	7
701	572	578	584	590	597	603	609	615	621	628	1
702	634	640	646	652	658	665	671	677	683	689	1
703	696	702	708	714	720	726	733	739	745	751	2
704	757	763	770	776	782	788	794	800	807	813	3
705	.84 819	.84 825	.84 831	.84 837	.84 844	.84 850	.84 856	.84 862	.84 868	.84 874	4
706	880	887	893	899	905	911	917	924	930	936	4
707	942	948	954	960	967	973	979	985	991	997	5
708	85 003	85 009	85 016	85 022	85 028	85 034	85 040	85 046	85 052	85 058	6
709	065	071	077	083	089	095	101	107	114	120	6
710	.85 126	.85 132	.85 138	.85 144	.85 150	.85 156	.85 163	.85 169	.85 175	.85 181	6
711	187	193	199	205	211	217	224	230	236	242	1
712	248	254	260	266	272	278	285	291	297	303	1
713	309	315	321	327	333	339	345	352	358	364	2
714	370	376	382	388	394	400	406	412	418	425	2
715	.85 431	.85 437	.85 443	.85 449	.85 455	.85 461	.85 467	.85 473	.85 479	.85 485	3
716	491	497	503	509	516	522	528	534	540	546	4
717	552	558	564	570	576	582	588	594	600	606	4
718	612	618	625	631	637	643	649	655	661	667	5
719	673	679	685	691	697	703	709	715	721	727	5
720	.85 733	.85 739	.85 745	.85 751	.85 757	.85 763	.85 769	.85 775	.85 781	.85 788	6
721	794	800	806	812	818	824	830	836	842	848	1
722	854	860	866	872	878	884	890	896	902	908	1
723	914	920	926	932	938	944	950	956	962	968	2
724	974	980	986	992	998	86 004	86 010	86 016	86 022	86 028	2
725	.86 034	.86 040	.86 046	.86 052	.86 058	.86 064	.86 070	.86 076	.86 082	.86 088	3
726	094	100	106	112	118	124	130	136	141	147	4
727	153	159	165	171	177	183	189	195	201	207	4
728	213	219	225	231	237	243	249	255	261	267	5
729	273	279	285	291	297	303	308	314	320	326	5
730	.86 332	.86 338	.86 344	.86 350	.86 356	.86 362	.86 368	.86 374	.86 380	.86 386	6
731	392	398	404	410	415	421	427	433	439	445	1
732	451	457	463	469	475	481	487	493	499	504	1
733	510	516	522	528	534	540	546	552	558	564	2
734	570	576	581	587	593	599	605	611	617	623	2
735	.86 629	.86 635	.86 641	.86 646	.86 652	.86 658	.86 664	.86 670	.86 676	.86 682	3
736	688	694	700	705	711	717	723	729	735	741	4
737	747	753	759	764	770	776	782	788	794	800	4
738	806	812	817	823	829	835	841	847	853	859	5
739	864	870	876	882	888	894	900	906	911	917	5
740	.86 923	.86 929	.86 935	.86 941	.86 947	.86 953	.86 958	.86 964	.86 970	.86 976	5
741	982	988	994	999	87 005	87 011	87 017	87 023	87 029	87 035	1
742	87 040	87 046	87 052	87 058	064	070	075	081	087	093	1
743	099	105	111	116	122	128	134	140	146	151	2
744	157	163	169	175	181	186	192	198	204	210	2
745	.87 216	.87 221	.87 227	.87 233	.87 239	.87 245	.87 251	.87 256	.87 262	.87 268	3
746	274	280	286	291	297	303	309	315	320	326	3
747	332	338	344	349	355	361	367	373	379	384	4
748	390	396	402	408	413	419	425	431	437	442	4
749	448	454	460	466	471	477	483	489	495	500	5
750	.87 506	.87 512	.87 518	.87 523	.87 529	.87 535	.87 541	.87 547	.87 552	.87 558	
N	0	1	2	3	4	5	6	7	8	9	

.84 510 - .87 558

7500 - 8000

N	0	1	2	3	4	5	6	7	8	9	Dif.
750	.87 506	.87 512	.87 518	.87 523	.87 529	.87 535	.87 541	.87 547	.87 552	.87 558	6
751	564	570	576	581	587	593	599	604	610	616	1
752	622	628	633	639	645	651	656	662	668	674	1
753	679	685	691	697	703	708	714	720	726	731	2
754	737	743	749	754	760	766	772	777	783	789	2
755	.87 795	.87 800	.87 806	.87 812	.87 818	.87 823	.87 829	.87 835	.87 841	.87 846	3
756	852	858	864	869	875	881	887	892	898	904	4
757	910	915	921	927	933	938	944	950	955	961	4
758	967	973	978	984	990	996	88 001	88 007	88 013	88 018	5
759	88 024	88 030	88 036	88 041	88 047	88 053	058	064	070	076	5
760	.88 081	.88 087	.88 093	.88 098	.88 104	.88 110	.88 116	.88 121	.88 127	.88 133	5
761	138	144	150	156	161	167	173	178	184	190	1
762	195	201	207	213	218	224	230	235	241	247	1
763	252	258	264	270	275	281	287	292	298	304	2
764	309	315	321	326	332	338	343	349	355	360	2
765	.88 366	.88 372	.88 377	.88 383	.88 389	.88 395	.88 400	.88 406	.88 412	.88 417	3
766	423	429	434	440	446	451	457	463	468	474	3
767	480	485	491	497	502	508	513	519	525	530	4
768	536	542	547	553	559	564	570	576	581	587	4
769	593	598	604	610	615	621	627	632	638	643	5
770	.88 649	.88 655	.88 660	.88 666	.88 672	.88 677	.88 683	.88 689	.88 694	.88 700	6
771	705	711	717	722	728	734	739	745	750	756	1
772	762	767	773	779	784	790	795	801	807	812	1
773	818	824	829	835	840	846	852	857	863	868	2
774	874	880	885	891	897	902	908	913	919	925	2
775	.88 930	.88 936	.88 941	.88 947	.88 953	.88 958	.88 964	.88 969	.88 975	.88 981	3
776	986	992	997	89 003	89 009	89 014	89 020	89 025	89 031	89 037	4
777	89 042	89 048	89 053	059	064	070	076	081	087	092	4
778	098	104	109	115	120	126	131	137	143	148	5
779	154	159	165	170	176	182	187	193	198	204	5
780	.89 209	.89 215	.89 221	.89 226	.89 232	.89 237	.89 243	.89 248	.89 254	.89 260	5
781	265	271	276	282	287	293	298	304	310	315	1
782	321	326	332	337	343	348	354	360	365	371	1
783	376	382	387	393	398	404	409	415	421	426	2
784	432	437	443	448	454	459	465	470	476	481	2
785	.89 487	.89 492	.89 498	.89 504	.89 509	.89 515	.89 520	.89 526	.89 531	.89 537	3
786	542	548	553	559	564	570	575	581	586	592	3
787	597	603	609	614	620	625	631	636	642	647	4
788	653	658	664	669	675	680	686	691	697	702	4
789	708	713	719	724	730	735	741	746	752	757	5
790	.89 763	.89 768	.89 774	.89 779	.89 785	.89 790	.89 796	.89 801	.89 807	.89 812	6
791	818	823	829	834	840	845	851	856	862	867	1
792	873	878	883	889	894	900	905	911	916	922	1
793	927	933	938	944	949	955	960	966	971	977	2
794	982	988	993	998	90 004	90 009	90 015	90 020	90 026	90 031	2
795	.90 037	.90 042	.90 048	.90 053	.90 059	.90 064	.90 069	.90 075	.90 080	.90 086	3
796	091	097	102	108	113	119	124	129	135	140	4
797	146	151	157	162	168	173	179	184	189	195	4
798	200	206	211	217	222	227	233	238	244	249	5
799	255	260	266	271	276	282	287	293	298	304	5
800	.90 309	.90 314	.90 320	.90 325	.90 331	.90 336	.90 342	.90 347	.90 352	.90 358	
N	0	1	2	3	4	5	6	7	8	9	

.87 506 - .90 358

8000 - 8500

N	0	1	2	3	4	5	6	7	8	9	Dif.
800	.90 309	.90 314	.90 320	.90 325	.90 331	.90 336	.90 342	.90 347	.90 352	.90 358	5
801	363	369	374	380	385	390	396	401	407	412	1
802	417	423	428	434	439	445	450	455	461	466	1
803	472	477	482	488	493	499	504	509	515	520	2
804	526	531	536	542	547	553	558	563	569	574	2
805	.90 580	.90 585	.90 590	.90 596	.90 601	.90 607	.90 612	.90 617	.90 623	.90 628	3
806	634	639	644	650	655	660	666	671	677	682	3
807	687	693	698	703	709	714	720	725	730	736	4
808	741	747	752	757	763	768	773	779	784	789	4
809	795	800	806	811	816	822	827	832	838	843	5
810	.90 849	.90 854	.90 859	.90 865	.90 870	.90 875	.90 881	.90 886	.90 891	.90 897	6
811	902	907	913	918	924	929	934	940	945	950	1
812	956	961	966	972	977	982	988	993	998	91 004	1
813	91 009	91 014	91 020	91 025	91 030	91 036	91 041	91 046	91 052	057	2
814	062	068	073	078	084	089	094	100	105	110	2
815	.91 116	.91 121	.91 126	.91 132	.91 137	.91 142	.91 148	.91 153	.91 158	.91 164	3
816	169	174	180	185	190	196	201	206	212	217	4
817	222	228	233	238	243	249	254	259	265	270	4
818	275	281	286	291	297	302	307	312	318	323	5
819	328	334	339	344	350	355	360	365	371	376	5
820	.91 381	.91 387	.91 392	.91 397	.91 403	.91 408	.91 413	.91 418	.91 424	.91 429	5
821	434	440	445	450	455	461	466	471	477	482	1
822	487	492	498	503	508	514	519	524	529	535	1
823	540	545	551	556	561	566	572	577	582	587	2
824	593	598	603	609	614	619	624	630	635	640	2
825	.91 645	.91 651	.91 656	.91 661	.91 666	.91 672	.91 677	.91 682	.91 687	.91 693	3
826	698	703	709	714	719	724	730	735	740	745	3
827	751	756	761	766	772	777	782	787	793	798	4
828	803	808	814	819	824	829	834	840	845	850	4
829	855	861	866	871	876	882	887	892	897	903	5
830	.91 908	.91 913	.91 918	.91 924	.91 929	.91 934	.91 939	.91 944	.91 950	.91 955	6
831	960	965	971	976	981	986	991	997	92 002	92 007	1
832	92 012	92 018	92 023	92 028	92 033	92 038	92 044	92 049	054	059	1
833	065	070	075	080	085	091	096	101	106	111	2
834	117	122	127	132	137	143	148	153	158	163	2
835	.92 169	.92 174	.92 179	.92 184	.92 189	.92 195	.92 200	.92 205	.92 210	.92 215	3
836	221	226	231	236	241	247	252	257	262	267	4
837	273	278	283	288	293	298	304	309	314	319	4
838	324	330	335	340	345	350	355	361	366	371	5
839	376	381	387	392	397	402	407	412	418	423	5
840	.92 428	.92 433	.92 438	.92 443	.92 449	.92 454	.92 459	.92 464	.92 469	.92 474	5
841	480	485	490	495	500	505	511	516	521	526	1
842	531	536	542	547	552	557	562	567	572	578	1
843	583	588	593	598	603	609	614	619	624	629	2
844	634	639	645	650	655	660	665	670	675	681	2
845	.92 686	.92 691	.92 696	.92 701	.92 706	.92 711	.92 716	.92 722	.92 727	.92 732	3
846	737	742	747	752	758	763	768	773	778	783	3
847	788	793	799	804	809	814	819	824	829	834	4
848	840	845	850	855	860	865	870	875	881	886	4
849	891	896	901	906	911	916	921	927	932	937	5
850	.92 942	.92 947	.92 952	.92 957	.92 962	.92 967	.92 973	.92 978	.92 983	.92 988	
N	0	1	2	3	4	5	6	7	8	9	

.90 309 - .92 988

8500 - 9000

N	0	1	2	3	4	5	6	7	8	9	Dif.
850	.92 942	.92 947	.92 952	.92 957	.92 962	.92 967	.92 973	.92 978	.92 983	.92 988	6
851	993	998	93 003	93 008	93 013	93 018	93 024	93 029	93 034	93 039	1
852	93 044	93 049	054	059	064	069	075	080	085	090	1
853	095	100	105	110	115	120	125	131	136	141	2
854	146	151	156	161	166	171	176	181	186	192	2
855	.93 197	.93 202	.93 207	.93 212	.93 217	.93 222	.93 227	.93 232	.93 237	.93 242	3
856	247	252	258	263	268	273	278	283	288	293	4
857	298	303	308	313	318	323	328	334	339	344	4
858	349	354	359	364	369	374	379	384	389	394	5
859	399	404	409	414	420	425	430	435	440	445	5
860	.93 450	.93 455	.93 460	.93 465	.93 470	.93 475	.93 480	.93 485	.93 490	.93 495	5
861	500	505	510	515	520	526	531	536	541	546	1
862	551	556	561	566	571	576	581	586	591	596	1
863	601	606	611	616	621	626	631	636	641	646	2
864	651	656	661	666	671	676	682	687	692	697	2
865	.93 702	.93 707	.93 712	.93 717	.93 722	.93 727	.93 732	.93 737	.93 742	.93 747	3
866	752	757	762	767	772	777	782	787	792	797	3
867	802	807	812	817	822	827	832	837	842	847	4
868	852	857	862	867	872	877	882	887	892	897	4
869	902	907	912	917	922	927	932	937	942	947	5
870	.93 952	.93 957	.93 962	.93 967	.93 972	.93 977	.93 982	.93 987	.93 992	.93 997	4
871	94 002	94 007	94 012	94 017	94 022	94 027	94 032	94 037	94 042	94 047	0
872	052	057	062	067	072	077	082	086	091	096	1
873	101	106	111	116	121	126	131	136	141	146	1
874	151	156	161	166	171	176	181	186	191	196	2
875	.94 201	.94 206	.94 211	.94 216	.94 221	.94 226	.94 231	.94 236	.94 240	.94 245	2
876	250	255	260	265	270	275	280	285	290	295	2
877	300	305	310	315	320	325	330	335	340	345	3
878	349	354	359	364	369	374	379	384	389	394	3
879	399	404	409	414	419	424	429	433	438	443	4
880	.94 448	.94 453	.94 458	.94 463	.94 468	.94 473	.94 478	.94 483	.94 488	.94 493	5
881	498	503	507	512	517	522	527	532	537	542	1
882	547	552	557	562	567	571	576	581	586	591	1
883	596	601	606	611	616	621	626	630	635	640	2
884	645	650	655	660	665	670	675	680	685	689	2
885	.94 694	.94 699	.94 704	.94 709	.94 714	.94 719	.94 724	.94 729	.94 734	.94 738	3
886	743	748	753	758	763	768	773	778	783	787	3
887	792	797	802	807	812	817	822	827	832	836	4
888	841	846	851	856	861	866	871	876	880	885	4
889	890	895	900	905	910	915	919	924	929	934	5
890	.94 939	.94 944	.94 949	.94 954	.94 959	.94 963	.94 968	.94 973	.94 978	.94 983	4
891	988	993	998	95 002	95 007	95 012	95 017	95 022	95 027	95 032	0
892	95 036	95 041	95 046	051	056	061	066	071	075	080	1
893	085	090	095	100	105	109	114	119	124	129	1
894	134	139	143	148	153	158	163	168	173	177	2
895	.95 182	.95 187	.95 192	.95 197	.95 202	.95 207	.95 211	.95 216	.95 221	.95 226	2
896	231	236	240	245	250	255	260	265	270	274	2
897	279	284	289	294	299	303	308	313	318	323	3
898	328	332	337	342	347	352	357	361	366	371	3
899	376	381	386	390	395	400	405	410	415	419	4
900	.95 424	.95 429	.95 434	.95 439	.95 444	.95 448	.95 453	.95 458	.95 463	.95 468	
N	0	1	2	3	4	5	6	7	8	9	

.92 942 - .95 468

N	0	1	2	3	4	5	6	7	8	9	Dif.
900	.95 424	.95 429	.95 434	.95 439	.95 444	.95 448	.95 453	.95 458	.95 463	.95 468	5
901	472	477	482	487	492	497	501	506	511	516	1
902	521	525	530	535	540	545	550	554	559	564	1
903	569	574	578	583	588	593	598	602	607	612	2
904	617	622	626	631	636	641	646	650	655	660	2
905	.95 665	.95 670	.95 674	.95 679	.95 684	.95 689	.95 694	.95 698	.95 703	.95 708	3
906	713	718	722	727	732	737	742	746	751	756	3
907	761	766	770	775	780	785	789	794	799	804	4
908	809	813	818	823	828	832	837	842	847	852	4
909	856	861	866	871	875	880	885	890	895	899	5
910	.95 904	.95 909	.95 914	.95 918	.95 923	.95 928	.95 933	.95 938	.95 942	.95 947	4
911	952	957	961	966	971	976	980	985	990	995	0
912	999	96 004	96 009	96 014	96 019	96 023	96 028	96 033	96 038	96 042	1
913	96 047	052	057	061	066	071	076	080	085	090	1
914	095	099	104	109	114	118	123	128	133	137	2
915	.96 142	.96 147	.96 152	.96 156	.96 161	.96 166	.96 171	.96 175	.96 180	.96 185	2
916	190	194	199	204	209	213	218	223	227	232	2
917	237	242	246	251	256	261	265	270	275	280	3
918	284	289	294	298	303	308	313	317	322	327	3
919	332	336	341	346	350	355	360	365	369	374	4
920	.96 379	.96 384	.96 388	.96 393	.96 398	.96 402	.96 407	.96 412	.96 417	.96 421	5
921	426	431	435	440	445	450	454	459	464	468	1
922	473	478	483	487	492	497	501	506	511	515	1
923	520	525	530	534	539	544	548	553	558	562	2
924	567	572	577	581	586	591	595	600	605	609	2
925	.96 614	.96 619	.96 624	.96 628	.96 633	.96 638	.96 642	.96 647	.96 652	.96 656	3
926	661	666	670	675	680	685	689	694	699	703	3
927	708	713	717	722	727	731	736	741	745	750	4
928	755	759	764	769	774	778	783	788	792	797	4
929	802	806	811	816	820	825	830	834	839	844	5
930	.96 848	.96 853	.96 858	.96 862	.96 867	.96 872	.96 876	.96 881	.96 886	.96 890	4
931	895	900	904	909	914	918	923	928	932	937	0
932	942	946	951	956	960	965	970	974	979	984	1
933	988	993	997	97 002	97 007	97 011	97 016	97 021	97 025	97 030	1
934	97 035	97 039	97 044	049	053	058	063	067	072	077	2
935	.97 081	.97 086	.97 090	.97 095	.97 100	.97 104	.97 109	.97 114	.97 118	.97 123	2
936	128	132	137	142	146	151	155	160	165	169	2
937	174	179	183	188	192	197	202	206	211	216	3
938	220	225	230	234	239	243	248	253	257	262	3
939	267	271	276	280	285	290	294	299	304	308	4
940	.97 313	.97 317	.97 322	.97 327	.97 331	.97 336	.97 340	.97 345	.97 350	.97 354	5
941	359	364	368	373	377	382	387	391	396	400	1
942	405	410	414	419	424	428	433	437	442	447	1
943	451	456	460	465	470	474	479	483	488	493	2
944	497	502	506	511	516	520	525	529	534	539	2
945	.97 543	.97 548	.97 552	.97 557	.97 562	.97 566	.97 571	.97 575	.97 580	.97 585	3
946	589	594	598	603	607	612	617	621	626	630	3
947	635	640	644	649	653	658	663	667	672	676	4
948	681	685	690	695	699	704	708	713	717	722	4
949	727	731	736	740	745	749	754	759	763	768	5
950	.97 772	.97 777	.97 782	.97 786	.97 791	.97 795	.97 800	.97 804	.97 809	.97 813	
N	0	1	2	3	4	5	6	7	8	9	

.95 424 – .97 813

9500 - 10000

N	0	1	2	3	4	5	6	7	8	9	Dif.
950	.97 772	.97 777	.97 782	.97 786	.97 791	.97 795	.97 800	.97 804	.97 809	.97 813	4
951	818	823	827	832	836	841	845	850	855	859	0
952	864	868	873	877	882	886	891	896	900	905	1
953	909	914	918	923	928	932	937	941	946	950	1
954	955	959	964	968	973	978	982	987	991	996	2
955	.98 000	.98 005	.98 009	.98 014	.98 019	.98 023	.98 028	.98 032	.98 037	.98 041	2
956	046	050	055	059	064	068	073	078	082	087	2
957	091	096	100	105	109	114	118	123	127	132	3
958	137	141	146	150	155	159	164	168	173	177	3
959	182	186	191	195	200	204	209	214	218	223	4
960	.98 227	.98 232	.98 236	.98 241	.98 245	.98 250	.98 254	.98 259	.98 263	.98 268	5
961	272	277	281	286	290	295	299	304	308	313	1
962	318	322	327	331	336	340	345	349	354	358	1
963	363	367	372	376	381	385	390	394	399	403	2
964	408	412	417	421	426	430	435	439	444	448	2
965	.98 453	.98 457	.98 462	.98 466	.98 471	.98 475	.98 480	.98 484	.98 489	.98 493	3
966	498	502	507	511	516	520	525	529	534	538	3
967	543	547	552	556	561	565	570	574	579	583	4
968	588	592	597	601	605	610	614	619	623	628	4
969	632	637	641	646	650	655	659	664	668	673	5
970	.98 677	.98 682	.98 686	.98 691	.98 695	.98 700	.98 704	.98 709	.98 713	.98 717	4
971	722	726	731	735	740	744	749	753	758	762	0
972	767	771	776	780	784	789	793	798	802	807	1
973	811	816	820	825	829	834	838	843	847	851	1
974	856	860	865	869	874	878	883	887	892	896	2
975	.98 900	.98 905	.98 909	.98 914	.98 918	.98 923	.98 927	.98 932	.98 936	.98 941	2
976	945	949	954	958	963	967	972	976	981	985	2
977	989	994	998	99 003	99 007	99 012	99 016	99 021	99 025	99 029	3
978	99 034	99 038	99 043	047	052	056	061	065	069	074	3
979	078	083	087	092	096	100	105	109	114	118	4
980	.99 123	.99 127	.99 131	.99 136	.99 140	.99 145	.99 149	.99 154	.99 158	.99 162	5
981	167	171	176	180	185	189	193	198	202	207	1
982	211	216	220	224	229	233	238	242	247	251	1
983	255	260	264	269	273	277	282	286	291	295	2
984	300	304	308	313	317	322	326	330	335	339	2
985	.99 344	.99 348	.99 352	.99 357	.99 361	.99 366	.99 370	.99 374	.99 379	.99 383	3
986	388	392	396	401	405	410	414	419	423	427	3
987	432	436	441	445	449	454	458	463	467	471	4
988	476	480	484	489	493	498	502	506	511	515	4
989	520	524	528	533	537	542	546	550	555	559	5
990	.99 564	.99 568	.99 572	.99 577	.99 581	.99 585	.99 590	.99 594	.99 599	.99 603	4
991	607	612	616	621	625	629	634	638	642	647	0
992	651	656	660	664	669	673	677	682	686	691	1
993	695	699	704	708	712	717	721	726	730	734	1
994	739	743	747	752	756	760	765	769	774	778	2
995	.99 782	.99 787	.99 791	.99 795	.99 800	.99 804	.99 808	.99 813	.99 817	.99 822	2
996	826	830	835	839	843	848	852	856	861	865	2
997	870	874	878	883	887	891	896	900	904	909	3
998	913	917	922	926	930	935	939	944	948	952	3
999	957	961	965	970	974	978	983	987	991	996	4
1000	.00 000	.00 004	.00 009	.00 013	.00 017	.00 022	.00 026	.00 030	.00 035	.00 039	
N	0	1	2	3	4	5	6	7	8	9	

.97 772 - .96 996

10000 - 10500

N	0	1	2	3	4	5	6	7	8	9
1000	.00 000	.00 004	.00 009	.00 013	.00 017	.00 022	.00 026	.00 030	.00 035	.00 039
01	043	048	052	056	061	065	069	074	078	082
02	087	091	095	100	104	108	113	117	121	126
03	130	134	139	143	147	152	156	160	165	169
04	173	178	182	186	191	195	199	204	208	212
05	.00 217	.00 221	.00 225	.00 230	.00 234	.00 238	.00 243	.00 247	.00 251	.00 255
06	260	264	268	273	277	281	286	290	294	299
07	303	307	312	316	320	325	329	333	337	342
08	346	350	355	359	363	368	372	376	381	385
09	389	393	398	402	406	411	415	419	424	428
1010	.00 432	.00 436	.00 441	.00 445	.00 449	.00 454	.00 458	.00 462	.00 467	.00 471
11	475	479	484	488	492	497	501	505	509	514
12	518	522	527	531	535	540	544	548	552	557
13	561	565	570	574	578	582	587	591	595	600
14	604	608	612	617	621	625	629	634	638	642
15	.00 647	.00 651	.00 655	.00 659	.00 664	.00 668	.00 672	.00 677	.00 681	.00 685
16	689	694	698	702	706	711	715	719	724	728
17	732	736	741	745	749	753	758	762	766	771
18	775	779	783	788	792	796	800	805	809	813
19	817	822	826	830	834	839	843	847	852	856
1020	.00 860	.00 864	.00 869	.00 873	.00 877	.00 881	.00 886	.00 890	.00 894	.00 898
21	903	907	911	915	920	924	928	932	937	941
22	945	949	954	958	962	966	971	975	979	983
23	988	992	996	01 000	01 005	01 009	01 013	01 017	01 022	01 026
24	01 030	01 034	01 038	043	047	051	055	060	064	068
25	.01 072	.01 077	.01 081	.01 085	.01 089	.01 094	.01 098	.01 102	.01 106	.01 111
26	115	119	123	127	132	136	140	144	149	153
27	157	161	166	170	174	178	182	187	191	195
28	199	204	208	212	216	220	225	229	233	237
29	242	246	250	254	258	263	267	271	275	280
1030	.01 284	.01 288	.01 292	.01 296	.01 301	.01 305	.01 309	.01 313	.01 317	.01 322
31	326	330	334	339	343	347	351	355	360	364
32	368	372	376	381	385	389	393	397	402	406
33	410	414	418	423	427	431	435	439	444	448
34	452	456	460	465	469	473	477	481	486	490
35	.01 494	.01 498	.01 502	.01 507	.01 511	.01 515	.01 519	.01 523	.01 528	.01 532
36	536	540	544	549	553	557	561	565	569	574
37	578	582	586	590	595	599	603	607	611	616
38	620	624	628	632	636	641	645	649	653	657
39	662	666	670	674	678	682	687	691	695	699
1040	.01 703	.01 708	.01 712	.01 716	.01 720	.01 724	.01 728	.01 733	.01 737	.01 741
41	745	749	753	758	762	766	770	774	778	783
42	787	791	795	799	803	808	812	816	820	824
43	828	833	837	841	845	849	853	858	862	866
44	870	874	878	883	887	891	895	899	903	907
45	.01 912	.01 916	.01 920	.01 924	.01 928	.01 932	.01 937	.01 941	.01 945	.01 949
46	953	957	961	966	970	974	978	982	986	991
47	995	999	02 003	02 007	02 011	02 015	02 020	02 024	02 028	02 032
48	.02 036	02 040	044	049	053	057	061	065	069	073
49	078	082	086	090	094	098	102	107	111	115
1050	.02 119	.02 123	.02 127	.02 131	.02 135	.02 140	.02 144	.02 148	.02 152	.02 156
N	0	1	2	3	4	5	6	7	8	9

.00 000 - .02 156

10500 - 11000

N	0	1	2	3	4	5	6	7	8	9
1050	.02 119	.02 123	.02 127	.02 131	.02 135	.02 140	.02 144	.02 148	.02 152	.02 156
51	160	164	169	173	177	181	185	189	193	197
52	202	206	210	214	218	222	226	230	235	239
53	243	247	251	255	269	263	268	272	276	280
54	284	288	292	296	301	305	309	313	317	321
55	.02 325	.02 329	.02 333	.03 338	.02 342	.02 346	.02 350	.02 354	.02 358	.02 362
56	366	371	375	379	383	387	391	395	399	403
57	407	412	416	420	424	428	432	436	440	444
58	449	453	457	461	465	469	473	477	481	485
59	490	494	498	502	506	510	514	518	522	526
1060	.02 531	.02 535	.02 539	.02 543	.02 547	.02 551	.02 555	.02 559	.02 563	.02 567
61	572	576	580	584	588	592	596	600	604	608
62	612	617	621	625	629	633	637	641	645	649
63	653	657	661	666	670	674	678	682	686	690
64	694	698	702	706	710	715	719	723	727	731
65	.02 735	.02 739	.02 743	.02 747	.02 751	.02 755	.02 759	.02 763	.02 768	.02 772
66	776	780	784	788	792	796	800	804	808	812
67	816	821	825	829	833	837	841	845	849	853
68	857	861	865	869	873	877	882	886	890	894
69	898	902	906	910	914	918	922	926	930	934
1070	.02 938	.02 942	.02 946	.02 951	.02 955	.02 959	.02 963	.02 967	.02 971	.02 975
71	979	983	987	991	995	999	03 003	03 007	03 011	03 015
72	03 019	03 024	03 028	03 032	03 036	03 040	044	048	052	056
73	060	064	068	072	076	080	084	088	092	096
74	100	104	109	113	117	121	125	129	133	137
75	.03 141	.03 145	.03 149	.03 153	.03 157	.03 161	.03 165	.03 169	.03 173	.03 177
76	181	185	189	193	197	201	205	209	214	218
77	222	226	230	234	238	242	246	250	254	258
78	262	266	270	274	278	282	286	290	294	298
79	302	306	310	314	318	322	326	330	334	338
1080	.03 342	.03 346	.03 350	.03 354	.03 358	.03 362	.03 366	.03 371	.03 375	.03 379
81	383	387	391	395	399	403	407	411	**415**	419
82	423	427	431	435	439	443	447	451	**455**	459
83	463	467	471	475	479	483	487	491	495	499
84	503	507	511	515	519	523	527	531	535	539
85	.03 543	.03 547	.03 551	.03 555	.03 559	.03 563	.03 567	.03 571	.03 575	.03 579
86	583	587	591	595	599	603	607	611	615	619
87	623	627	631	635	639	643	647	651	655	659
88	663	667	671	675	679	683	687	691	695	699
89	703	707	711	715	719	723	727	731	735	739
1090	.03 743	.03 747	.03 751	.03 755	.03 759	.03 763	.03 757	.03 771	.03 775	.03 778
91	782	786	790	794	798	802	806	810	814	818
92	822	826	830	834	838	842	846	850	854	858
93	862	866	870	874	878	882	886	890	894	898
94	902	906	910	914	918	922	926	930	933	937
95	.03 941	.03 945	.03 949	.03 953	.03 957	.03 961	.03 956	.03 969	.03 973	.03 977
96	981	985	989	993	997	04 001	04 005	04 009	04 013	04 017
97	04 021	04 025	04 029	04 033	04 036	040	044	048	052	056
98	060	064	068	072	076	080	084	088	092	096
99	100	104	108	112	116	120	123	127	131	135
1100	.04 139	.04 143	.04 147	.04 151	.04 155	.04 159	.04 163	.04 167	.04 171	.04 175
N	0	1	2	3	4	5	6	7	8	9

.02 119 - .04 175

Index

A

Acids,
  common strong, 152
  in half-reactions, 203
  strong,
    titration with weak acid anions, 185
Acid-base indicators, 156
Acid-base reaction, 150
  transfer of protons to produce new acid and new base, 202
Acid phthalate, determination of, in an unknown, 193
Accuracy, definition of, 104
Activity,
  coefficient, 48
  definition of, 48
  unit, 216
Adsorption,
  by flocculated colloids, 92
  contamination by, 92
  effect of, on recrystallization, 88
  indicators, use of, 141
  of ions and molecules, 88
  of lattice ions, 88
  primary, 88, 89
  surface, 19
Agglomeration, of particles, 88
Air,
  buoyancy, effect on weighing, 121
  water content of, 18
Alkali metals, as foreign cations, 78
Alkalinity,
  total, determination in a carbonate-bicarbonate mixture, 194
Ammonium ion,
  in iron precipitation, 97
  use of,
    in the decrease of coprecipitation of non-volatile compounds, 98
Analysis,
  colorimetric, and related methods, 257
  gravimetric, 2
  physicochemical, 2, 256

quantitative, nature of, 1
  volumetric, 2, 34
Anions,
  foreign, coprecipitation, of, 78
  in formation of insoluble ferric salts, 97
  weak acid, titration of, 185
Anode, definition of, 214
Apparatus, volumetric, 114
Arithmetic mean, 104
Atomic theory, 28
Atomic weights, inside back cover

B

Bacteria, in thiosulfate solutions, 244
Balance,
  analytical, use of, 6
  macro, 9
  operation of, 9
  sensitivity of, 15
  systematic errors in use of, 17
Barium chloride dihydrate,
  determination of water in, 23
Barium diphenylamine sulfonate,
  as an indicator, 228, 230
Barium iodate, estimation of solubility of, 65
Barium sulfate,
  as solvent for lead sulfate, 93
  crystal lattice, 93
  in gravimetric determination of sulfate, 78, 79
  precipitate, in gravimetric determination of sulfate, 82, 83, 84
  solubility of, 71
Bases,
  acid-base indicators, 155
  acid-base reaction, 150
  common strong, 152
  excess, estimation of pH in presence of, 164
  mono-acidic, titration with a strong acid, 167

Bases—Continued
 standardization of, 193
 strong, problems in use of, 189
Bicarbonate,
 determination of, in a mixture, 194, 195
 equivalence-point, 183
 solution, estimation of pH in, 178
Buffer capacity, 173
Buffer region, extent of, 163
Buffer solutions,
 bicarbonate-carbonate, estimation of pH in, 178
 capacity of, 173
 carbonic acid-bicarbonate, estimation of pH in, 177
 composition of, 171
 definition of, 162, 170
 quantitative considerations of, 172
Buret,
 calibration of, 120
 cleaning and care of, 115
 manipulation of, 119
 reading of, 119
 use of, 118

C

Calcium,
 as foreign cation, 78
 in precipitation of calcium oxalate, 239
 permanganate determination of, 236
Calcium chloride, as a desiccant, 21
Calcium oxalate,
 precipitation of, 237
 solution and titration of, 240
Calculations,
 common volumetric, 34
 in gravimetric methods, 29
 numerical, a method of, 33
 of percent composition, 32
 stoichiometric, 40
Calibration,
 of buret, 120
 of pipet, 124
 of volumetric flask, 127
Carbon dioxide,
 effect of, on common strong base, 189
 in standardization of sodium hydroxide, 191
 solubility of, in water, 175
Carbonate,
 equivalence-point, use of, 183
 in a mixture, determination of, 194

ion, titration of, 181
Carbonate systems, 175
 carbonate ion, titration of, 181
 carbonate solutions, estimation of pH in, 181
Carbonic acid,
 bicarbonate buffers, estimation of pH in, 177
 equivalence-point, use of, 184
 estimation of pH in, 176
 titration of, 181
Cathode, definition of, 214
Cations,
 foreign, 78
 formation of insoluble hydroxides, 97
Cells, electrolytic, 214
Chloride,
 coprecipitation of, 78
 gravimetric determination of, 51
 ion concentration, 135
 Mohr method of determining, 139
 titration of, use of adsorption indicators in, 141
 volumetric determination of, 144
Cohesive forces, between molecules or ions, 87, 89
Colloid,
 flocculated, 92
 formation of, 91
Colloidal suspensions,
 effect of temperature on, 90
 formation and flocculation, 88
 formation of, 91
Color,
 changes in acid-base indicators, 159
 in acid-base indicators, 156
 transition, 157
Colorimetric methods of analysis, 257
Common ion effect,
 definition of, 60
 estimation of, 63
Composition,
 of solution, effect on solubility, 60
 percent, 32
Concentration units, 35
Contamination,
 by occlusion, 92
 of a precipitate, 92
 reduction of, 93
Copper,
 determination of, 245
 titration of, 248
Copper sulfate, effect on composition when exposed to air, 21

INDEX

Counter ions,
  definition of, 89
  region, 89
Crucible,
  filter, use of, 53
  Gooch, preparation and use of, 54, 56
  sintered, 56
Cupric solution,
  chemistry of, 246
  preparation of, 245

D

Data,
  recording of, 4
  solubility, 62
Derived standard, 130
Desiccants, 21
Desiccator, use of, 21
Determination,
  methods of, 2
  of acid phthalate, in an unknown, 193
  of carbonate and bicarbonate in a mixture, 194
  of chloride, gravimetric, 51
    volumetric, 144
  of copper, 245
  of iron,
    dichromate determination, 228
    gravimetric, 97
  of sulfate, 78
Dichloro-fluorescein indicator, 144
Digestion of precipitates, 88
Diphenylamine, 232, 233
Diphenylbenzidine, 225, 232, 233

E

Electrode,
  inert, 217
  reactions, 214
  standard hydrogen, 217
Electrons,
  exchange of, 203
  in balancing equations, 206
  in oxidation-reduction, 207
End-point,
  definition of, 131
  detection,
    acid-base, 138
    in acid-base titrations, 156
    in oxidation-reduction, 242
    physicochemical methods of, 259
    potentiometric methods of, 259
  permanence of, in standardization of sodium hydroxide, 192
Equations,
  balancing,
    use of half-reactions in, 206
    use of oxidation numbers in, 208, 210
Equilibria,
  adsorption, 142
  in simple hydrate systems, 49
  solubility, 50
Equilibrium,
  concept of, 43
  constant, 45
  establishment of, 47
  in simple hydrate systems, 49
  solubility, 50
  state of, 43
Equilibrium constant,
  as related to the standard potential, 216
  calculation of, from oxidation potentials, 213, 219
  for the reaction between ferric and iodide ions, 220
Equivalence-point,
  estimation of pH at the, 163
  in acid-base titration, 151
  in oxidation-reduction titration, 212
  in titration of acetic acid, 160
  use of term, 131
  use of the bicarbonate, 183
  use of the carbonate, 183
Equivalent weight,
  of a base, 150
  of an acid, 150
  of an oxidizing agent, 210
  of a reducing agent, 210
Errors,
  propagation of, in calculations, 108
  random or indeterminate, 104
  systematic balance, 17
  systematic or corrigible, 104

F

Factor,
  chemical, 32
  gravimetric, 32
Ferric oxide, hydrous,
  difficulty in filtration, 97
  filtration and washing, 99
  precipitation of, 97
  solubility of, 97
Filter, sintered glass, cleaning of, 53

Filtration,
  in gravimetric determination of chloride, 56
  in gravimetric determination of iron, 99
  in gravimetric determination of sulfate, 81
Flocculation,
  effect of temperature on, 90
  of colloidal suspensions, 88, 91
Fluorescein, as an adsorption indicator, 141
Fluorescence, methods of analysis, 257
Formality, 36

G

Gooch crucible, 56
Gram atom, definition of, 29
Gram per unit volume, relation of, to molarity, 36
Gravimetric calculations, methods of, 29
Gravimetric determination,
  of chloride, 51
  of iron, 97
  of sulfate, 78
Gravimetric factors, 32
Gravimetric techniques, 51

H

Half-reactions, 202
  definition of, 203
  electrons involved in, 207
  principles applied to, 204
Hydrate,
  simple systems, 49
  stability of, 20
Hydration, water of, 20
Hydrogen electrode, standard, 217
Hydrogen ion,
  basis of end-point detection, 156
  basis of equilibrium of indicator, 157
  concentration in chloride determination, 140
  effect on solubilities of silver acetate and barium sulfate, 71
  effect on solubility of salts of weak acids, 67
  qualitative effect on solubility of common salts, 73
  use of, in half-reactions, 205
Hydrolysis, of acetate ion, 160
Hydroxyl ion,
  control of concentration of, 98
  in buffer solutions, 171
Hygroscopic, definition of, 19
Hygrostat, 21

I

Ignition,
  in gravimetric determination of iron, 100
  in gravimetric determination of sulfate, 83
Indicator,
  acid-base, 156
  chemistry of, 232
  equivalence-point, 183
  one color, 157
  oxidation-reduction, 225
  provision of a precise end-point, 159
  selection, 164
  transition ranges and color changes, 159
  use in determination of bicarbonate, 183
International atomic weights, inside front cover
Iodide,
  as analytical reagent, 240
  use in connection with thiosulfate, 241
Iron,
  dichromate determination of, 228
  gravimetric determination of, 97
  quantitative oxidation of ferrous ion, 233
Isotopes, 28

L

Laboratory notebook, 3
Laboratory records, recording data, 3
Laboratory time, organization of, 5
Lattice ion, regular arrangement of, 95
Law,
  of Combining Weights, 28
  of Constant Proportions, 28, 29
  of Mass Action, 48
  of Simple Multiple Proportions, 28
Logarithms, use of, Appendix 6

M

Magnesium, in precipitation of calcium oxalate, 239
Magnesium perchlorate, as desiccant, 21
Mass, measurement of, 6
Meniscus, clarification of, 120

INDEX

Micron, 85
Millimicron, 85
Mixed indicator, use in determination of bicarbonate equivalence-point, 183
Mohr method,
 for determination of chloride, 139
 limitations of, 140
Molarity,
 conversion of percent concentration, 37
 definition of, 35
 relation of grams per unit volume to, 36
 use of term, 36
Mole,
 definition of, 29
 ratio, 162
Muffle furnace, preparation of, 24

N

Nephelometric methods of analysis, 257
Neutralization, use of term, 159
Normality,
 definition of, 35
 use of term, 36
Normal solution, definition of, 151
Nuclei, initial units of precipitate, 95

O

Observation, rejection of an, 105
Occluded substances, 92
Occlusion,
 contamination by, 92
 reduction of contamination, 93
Oxidation numbers,
 assignment of, 206, 207
 conventions followed in, 208
Oxidation potentials, 213, 219
 standard,
  definition of, 216, 217
  table of, 218
Oxidation-reduction, 202
 indicators, 225
 reactions, 203
 use of equivalent weights in, 210
Oxidizing agent, definition of, 203

P

Particle,
 agglomeration, 88
 growth of large, 95
 primary, 94
 rate of growth of, 87

size of precipitates, 85
solubility of, 86
Peptization,
 definition of, 91
 prevention of, 91
Permanganate,
 solution, standardization of, 233
 titration of, 234
 use of, in determination of calcium, 236
pH,
 adjustment in titration, 155
 as cause of change near equivalence-point, 165
 as dependent upon ratio of concentrations, 172
 at equivalence-point,
  in titration of a weak mono-acidic base with a strong acid, 168
  in titration with strong base, 163
 estimation of,
  in buffer region, 161
  the initial, 161
 in bicarbonate-carbonate buffers, 178
 in buffer region, 168
 in carbonic acid-bicarbonate buffers, 177
 in carbonic acid solutions, 176
 in presence of excess acid, 169
 in presence of excess base, 164
Phenolphthalein,
 indicator in standardization of sodium hydroxide, 190
 one-color indicator, 157
 to determine bicarbonate equivalence-point, 183
Phenol-red, use as indicator, 156
Phosphate systems, titrations in, 187
Phosphorus pentoxide, as desiccant, 21
Physicochemical analysis, methods of, 2
Pipet,
 calibration of, 124
 cleaning of, 123
 use of, 124
Policeman, 58, 82
Potassium dichromate,
 as an oxidizing agent, 228
 as a titrant, 228
Potentiometric methods, of end-point detection, 259
Precipitate,
 contamination of, 92
 effect of acidity regulation, 95
 effect of elevated temperature, 95
 formation, of simple inorganic, 97

Precipitate—Continued
  increase in size and purity, 94
  particle size of, 85
  particle solubility of, 86
  rate of growth of, 87
  reprecipitation of, 79
  separation of, 85
  washing of, 59
Precipitation,
  conditions of, effect on size and purity, 94
  general use of, 51
  in gravimetric determination,
    of iron, 99
    of sulfate, 80
  methods, application of, 144
  of calcium oxalate, 237
  of silver chloride, 56
  post, 93
    definition of, 94
    importance of, 94
Precision, use of term, 104
Primary particles, initial units, 94
Primary standard, 130
Product, best value of, 107
Propagation, of errors in calculations, 108
Protons, exchange of, 202

Q

Quantitative analysis,
  definition of, 1
  general discussion of, 256
  related methods, 257

R

Reaction, acid-base, 150
Reagents, for oxidation-reduction, 226
Records, laboratory, 3
Recrystallization,
  in adsorption, 88
  limited occurrence, 94
Reducing agent, definition of, 203
Reduction, in dichromate determination of iron, 231
Reprecipitation, 93
Rest point, of balance, 14

S

Sample, weighing of, 55
Salt bridge, 214
Secondary standard, 130

Sensitivity, of balance, 15
Separation, mechanical, of suspension groups, 85
Significant figures, 102
Silica gel, as desiccant, 21
Silver acetate, solubility of, 67, 71
Silver chloride,
  adsorption of fluorescein on, 141
  colloidal dispersion of, 91
  peptization of, 91
  precipitation of, 56
  precipitate, stabilization of, 142
  primary adsorption on, 89
  solubility of, 67
Silver iodide, application of Volhard method to, 143
Silver nitrate, standardization of, 144
Silver thiocyanate, 143
Sodium carbonate, in standardization of hydrochloric acid, 194
Sodium hydroxide,
  preparation and storage of, 190
  preparation of standard solution of, 130
  solid, sodium carbonate content, 130
  standardization of, 190
Sodium thiosulfate,
  growth of thiobacteria in, 244
  oxidation in the presence of air, 243
Solid solutions, formation of, 93
Solids,
  drying and storing of, 18
  surface adsorption on, 19
  water in, 18
Solubility,
  and particle size, 86
  control of, 60
  effect of,
    complex ion formation on, 71
    hydrogen ion on, 73
    temperature on, 60
    the composition on, 60
  equilibria, 50
  loss due to, 61
  products from solubility data, 62
  to decrease, 60
  to increase, 61
Spectrographic methods of analysis, 257
Spectrophotometric methods of analysis, 257
Standard solution,
  definition of, 130
  preparation of, 130

INDEX

Standardization,
 of hydrochloric acid with sodium carbonate, 194
 of thiosulfate solutions, 243
Stoichiometry,
 basic laws of, 28
 calculations,
  in terms of normality, 212
  terms used in, 35, 40
  definition of, 28
  in volumetric methods, 131
  of acid-base titrations, 150
Sulfate, gravimetric determination of, 78
Sulfuric acid, as desiccant, 21
Surface, of a solid, definition of, 86
Suspension group, particle size range of, 85

T

Temperature,
 effect on,
  formation and flocculation of colloidal suspensions, 90
  solubility, 60
  volumetric measurements, 114
 elevated, use to increase solubility of precipitate, 95
Thiosulfate,
 methods of standardization, 244, 245
 reaction with tri-iodide, 240
 solutions, preparation and standardization of, 243
 stability of, 243
 use of iodide in connection with, 241
Thymol blue, indicator for bicarbonate equivalence-point, 183
Titrant, 130
Titration,
 back, or indirect, 143
 curve,
  acid-base, definition of, 133
  oxidation-reduction, 222
  definition of, 130
  in determination of copper, chemistry of, 248
  limitations, 165
 of carbonic acid or carbonate ion, 181
 of hydrochloric acid with base, 192
 of strong acids with strong bases, 152
 of weak acid with weak base, 169
 of weak monobasic acid with strong base, 159
 with tri-iodide, 242
Transition ranges, of some acid-base indicators, 159
Tri-iodide,
 as an analytical reagent, 240
 reaction with thiosulfate, 240
 titrations with, 242

V

Vacuo, drying of hydrate, 21
Volhard method, titration, 142, 143, 146
Volumetric analysis, methods of, 2
Volumetric calculation, 34
Volumetric flask,
 calibration of, 127
 cleaning of, 126
 use of, 126
Von Weirmarn, thesis of supersaturation, 95

W

Washing, technique in gravimetric determination of,
 chloride, 59
 iron, 99
 sulfate, 81
Water,
 content of air, 18
 determination of, in barium chloride dihydrate, 23
 indirect determination of, 25
 in solids, 18
 of hydration, 20
 surface adsorption, 19
Weighing,
 bottle, preparation and manipulation, 24
 by difference, 16
 direct method for, 14
 of samples, 55
Weights,
 calibration of, 8
 care in handling, 7
 errors in recording, 17
 placement of, 15
 standard, 6
 use of, 7
Witt plate, 54

Z

Zero point, of balance, 12
Zinc,
 in electrolytic cell, 213
 ions, in precipitation of ferric hydroxide, 93